Multiple Cropping

ASA Special Publication Number 27

Proceedings of a symposium sponsored by Divisions A-6, S-4, S-6, A-3, A-4, and C-3 of the American Society of Agronomy, Crop Science Society of America and Soil Science Society of America. The papers were presented during the annual meetings in Knoxville, Tennessee, August, 1975.

Editorial Committee
R. I. Papendick, Chairman
P. A. Sanchez
G. B. Triplett

Organizing Committee
P. A. Sanchez, Chairman
R. R. Allmaras
G. R. Carlson
D. H. Myhre

Editor-in-Chief: Matthias Stelly
Managing Editor: David M. Kral
Assistant Editors: Linda C. Eisele
Judith H. Nauseef

1976

Published by the

AMERICAN SOCIETY OF AGRONOMY
CROP SCIENCE SOCIETY OF AMERICA
SOIL SCIENCE SOCIETY OF AMERICA
677 South Segoe Road
Madison, Wisconsin 53711

American Society of Agronomy
Crop Science Society of America
Soil Science Society of America
677 South Segoe Road, Madison, Wisconsin 53711 USA

Library of Congress Catalog Card Number: 76-22285
Standard Book Number: 0-89118-045-1

Printed in the United States of America

Contents

Foreword

This symposium is the first major publication of the three societies on one aspect of increasing food production beyond increasing cultivated area and increasing yields; that is, harvesting more than one crop from the same piece of land in a year. It provides recognition to this aspect of crop intensification as one of the major tools for preventing food shortages throughout the world.

The purpose of the symposium was to bring together the available knowledge about multiple cropping systems, both ancient and new. A uniform terminology was presented and used throughout. The ancient traditional tropical multiple cropping systems were summarized from a regional perspective never attempted before. New systems developed in the U. S. during the last decade are described in detail. Both fundamental and applied aspects of multiple cropping are presented from a multidisciplinary viewpoint. It is hoped that this publication will serve as a basic reference of what is known about multiple cropping as of 1976.

The breadth of the publication is illustrated by the viewpoints and contributions of authors from different parts of the world and representing several disciplines. The authors range from all regions of the U. S., Australia, Colombia, Costa Rica, Guatemala, India, Lebanon, Nigeria, the Philippines, and the United Kingdom. They are agricultural engineers, agricultural economists, agrometeorologists, agronomists, crop physiologists, entomologists, soil chemists, soil physicists, soil fertility specialists, soil conservation specialists, and weed control specialists.

The Symposium was cosponsored by Divisions A-3, A-4, A-6, C-3, S-4, and S-6 with Division A-6 carrying leadership for organization of the papers. We extend a special appreciation to the organizing committee: D. H. Myhre, G. R. Carlson, R. R. Allmaras, and P. A. Sanchez, Chairman, and to the editorial committee: G. B. Triplett, P. A. Sanchez, and R. I. Papendick, Chairman.

F. L. Patterson, President
American Society of Agronomy

R. L. Mitchell, President
Crop Science Society of America

C. B. Davey, President
Soil Science Society of America

Preface

Multiple cropping is not a new concept but instead a centuries-old technique of intensive farming that has persisted in many areas of the world as a method to maximize land productivity per unit area per season. As defined in this publication, multiple cropping means growing two or more crops on the same field in a year. The practice is most prevalent in areas of high rainfall in the tropics where temperature and moisture are favorable for year-round crop production. Systems in use today have evolved largely from experience and in response to high food demand in densely populated areas.

Recent world food shortages and prospects of inadequate supplies in the future have prompted accelerated interest in methods for increasing food production. Gains in production per unit area with monoculture cropping with single harvests per season have not been impressive in recent years, and the potential for improvement through new technology remains uncertain. More promising for many areas to increase food output is development and application of new technology for multiple cropping systems. Though the history of multiple cropping is old, the concept has received only limited attention from the scientific viewpoint, and that only in relatively recent times. In limited instances where new technology has been applied to exploit space, moisture, and radiation resources, phenomenal gains in food output have been reported.

The development and application of technology to improve the efficiency of multiple cropping systems will not be an easy task. In parts of the tropics, systems in use are extremely complex, and the basis for established cropping patterns are often poorly understood. In the northern latitudes where farming methods are highly mechanized, development of systems is only in the beginning stages relative to those in the warmer, more populated areas.

The papers in this publication are the result of a symposium on "Multiple Cropping" held at the 1975 American Society of Agronomy annual meetings. Organizers were P. A. Sanchez of North Carolina State University, R. R. Allmaras, D. L. Myhre, and G. Carlson, all of the Agricultural Research Service, U. S. Department of Agriculture. The objectives of the Symposium were to bring together the present knowledge about multiple cropping systems on a worldwide basis. The papers cover (i) a description of what farmers and researchers are doing in specific geographical regions, (ii) basic concepts of crop performance in multiple cropping systems, and (iii) specific agronomic practices. Although the papers do not include all of the aspects of the subject, they should provide a basis upon which the potential for improvement in land productivity through multiple cropping can be assessed.

R. I. Papendick
P. A. Sanchez
G. B. Triplett
editors

The Importance of Multiple Cropping in Increasing World Food Supplies

D. J. Andrews and A. H. Kassam[1]

Multiple cropping describes forms of cropping practices where total production from a unit area of land in a farming year is achieved through growing crops simultaneously, sole crops in sequence, or a combination of mixed and sole crops in sequence.

Multiple cropping for food production is in widespread use by farmers in the warmer parts of the world at all levels of agricultural technology. However, the form of multiple cropping varies from area to area depending on the farmers' total resources. Under conditions of "low level equilibrium" farming, as exists in much of the developing world (e.g., Africa, Latin America, parts of India), farmers operate with difficulties arising from low capital, unfavorable price relations, unsophisticated markets, and rudimentary infrastructure. Multiple cropping involving the growing of rain-fed crops in mixtures matches well the total resources available to these farmers in maintaining low but often adequate and relatively steady production. In conditions of "high level equilibrium" farming, as exists in areas such as the U. S., Taiwan, and parts of India, on-farm agricultural technology is geared towards commercial production. Here multiple cropping mostly involves the growing of sole crops in sequence, but in some cases where farming is both capital and labor intensive due to a high population and an absolute land shortage, growing crops in mixtures has become economically more attractive.

In the future much of the food needed by the world's rural and urban population in the areas presently under conditions of low level equilibrium farming will have to be produced by farming communities under conditions of change in agricultural technology. While efforts by governments to improve institutional and administrative structures and support facilities will

---

[1]Plant breeder and Plant physiologist, International Crops Research Institute for the Semi-Arid Tropics, Hyderabad, India.

play a major part, upgrading the farmers' whole system of cropping will have to parallel any improvement in resources and services made available. In this context multiple cropping can play an important role, the potential of which has been recognized by many research bodies who in the last decade have initiated investigations into the basic principles involved in various forms of multiple cropping. With the ever growing need to achieve stable increases in the world food supplies, a wider and more intensive use of multiple cropping offers additional means to intensify production per unit area on the existing and potential cultivable area.

PATTERNS AND FEATURES OF MULTIPLE CROPPING

Definitions

Eight major multiple cropping patterns, together with other related terms currently in use, are defined in Tables 1 and 2. The various patterns of

Table 1. Definitions of the principle multiple cropping patterns with modifications from P. A. Sanchez, North Carolina State University (personal communication)

MULTIPLE CROPPING: The intensification of cropping in time and space dimensions. Growing two or more crops on the same field in a year.

---

1. SEQUENTIAL CROPPING: Growing two or more crops in *sequence* on the same field per year.* The succeeding crop is planted after the preceding crop has been harvested. Crop intensification is only in the time dimension. There is no intercrop competition. Farmers manage only one crop at a time in the same field.

   1.1 *Double cropping:* Growing two crops a year in sequence.
   1.2 *Triple cropping:* Growing three crops a year in sequence.
   1.3 *Quadruple cropping:* Growing four crops a year in sequence.
   1.4 *Ratoon cropping:* The cultivation of crop regrowth after harvest, although not necessarily for grain.

2. INTERCROPPING: Growing two or more crops *simultaneously* on the same field. Crop intensification is in both time and space dimensions. There is intercrop competition during all or part of crop growth. Farmers manage more than one crop at a time in the same field.

   2.1 *Mixed intercropping:* Growing two or more crops simultaneously with no distinct row arrangement.
   2.2 *Row intercropping:* Growing two or more crops simultaneously where one or more crops are planted in rows.
   2.3 *Strip intercropping:* Growing two or more crops simultaneously in different strips wide enough to permit independent cultivation but narrow enough for the crops to interact agronomically.
   2.4 *Relay intercropping:* Growing two or more crops simultaneously during part of the life cycle of each. A second crop is planted after the first crop has reached its reproductive stage of growth but before it is ready for harvest.

---

* The farming year is 12 months except in aridic areas where only one crop can be grown every 2 years due to moisture limitations. In these areas sequential cropping involves growing two or more crops every 2 years.

Table 2. Related terminology used in multiple cropping systems with modifications from P. A. Sanchez, North Carolina State University (personal communication)

Sole cropping: One crop variety grown alone in pure stands at normal density. Synonymous with solid planting; opposite of intercropping.

Monoculture: The repetitive growing of the same sole crop on the same land.

Rotation: The repetitive cultivation of an ordered succession of crops (or crops and fallow) on the same land. One cycle often takes several years to complete.

Cropping pattern: The yearly sequence and spatial arrangement of crops or of crops and fallow on a given area.

Cropping system: The cropping patterns used on a farm and their interaction with farm resources, other farm enterprises, and available technology which determine their makeup.

Mixed farming: Cropping systems which involve the raising of crops, animals, and/or trees.

Cropping index: The number of crops grown per annum on a given area of land $\times$ 100.

Land Equivalent Ratio (LER): The ratio of the area needed under sole cropping to one of intercropping at the same management level to give an equal amount of yield. LER is the sum of the fractions of the yields of the intercrops relative to their sole crop yields.

Income Equivalent Ratio (IER): The ratio of the area needed under sole cropping to produce the same gross income as one hectare of intercropping at the same management level. IER is the conversion of LER into economic terms.

---

multiple cropping reflect essentially two underlying principles that of growing crops simultaneously in mixtures, i.e., intercropping; or of growing individual crops in sequence, i.e., sequential cropping. Mixed, row, strip, and relay intercropping work on the former principle, while double (and triple, etc.) and ratoon cropping use the latter. There are several other derived forms of multiple cropping patterns, but these originate through synthesis of the simultaneous and sequential cropping practices.

Availability of Water

In vast areas of rain-fed agriculture where full irrigation is an economic impossibility, the extent of crop growth is limited by the duration of the wet season moisture supply. In India and Africa, settled farming is possible in areas where annual rainfall is greater than 300 mm. In areas with rainfall between 300 and 600 mm, simultaneous cropping is practiced with crops of similar maturity, although there is usually a component crop in the mixture which allows fuller use of the end of wet season moisture. In areas of higher rainfall up to 1,000 mm, crop mixtures, especially those involving different maturities, are common. Here the slow-growing, later maturing components generally tend to mature under better end-of-season moisture conditions. In areas with above 1,000 mm of rainfall, multiple cropping both on the simultaneous and sequential principle is practiced (Ruthenberg, 1971; Krishnamoorthy, 1974).

Sequential cropping is possible in climatic areas where conditions for plant growth exist beyond the duration of one early maturing crop. In temperate regions the total growing season is limited mainly by low temperature (and low solar radiation) in the winter months. However, in frost-free areas, the restriction is usually one of availability of soil moisture. Within these warmer regions with a long wet season, as in the humid tropics, or a shorter wet season, as in the dry tropics with irrigation facilities, crops can be grown through much of the year or all year round. It is in such areas that a strong association with multiple cropping emerges (Dalrymple, 1971), and rice (*Oryza sativa* L.) in monoculture more than any other crop is involved in areas closer to the equator, while rice in combination with other crops, e.g., wheat (*Triticum aestivum* L.), in areas away from the equator. However, the cropping intensity index varies from area to area and country to country. The cropping index in India is about 115 over about 20 million ha, which can be double cropped out of approximately 100 million ha. In Taiwan the cropping index is 185, with certain districts as high as 230, though figures for individual fields may exceed 400 (Dalrymple, 1971).

Utilization of Space and Time

Crops may be grown sequentially one after another so that time is used to obtain more production, or crops can be mixed and grown together simultaneously intercropped. With the latter, since different crops have different growth requirements, a mixture of crops of similar maturity can have higher total productivity than a single crop. However, crops commonly used in mixtures usually differ in maturity, so their growth requirements are further separated in time and competition between them is less.

The intercropped patterns aim at utilizing both extra time and spatial arrangements of component crops, and one species may even provide support for another, as in the case of climbing beans (*Phaseolus* sp.) and maize (*Zea mays* L.) (CIAT, 1973). In a successful crop mixture of both similar and different maturities, the sum of the intercrop competition should be less than the sum of the intracrop competition of the component crops when grown alone. Gain originates in crop mixtures because either individual plants yield more and/or higher total plant population densities are possible. In mixtures of crops of similar maturity, yield advantages accrue basically through a lower "instantaneous" intercrop competition in space, both aerial and adaphic. In mixtures of crops of different maturities, yield advantages accrue through a low intercrop competition in space and time for the more rapidly growing, early maturing components and through a lower intracrop competition in space and time for the slow-growing, later maturing components.

The successive patterns of cropping aim at multiplying the net return per unit area by growing extra crop(s). Time is therefore the extra dimension used. The breeding of high-yielding, early maturing crop cultivars has greatly contributed to the flexibility of successive cropping patterns. For example, the replacement of the photosensitive 'Kharif' (wet season) sorghums (*Sorghum bicolor*) with early maturing hybrids in India has allowed double cropping where only single cropping existed before. Further, where double cropping already existed, it has permitted earlier planting with consequent higher yields of the second crop (*Rabi* post-monsoon, residual moisture crop) such as wheat, chickpea (*Cicer arietinum*), safflower (*Carthamus tinctorius*), linseed (*Linum* sp.), and sunflower (*Helianthus annuus*) (IARI, 1972; Krishnamoorthy, 1974; Rao, 1975). The principles used to increase yields of sole crops can be more easily transferred to sequential cropping where crops are usually grown alone, rather than to intercropped mixtures. However, a note of caution has to be sounded when adopting new sequential cropping sequences due to possible negative carryover effects from one crop to another. The first crop may adversely affect the performance of the second crop by an undue depletion of nutrients or soil moisture reserves and an increase in the population of pests and diseases, particularly critical in monoculture sequences. On the other hand, complementary effects can be noted with sequences involving legumes and pest and disease control when different crops are used.

The principles of yield increases resulting from a better use of space in mixtures are complementary to utilizing time with crops in sequences. Theoretically, therefore, maximum cropping should be obtained with sequences of high-yielding crops in compatible mixtures. In practice, this pattern has evolved in relation to the traditional resources where several crops are planted and harvested in mixtures at different times (Ruthenberg, 1971; Baker & Norman, 1975).

Yield Advantages in Crop Mixtures

The extent of the extra contribution to production per unit area from crop mixtures has been particularly difficult to define in surveys because the land equivalent ratio (LER) of a mixture is not readily apparent without the corresponding yield figures of all the component crops in the mixture grown as sole crops under similar management. However, LERs of up to 1.6 have been reported for farmers' fields in northern Nigeria (Baker & Norman, 1975).

Experiments have been conducted to discover if and how crop mixtures can be improved, and LERs of up to 2.0 have been reported (Andrews, 1972; Government of India, 1975; IRRI, 1974; Krantz et al., 1974; and Rao, 1975). Cultivars bred for high yields under sole cropping show less interplant competition, which also makes them more favorable for growing in mixtures provided any shift in the interplant competition equilibrium in mixtures is restored by adjusting the relative crop plant densities. Work at IRRI (1974) has indicated that some mixtures show a higher LER at a low level of management, while others, e.g., rice-maize, respond to good management.

Further instances of good responses at higher production levels have been demonstrated with sorghum-millet (*Pennisetum americanum*)-cowpea (*Vigna* sp.) mixture (Andrews, 1974), sorghum-millet-maize (Baker, 1974), sorghum-beans (Osiru & Willey, 1972), and maize-beans (Willey & Osiru, 1972).

High-yielding cultivars tend to give optimum yields over a wide range in population density; therefore, intercropped row widths are less critical at high densities. This facilitates intercropping and contributes to better utilization of space. Work comparing row versus mixed intercropping (Dalal, 1974; Evans, 1960) has indicated that there need not be a substantial loss in re-orientating mixed crops into rows, which patently has many advantages and is a necessity to allow more improved production techniques to be applied to mixtures. On a row basis, many crop-specific cultural operations are possible from sowing to harvest, and there is a wide scope for using animal and motorized power in intercrops without having to resort to strip cropping, where the benefits from crop contact over space and time are less.

Since yield levels have been shown to be higher with crop mixtures in the semiarid tropics where availability of water for crop growth is often limiting, total crop water use efficiency of mixtures may well be higher particularly for the wet season as a whole (Baker & Norman, 1975). Similarly, investigations into nitrogen use efficiency have indicated with some exclusions (S. P. Liboon, and R. R. Harwood. 1975. Nitrogen response in corn-soybean intercropping. Sixth Annual Sci. Meeting, Philippines Crop Sci. Soc., Bacolod City, Philippines) that mixtures can make better use of nitrogen than sole crops (IRRI, 1974; Kasam & Stockinger, 1973). Further, weed control and use of total available labor has been shown to be better in crop mixtures (Baker & Norman, 1975).

Security Factors in Multiple Cropping

A significant feature of multiple cropping is a greater dependability of return compared with sole cropping. This is important at all levels of production but especially to small farmers at low yield levels where alternatives to production are much more restricted and the farmer therefore has to be more certain that his investments of labor and capital (if any) are protected. In the tropics, at low levels of production, it has become abundantly clear that the adoption of sole cropping practices for many food crops offers less dependable returns (Evans, 1960; Ogunfowora & Norman, 1973; Ruthenberg, 1971; Webster & Wilson, 1966). In this context increases in production are more likely to come through multiple cropping which satisfies the farmer's security motives.

Sequential cropping is intrinsically more secure in providing some measure of return because two (or more) crops will be attempted during the year. In the rain-fed areas, the potentiality of multiple cropping attracts the development of soil and water resources which is accompanied by an array of stabilizing features such as less risk of drought and erosion.

A crop mixture is more dynamic biologically than a sole crop and is less likely to succumb to adversities of nature. Reduced performance of some of the component crops may be compensated by those remaining. There is good evidence (Caswell & Raheja, 1972; Hayward, 1975; IRRI, 1974) that pest attack may be lower on crops grown in mixtures involving maize, cowpea, pigeon pea (*Cajanus cajan*), and probably other legumes. This is possible also for diseases where the severity of attack is proportional to the host plant density. Further, there is some evidence to suggest that the pest population dynamics may be more stable than in sole crops (IRRI, 1974). While verification of lower pest incidence in mixtures at higher levels of production is required, it remains likely that pest control could be easier in some mixtures.

MULTIPLE CROPPING AND FARMERS' RESOURCES

The Present Scene

The actual form of multiple cropping used and benefits that a farmer derives from it are dictated by the farmer's yield-sustaining resources on the farm and his own understanding of how best to achieve maximum profit and security within the limitations of his total environment. In areas where the rainy season is long and favorable enough to grow more than one crop of different maturities simultaneously or successively, or where irrigation is available, the potential benefits of multiple cropping have been long appreciated and are being realized. Where farming has become capital intensive, production is at a high level even in the developing world. However, it is in the dryland areas of the developing world with low production where the benefits of multiple cropping at a high level of production are yet to be realized on a large scale. The natural reasons for the fluctuations of world food supplies are adversities of climate and weather. Most vulnerable to these factors are the low level equilibrium farmers whose failures to meet basic production requirements in poor years strain available food reserves. To consider the potential of multiple cropping in increasing world food supplies, it is essential to recognize that the problems of increasing production in areas where farming is already capital or labor intensive are markedly different from those of increasing food supplies in areas where farming communities depend solely on their own labor (with or without animal power) for survival. It is in these latter areas, which comprise about 80% of the farmers in the poorer countries, where cropping practices have to produce not only more food but to provide productive work for the rural population, food for the urban population, raw material for industries and export, markets for the products of indigenous industries, and funds for general rural development. Hunger has often been thought of as the main problem of these areas, but it has long been evident that in most of the poorer countries, hunger is but one facet of poverty (Bunting, 1972). It is further evident that as human populations have increased in the poorer countries the output of food has increased with them, so that except in certain parts of Africa, estimated average output of food per head has generally risen (Bunting, 1972).

The Green Revolution

The green revolution with rice and wheat is commonly associated with high-yielding varieties, some of which can indeed out yield the traditional cultivars even when the cultural practices remain unchanged. However, the impact of new varieties of rice and wheat on production has occurred mainly through improved conditions of production, particularly in respect to irrigation, fertilizers, and control of pests and diseases. Consequently, the logistics of the green revolution have had to include schemes to ensure that the necessary inputs are available to the farmers in the right form, that the farmer has means to buy them on fair terms, and that there is a reliable market at the end of the season at a price sufficient to ensure a profit and an adequate incentive. In other words, the use of high-yielding varieties and the sequential cropping practices in much of the green revolution areas are interlocked with better total resources and services made available (Bunting, 1972).

TECHNICAL RESEARCH AND PROSPECTS

In irrigated agriculture, sequential multiple cropping practices are usually more technologically advanced even in the developing world. The use of irrigation requires complementary land development and soil and water management practices, which also create a stable framework in which improved cultural practices become reliably more profitable and newer techniques can be more easily adopted. In the rain-fed agriculture in the tropics, rainstorm systems and soil water regimes are such that crop production is caught between drought, leaching and excess water. Further, the high energy load and concentrated nature of individual rainstorm systems present serious erosion hazards during the whole wet season on all types of soil. All this leads to problems of soil, water, and crop management largely unknown under the gentler rainfall conditions of the temperate and subtropical climates. Proper understanding of the characteristics of rainfall and its management, use, and conservation is a fundamental requisite for creating a stable basis for improving production. Control of soil erosion, improvement of soil moisture penetration and retention, reduction of runoff, and harvesting that which does occur for reuse during the wet season or extending the growing season, are basic concepts (ICRISAT, 1974). Within this context, multiple cropping with its quicker, greater, and longer crop cover offers a better and stable yield-producing system (Krantz et al., 1974). However, a proper understanding of nutrient, pest, and disease balance and their control and management is needed in both the semiarid and humid tropics. The possible benefits of legumes in mixtures and sequences must be more clearly studied in relation to the whole question of the nitrogen cycle. Since the success of multiple cropping depends largely on the utilization of time, its management becomes important in terms of operations needed in respect to the seasons and state of the component crops. The use of power (animal and/or machine) and implements has been recognized as being an important input in relation to the timeliness of operations, reducing drudgery of farming, removing labor bottlenecks, and generating employment through increased production. However, more information is needed on the economics of various sources and types of power and implements which are likely to be suitable for multiple cropping. Finally, all the above aspects of multiple cropping need to be considered in the overall context of the cropping system, and it is here that the results of cropping systems research supported by appropriate socio-economic studies, such as that conducted at IRRI, ICRISAT, CIAT, IITA, and national centers, are most needed.

The prospects of increasing world food supplies through multiple cropping in the rain-fed farming areas of the poorer countries must be seen in perspective, i.e., it is only one element in the fight against poverty. Rural populations in these areas will continue to increase for many years, and if their well-being is to improve, agriculture will have to provide more productive work and better food the year round than it does now. Multiple cropping at high production through the use of intensive capital investments, heavy farm machinery, and labor-saving means is unlikely to offer a solution to the large majority. The object will be how to use productively as much of the labor available with limited capital. The use of animal power and/or mechanization should be aimed at increasing labor productivity, not by reducing the total labor required but by reducing labor bottlenecks, particularly that of weeding and other activities, related to the pronounced labor peak early in the season, so that labor may be more productive at other times of the season. Low capital mechanization which is production-enhancing, and where possible, employment-generating will therefore be more appropriate. Multiple cropping, particularly intercropping, is labor intensive and can be more productive per unit area, which, for many of the populous regions with absolute land limitations is a more realistic yardstick to use when considering the social objectives and economics of human labor, although production per unit total costs will always be of prime importance for production geared toward commercial markets.

LITERATURE CITED

Andrews, D. J. 1972. Intercropping with sorghum in Nigeria. Exp. Agric. 8:139–150.

Andrews, D. J. 1974. Responses of sorghum varieties to intercropping. Exp. Agric. 10: 57–63.

Baker, E. F. I. 1974. Research into intercropping aspects of farming systems in Nigeria. Mixed cropping with cereals—a system for improvement. p. 287–301. In Proceedings of the Farming Systems Workshop, ICRISAT, Hyderabad, India.

Baker, E. F. I., and D. W. Norman. 1975. Cropping systems in northern Nigeria. In Proceedings of the Cropping Systems Workshop, IRRI, Los Banos, Philippines.

Bunting, A. H. 1972. Pests, population, and poverty in the developing world. The John Curtis 'Woodstock' Lecture. J. R. Soc. Arts, p. 227–239.

Caswell, G. H., and A. K. Raheja. 1972. Report to the Board of Governors. Inst. for Agric. Res., Samaru, Nigeria.

Centro Internacional de Agricultura Tropical. 1973. Annual report. CIAT, Palmira, Colombia.

Dalal, R. C. 1974. Intercropping maize with pigeonpeas. Exp. Agric. 10:219–225.

Dalrymple, D. G. 1971. Survey of multiple cropping in less developed nations. Foreign Agric. Econ. Rep. 91., USDA, Washington, D. C.

Evans, A. C. 1960. Studies of intercropping. I. Maize or sorghum with groundnuts. East Afr. Agric. For. J. 26:1–10.

Government of India. 1975. Dep. Agric. Res. Educ. Rep., New Delhi, India.

Hayward, J. H. 1975. Cropping scheme meeting. Inst. for Agric. Res., Samaru, Nigeria.

Indian Agricultural Research Institute. 1972. Recent research on multiple cropping. IARI Bull. 8, New Delhi, India.

International Center and Research Institute for the Semiarid Tropics. 1974. Annual report. ICRISAT, Hyderabad, India.

International Rice Research Institute. 1974. Annual report. IRRI, Los Banos, Philippines.

Kasam, A. H., and K. Stockinger. 1973. Growth and nitrogen uptake of sorghum and millet in mixed cropping. Samaru Agric. Newsl. 15:28–33.

Krantz, B. A., and Sardar Singh. 1974. Cropping patterns for increasing and stabilizing agricultural production in the semi-arid tropics. p. 217–248. *In* Proceedings of the Farming Systems Workshop, ICRISAT, Hyderabad, India.

Krishnamoorthy, Ch. 1974. Present cropping systems including trends of change and advances of approach for improvement. p. 277–286. *In* Proceedings of Farming Systems Workshop, ICRISAT, Hyderabad, India.

Ogunfowora, O., and D. W. Norman. 1973. An optimization model for evaluating the stability of sole cropping and mixed cropping systems under changing resource and technology levels. Bull. Rural Econ. Soc. 8:77–96.

Osiru, D. S. O., and R. W. Willey. 1972. Studies on mixtures of dwarf sorghum and beans (*Phaseolus vulgaris*) with particular reference to plant population. J. Agric. Sci. Camb. 71:531–540.

Rao, N. G. P. 1975. Sorghum production programmes. All India Sorghum Improvement Programme. IARI, Hyderabad, India.

Ruthenberg, H. 1971. Farming systems in the tropics. Clarendon Press, Oxford, United Kingdom.

Webster, C. C., and P. N. Wilson. 1966. Agriculture in the tropics. Longmans, London.

Willey, R. W., and D. S. O. Osiru. 1972. Studies on mixtures of maize and beans (*Phaseolus vulgaris*) with particular reference to plant population. J. Agric. Sci. Camb. 79:519–529.

Multiple Cropping in Tropical Asia

R. R. Harwood and E. C. Price[1]

Present and potential multiple cropping patterns are determined by a wide range of physical and socio-economic conditions against a background of available technology. We have therefore chosen to present multiple cropping in tropical Asia in several parts which describe first the economic and physical factors which influence multiple cropping, then the present farming systems within which multiple cropping is practiced and their direction of change, and finally, the major multiple cropping patterns. Relevant research needs are summarized.

Tropical Asia includes the area between the Himalayan mountains and the equator from Pakistan and India to Indonesia, New Guinea, the Philippines, southern Taiwan, the southeastern portion of the People's Republic of China and mainland southeast Asia. The dominant crops in the region are mainly determined by water supply. Cropping systems in the drier regions of India and Pakistan are based on corn (*Zea mays* L.) sorghum (*Sorghum* spp.), millet (*Setaria italica*), and wheat (*Triticum aestivum* L.), while the wetter areas of these same countries and nearly all of east Asia, having high rainfall, are rice (*Oryza sativa* L.) based.

THE ECONOMIC SETTING OF CROPPING SYSTEMS IN TROPICAL ASIA

While most of the economic features in tropical Asia that affect multiple cropping are changeable to some degree, two of the more permanent conditions can be identified: a smallholder structure, and allied with this, a highly dispersed production that leads to high marketing costs. Other factors which strongly influence cropping systems, but which are more variable over time and locale, are agricultural wage rates, the levels of human and physical capital in agriculture, and prices of agricultural products and cash inputs.

---

[1] Agronomist and associate economist, The International Rice Research Institute, Los Banos, Philippines.

Table 1. Farm size distribution in south, southeast, and east Asia (IRRI, undated)

Location	Total farm area	Distribution of size in hectares					
		<0.5	0.5-1.0	1.0-2.0	2.0-3.0	3.0-4.0	>4.0
	000 ha	———————————— % ————————————					
South Asia	64115	22	19	22	12	7	18
India	49874	21	19	22	12	7	18
Bangladesh	6139	28	24	26	11	4	7
Nepal	2076	30	14	15	8	8	24
Pakistan	4860	17	15	17	12	8	31
Sri Lanka	1166	39	26	19	6	6	4
Southeast Asia	19899	33	20	21	10	5	11
Indonesia	12237	44	26	18	6	2	4
Malaysia (West)	450	15	22	31	16	6	10
Philippines	2166	4	7	30	21	12	26
Thailand	3174	10	7	22	17	11	32
Vietnam	1872	37	19	22	10	4	8
East Asia	8405	38	31	25	6*		
Japan	5176	38	31	25	6		
Korea	2452	36	32	26	6		
Taiwan	777	37	29	24	10		

* 2 hectares and above.

Farm Size

There is a prevalence of small farms in tropical Asia (Table 1). One-third of the farms in southeast Asia are less than 0.5 ha in size, one-half of all farms are less than 1 ha, and three-quarters are of less than 2 ha. The average farm size in southeast Asia is 1.8 ha, compared to 1.1 ha in east Asia, 2.4 in south Asia, and about 120 ha in the U. S. (Table 2).

Several researchers have found size of farm and number of crops per year inversely related. In Bangladesh, Amed (1965) found that on farms of less than 1 ha the average cropping intensity index was 167, compared to an index of 117 on farms larger than 16 ha (Table 3). In a study of vegetable farmers in Taiwan, Menegay (1975) also reported that "farm size decreased as the relative intensity of vegetable production increased." But the available research does not clearly say whether diminishing farm size over time forced farmers toward intensification or, alternatively, whether it was the drive toward intensive agriculture that resulted in small farms.

The latter is hypothesized here. More specifically, we suggest that (i) in a tropical regime, annual production per unit area responds positively to the management input at much higher rates of applications than in a temperate regime, and (ii) the resulting economic incentive to increase the management input has directly contributed to the reduction in farm size in tropical Asia. The argument is given in greater detail.

Because tropical climatic conditions are suitable for field crop production during much of the year, cropping pattern alternatives are numerous. As the number of possible sequential crops per year increases, the number of

Table 2. Arable land, farm size, portion of labor in agriculture, people per square kilometer of arable land (IRRI, undated)

Location	Arable land		Farm size	Portion of labor force in agriculture		People	
	1960	1970		1960	1970	1960	1970
	000 ha		ha	%		number/km^2	
South Asia	149994	199950	2.4	74	68	368	350
India	120268	164610	2.5 (1960)	74	68	360	327
Bangladesh	11283	12146	1.4 (1960)	76	70	476	615
Nepal	1831	1980	1.2 (1961/62)	94	92	501	569
Pakistan	15074	19235	3.5 (1960)	76	70	309	323
Sri Lanka	1538	1979	1.6 (1962)	56	52	643	637
Southeast Asia	53510	67687	1.8	76	70	373	387
Burma	17425	18920	*	68	64	127	147
Indonesia	11698	18000	1.1	75	70	799	673
Khmer Republic	2353	2984	2.0 (1960)	82	76	231	238
Laos	1000	950	na	83	78	233	314
Malaysia (Sabah, Sarawak, West Malaysia)	2135	3523	5.7 (1961)	63	56	411	306
Philippines	6696	8977	3.6 (1960)	74	69	409	425
Thailand	9782	11415	3.5 (1963)	84	76	270	317
Vietnam	2421	2918	1.3 (1960)	80	74	582	615
East Asia	8947	8688	1.1	39	28	1446	1738
Japan	6046	5510	1.2 (1960)	33	21	1556	1894
Korea	2109	2311	0.8 (1970)	66	58	1171	1389
Taiwan	792	867	1.3 (1960)	47	42	1340	1675
China	109354	110300	na	75	67	582	688
U.S.	182501	192318	122.5 (1959)	7	4	99	107

* 1960 survey indicated that 40% of the farms were less than 2 ha and only 14% were more than 8 ha.

Table 3. Cropping intensity as influenced by size of farm in Bangladesh (Amed, 1965)

Size of farm	Cropping intensity
	%
Small (under 1 ha)	167
Medium (1 to 5 ha)	148
Large (5 to 16 ha)	130
Over 16 ha	117

pattern alternatives expands rapidly. At one of the sites in the Philippines where the International Rice Research Institute (IRRI) cropping systems research has been conducted for 2 years, more than 170 cropping patterns have been identified among 50 farmers. More than 100 different farm operations are performed on those crops.

Choosing the most profitable pattern likely requires a higher level of management where sequential crops can be grown than in a one-crop regime. Put another way, marginal return to management remains positive at much higher rates of application under tropical regimes than under temperate ones (Fig. 1). However, the maximum return across variable management levels in tropical regimes may either be lower or higher than in temperate ones, depending on the quality of other resources.

Income from crops (per hectare)

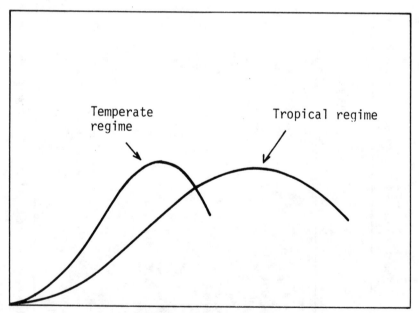

Units of management per hectare

Figure 1. Relation of farm income to management in tropical and temperate regimes.

The high complementarity between management and physical resources in the tropics, suggested here, is a hypothesis that has yet to be tested. Even more tentative is the following suggestion of the manner in which high ratios of management to land have been reached in southeast Asia. In the absence of education which might have augmented the management capacity of farmers, and before management-augmenting capital or technology became available, higher ratios of managerial capacity to land were achieved through the reduction of farm size. The size of holdings continued to decrease until the marginal return to farm operators declined to the level of the labor wage, or whatever was the highest level of return to managers in alternative employment.

One might further speculate that the same process that resulted in more managers also produced a high proportion of laborers, as siblings and offsprings of farm operators. Therefore, the redundancy of agricultural labor has perhaps been a by-product, not the major cause, of the drive to achieve intensive resource management. Whatever surplus labor that remains in southeast Asia today may be a condition that is largely incidental to the existence of intensive farming. Of course, the rational operator tended to use more labor when it was cheap than when its price was high.

Cheap labor is apparently not necessary for intensive agriculture. Taiwanese farms, for example, are now comparatively mechanized, occupying 42% of the labor force, compared with 70% for southeast Asia as a whole. Yet the cropping intensity in Taiwan is far greater than in any part of southeast Asia, about 175 (Chao, 1975). The index levels in the more labor intensive locales in southeast Asia do not exceed 150 (Manu, 1975; Oshima, 1973).

Seen in this light, it was perhaps not population pressure that has forced agricultural intensification, but rather the reverse. The evolution of small farms in tropical Asia may have been a rational response to profitable opportunities for the intensive land cultivation that is possible in these portions of the tropics. Two relatively permanent features associated with the long tropical growing season, which strongly influence cropping systems, are high complementarity of the management input with land and a consequently small optimum farm-size.

Markets

Associated with smallholder agriculture are high marketing costs for agricultural produce. Numerous middlemen and transactions are required to collect produce from many small producers and distribute it to consumers.

Summarizing some of the work presented at a workshop on multiple cropping, Oshima (1973) concluded that

> . . .Small amounts of surplus output from tiny, innumerable farms producing more than one commodity require a wide network of assembly and collecting stations, small processing plants, and marketing stalls and

centers. This suggests that the income from the sale of these surpluses are small and scattered requiring small shops and stores to sell farm inputs and consumer goods to the small farmers. Accordingly, small farms mean small stores, outlets, and other selling and service units.

A number of studies have shown markets in southeast Asia to be quite efficient, meaning that the difference between the price which the farmer receives and that paid by consumers closely reflects the cost to middlemen for performing their functions (Thodey & Anee, 1974; Mears, 1974).[2] This feature of high marketing costs has caused some misunderstanding between economists and agronomists, not unknown to those studying cropping systems. Having developed the biological technology for producing a crop to fit an ecological niche and perhaps noting that a respectable price for the crop prevails in central markets, the agronomist is likely to declare that production problems have been solved, and only economic ones remain. In truth, it is the structure of production that often causes the unprofitable operations of smallholders, a problem neither scientist can alter.

To some extent, the high density of southeast Asia populations compensates for the marketing problems associated with the smallholder by providing consuming points that are generally near production. Southeast Asian produce travels much less distance from producer to consumer than in many developed countries.

A more changeable component of marketing costs is transportation. In recent years new roads and highways have linked the interior of most countries to the population centers. This has increased the cropping alternatives for outlying areas, as in northeast Thailand, where a number of new field crops have entered cropping patterns both before and after rice, or where the the new crops have replaced rice altogether.

Superimposed on the relatively permanent economic features of tropical Asian agriculture are certain influential conditions that recently have changed as at no time since World War II. Those conditions which now appear to be rapidly shifting, with strong implications for cropping systems, are the availability of labor, levels of human and financial capital in the rural sectors, and product demand and input prices.

Agricultural Labor and Wages

The large labor pools of southeast Asia may have resulted from the spurts of entrepreneurial response to the opportunities for intensification. If there was a causal link between the drive toward intensive land management, and growth of the labor force, it was broken when education and management augmenting capital and technology became available. Increasing numbers of decision-makers per unit land area were no longer necessary, and the most explosive force in population growth relented. Industries

---

[2]E. C. Price, Jr., 1973. Aggregate supply of bovines in northeast Thailand. Ph.D. Dissertation, Department of Agricultural Economics, University of Kentucky, Lexington.

gradually absorbed the redundant labor. In recent years industrialization has been fairly rapid in southeast Asia, and surplus labor has disappeared. The real agricultural labor wage is already high in Malaya, is edging up in Thailand, and is likely to move higher in the Philippines. On the other hand, the agricultural labor wage is still low in Indonesia—at less than half the rate paid in the Philippines and Thailand.

Human Capital

A burgeoning class of agricultural technicians, educated in both the newly advanced curriculum of Asian universities and in universities abroad, is now of size to have a measurable impact on the technology readily available to farmers. The number of research scientists and extension workers in southeast Asia each doubled between 1965 and 1974 (Boyce & Evenson, 1975). In south Asia the rate of manpower increase, though lower, still was substantial. Furthermore, in 1974, south and southeast Asia combined had 36% of the world's extension workers, but only about 4% of the agricultural researchers (Boyce & Evenson, 1975).

Financial Capital

The investment of financial capital is also increasing, assisted by aggressive government programs which provide low interest rate loans for either operating or investment capital in agriculture. A recent Presidential decree in the Philippines requires that all banks operating in the country allocate 25% of their loan value to agriculture.

Still the rural interest rates are high. Farmers must rely heavily upon private lenders whose rates frequently exceed 100% per annum. An estimate of average interest rate on loans from all sources in northeast Thailand is 80% per annum.[3]

Product Demand and Prices

Two factors have radically changed the demand for agricultural products in southeast Asia: the entry of aggressive buyers for the large Japanese markets and the depletion of U. S. grain reserves which for 25 years had helped to stabilize world prices. The former development has not only increased the demand for commodities with established markets, but has created markets where none, or only weak ones, had existed. Soybean (*Glycine max* L. Merr.), corn, and sorghum buying particularly by agents who willingly seek out and contract for small but long-term supplies, has had a strong impact on producers' cropping decisions.

---

[3]E. C. Price, Jr., 1973. Bovines in northeast Thailand.

IMPLICATIONS OF ECONOMIC CONDITIONS FOR CROPPING SYSTEMS

The main characteristics of the economic setting in southeast Asia that have been presented are small farm size, dispersed production, a low real wage rate in certain areas but a rising wage in others, an increasingly large research and extension capacity, generally high interest rates but availability of low interest loans for high-priority projects, and a strong demand for agricultural produce but increasingly unstable prices. These factors are related to cropping systems.

Dispersed Production

Highly dispersed production can quite efficiently supply a similarly dispersed pattern of consumption, such as that which results from high population densities. But such structures are less responsive to new crop possibilities, since local demand for the crops must develop along with production. The alternative of shipping crops to terminals that are linked to external points of consumption, is hampered by the high costs of collecting crops.

The problem may not be as difficult to solve as it first appears. The development in several southeast Asian countries of an active local trade in melons (*Cucumis* spp.), green corn, yambean (*Pachyrhizus* spp.), soybean, and other produce shows the rapid growth in local demand for new crops. New feedgrain crops have been used by local livestock industries in northeast Thailand where corn has become a major crop both for export and domestic feed mills.

Labor

An increase in the labor wage, with industrialization, has no predictable impact on cropping patterns. While cheap labor assisted the early development of intensive agriculture, mechanization is also consistent with a high cropping index, as demonstrated in east Asia. Labor is only one cost of production. The returns, say, from producing a high valued crop, perhaps utilizing land in a period when it has a low opportunity cost, may well be sufficient to encourage production even under conditions of high labor costs. For example, ditch and dike vegetable cultivation can be seen in even the high-wage areas of southeast Asia. Furthermore, the high prices for field crops, such as soybeans, that have usually been grown by land-extensive technology, may now support a more intensive technology.

Human Capital

Higher levels of human capital in the farm sector, particularly when manifest in the managerial capacity of farmers, increase the potential for intensive resource utilization without resorting to a reduction of the size of holdings. The increasing number of extension workers and researchers in southeast Asia presumably will lead to high levels of on-farm human capital through training and advisory services.

Demand

Higher prices will permit more intensive cultivation, but the mix of crops may also shift. Since 1973 the prices of grain legumes in the Philippines have increased about 80% while cereal grains cost only about 30% higher. A consequent shift in the components of cropping patterns, and advisedly in the attention of researchers, may result.

Little can be found that is unique about the relationship of cast inputs to cropping systems in southeast Asia. The universal case is that with much higher prices of chemical inputs, with expanding crop production, chemical-saving technology now has a higher return. The biological control of insect and weed pests that is possible through multiple cropping is more profitable than before. More efficient use of fertilizer through sequential planting is now an important consideration in the design of cropping patterns.

PHYSICAL FACTORS INFLUENCING MULTIPLE CROPPING

Rainfall

In nonirrigated areas in tropical Asia, cropping patterns are determined primarily by duration and amount of rainfall, with most of the area subject to a monsoon climate. The dry areas of India that have less than 1,000 mm of rain per year have sorghum and millet-based patterns. Those that have intermediate rainfall grow corn or wheat. Corn-based patterns best fit the zone of 1,000 to 1,500 mm annual rainfall. The driest portions of southeast Asia fit this category. Rice-based patterns require an annual rainfall of 1,500 mm or more and at least 200 mm/month rainfall for 3 consecutive months. Most of eastern Asia falls into this latter category. Much of northeast Thailand, having slightly less than 1,500 mm annual rainfall and with 2 to 3 months of 200 mm/month is a marginal area for rain-fed rice; a portion of the area is not planted each year because of lack of water.

The type of rice culture or the type and intensity of cropping pattern depends on the specific characteristics of the rainfall curve. A rainfall classification scheme, based on cropping potential (Table 4), has been developed for Asia (Coulter et al., 1974). The amount and the duration of rainfall determine the number and types of crops possible. The gradual or rapid onset, or decline, of heavy rains determines the type of culture for rice, which crops should be used as second or third crops in the pattern, and the relative difficulty of tillage operations. Bangladesh, Indonesia, and the Philippines are being mapped using this system. The portions of land in Bangladesh, the

Table 4. Rainfall classification for southeast Asia (Coulter et al., 1974)

Zone & subzone	Description
I	less than 3 consecutive wet months (No rain-fed rice crop possible)
I 1	more than 6 consecutive dry months
I 2	5-6 consecutive dry months
I 3	2-4 consecutive dry months
I 4	less than 2 consecutive dry months
II	3-4 consecutive wet months
II 1	more than 6 consecutive dry months (always "sharp end")
II 2.1	5-6 consecutive dry months (with "sharp end")
II 2.2	5-6 consecutive dry months (with "gradual end")
II 3.1	2-4 consecutive dry months (with "sharp end")
II 3.2	2-4 consecutive dry months (with "gradual end")
II 4.1	less than 2 consecutive dry months ("bimodal")
II 4.2	less than 2 consecutive dry months ("unimodal")
III	5-6 consecutive wet months
III 1	more than 6 consecutive dry months (hypothetical)
III 2.1	5-6 consecutive dry months (always "sharp end")
III 3.1	2-4 consecutive dry months (with "sharp end")
III 3.2	2-4 consecutive dry months (with "gradual end")
III 4.1	less than 2 consecutive dry months ("bimodal")
III 4.2	less than 2 consecutive dry months ("unimodal")
IV	7-8 consecutive wet months
IV and IV 2	not applicable
IV 3.1	2-4 consecutive dry months (with "sharp end")
IV 3.2	2-4 consecutive dry months (with "gradual end")
IV 4.1	less than 2 consecutive dry months ("bimodal")
IV 4.2	less than 2 consecutive dry months ("unimodal")
V	more than 8 consecutive wet months
V 3	with 2 or more dry months
V 4	less than 2 dry months

Philippines, and the Island of Java that fall under each major rainfall zone are shown in Table 5.

Irrigation

Most of Asia's irrigation is "partial" irrigation, with water being available for only part of the year. Because rivers are short and valleys are steep in much of the area, large water storage dams are feasible only in selected locations. Irrigation only in the wet season is valuable, however, in reducing crop risk in an uncertain monsoon climate. Higher levels of crop management and inputs can be justified with some guarantee of available water. The partially irrigated areas of southeast Asia now offer great potential for increasing crop intensity as other crops are added to a single crop to make better use of available water in a growing season lengthened slightly by irrigation.

Table 5. Percentages of land in Bangladesh, Indonesia, and the Philippines that fall under five major rainfall categories

	Rainfall category	Bangladesh	Indonesia	Philippines
			%	
I	less than 3 wet months	0	25	12
II	3-4 wet months	23	40	28
III	5-6 wet months	72	30	37
IV	7-8 wet months	5	5	21
V	more than 8 wet months	0	0	2

A summary of irrigated areas in the region is available (Table 6), but figures on duration and quality of water in those systems are not available. Southeast Asia has the lowest percentage of irrigated land in Asia, 19%, compared with 21% in south Asia and 47% in east Asia. Fifty-four percent of the irrigated land in southeast Asia is in Indonesia.

The fully irrigated areas (year-round) already have a high cropping intensity. Since multiple cropping of rice depends upon a reliable water supply, irrigation and multiple cropping show a high statistical relationship. East Asia, with the largest percentage of arable land under irrigation, has high indexes of cropping intensity of between 150 and 200 (Chao, 1975).

Table 6. Percentages of arable land in rice and the percentage of land irrigated in 1970 (FAO, 1950, 1962, 1971, 1972; Munsoon, 1962; NEDA, 1974; National Statistical Office, 1971)

	Arable land in rice	Irrigated land percent of arable
	%	
South Asia	25	21
India	23	17
Bangladesh	82	6
Nepal	61	9
Pakistan	8	65
Sri Lanka	31	23
Southeast Asia	43	19
Burma	45	4
Indonesia	45	38
Khmer Republic	80	3
Laos	70	2
Malaysia (Sabah, Sarawak, West Malaysia)	20	7
Philippines	35	9
Thailand	59	28
Vietnam	86	20
East Asia	56	47
Japan	53	51
Korea	52	53
Taiwan	90	58
China	30	69
U.S.	0.4	8

The irrigated areas of India (Rao, 1975), Indonesia (Oshima, 1973), and Thailand (Manu, 1975) have moderately high cropping indexes of between 125 and 150, and countrywide the Philippines has little irrigation and a cropping intensity index nearer 100.

However, if rice data are removed, the relationship would probably not be so clearly demonstrated. Highly intensive cultivation of unirrigated upland crops is found in several countries. The Gunung Kedil area of Java and Batangas Province of the Philippines are examples of such cultivation.

Soil

Soil conditions influence cropping patterns primarily from the standpoint of water movement and drainage and tillage capability under high rainfall. Many soils of the high-rainfall area are high in clay, predominantly montmorillonite. The paddy rice system is the only feasible alternative for these areas during the peak of the monsoon, when the soil cannot be tilled and maintained in an upland (i.e., nonpaddy) condition. In upland areas with rolling topography, upland rice may be grown only where the soil has good internal drainage. The suitability of fresh-water alluvial areas (having a relatively high calcium level) to upland crops like sugarcane (*Saccharum officinarum* L.) hinges on this improved internal drainage. The north shore of Java is thus suited to cane, while seemingly similar areas in the Bangkok flood plain and Mekong Delta, being marine in origin, have higher sodium content, less internal water movement, and limited potential for nonrice crops. Where soil water movement is limited, the paddy system is used.

The potential for growing a second or third upland crop after paddy rice in areas where rainfall is not adequate for additional rice hinges on the capability of converting soil from the puddled to an "upland" condition. If the soil is alluvial and high in silt, the puddled soil can often be tilled at a relatively high moisture level. The 1:1 clay types (red soils) are included in this category. The more common montmorillonite clay types are more difficult to cultivate. They must be tilled dry (requiring considerably more power), then allowed to alternately wet and dry, permitting shrinking and swelling to fracture the large clods and regain structure for upland crops. This process cannot be accomplished in periods of high rainfall. The rotation of upland crops with paddy rice is thus a complex practice that requires a careful blend of power, tillage methods, and choice of crop to fit the specific environment. With continuous irrigation, it is thus far easier to maintain a rice-only pattern. Where water is limiting, however, sequences of rice and upland crops make more efficient use of the water resource. Here the tillage problem is a major constraint to high crop productivity.

For upland crops on heavy soil, tillage for land preparation and weed control is likewise difficult during periods of high rainfall. This is one of the reasons why sugarcane or tree crops are suitable on the well-drained, heavy soils. Mid-season tillage requirements for these crops are minimal, with land preparation being done primarily in the dry season.

Native soil fertility is a determinant of cropping patterns, primarily in small farm agriculture where cash inputs are scarce or unavailable. Continuous cropping, especially with cereals, requires high levels of nutrient inputs, unlike the one-crop-a-year patterns which in the high rainfall tropics can do reasonably well without added nutrients (Geertz, 1963). Single-crop paddy rice is especially efficient in using available nutrients under anaerobic soil conditions of the paddy. Low cash-flow farming systems can achieve the nutrient inputs needed in crop areas by the cycling of human and animal wastes, as in the hills of Nepal or in parts of China. The cycling of human and animal wastes in rural areas is a labor-intensive process, however, and works well only under certain socio-economic and physical conditions. The cycling of urban wastes may have more potential in the future. The lower requirements for applied nutrients in the cereal-legume sequences make them more desirable to the farmer with limited access to cash inputs.

In Thailand and in similar soils the higher fertility requirements of paddy-upland crop rotations on low fertility soils are limiting to crop intensification and diversification. The favorable nutrient availability in the paddy leaves the following upland crop with a depleted nutrient status which may be uneconomical to correct for many upland crops. The transitional soils bordering the Bangkok flood plain fall into this category and have limited potential for cropping with upland field crops after rice, because of both nutrient and drainage problems (Ministry of Agriculture and Cooperatives, 1975. Preliminary report of the 1973–74 Chao Phya research project. Bangkok, Thailand. Unpublished report).

Elevation and Temperature

For most of southeast Asia the relatively small arable areas of higher elevation are used for the production of vegetable crops. At higher latitudes and on the drier Deccan Plateau of India, winter temperatures influence the crop pattern, but year-round cropping is not prohibited by temperature in most areas.

FARMING SYSTEMS IN WHICH MULTIPLE CROPPING IS PRACTICED IN ASIA

The Homestead Area

Asian farms are characterized by a diversity of crop, animal, and off-farm enterprises which contribute to the cash flow of the farming system and a homestead production area which is aimed primarily at farm family comfort and subsistence.

The area around the house or farmyard is normally planted to a wide assortment of crops which not only offer shelter and privacy, but also contribute diversity and quality to the diet of the farm family. The relative importance of this area to the family depends on both farm size and its cash flow. If the family has a low income, the extent and quality of the homestead area is crucial to the quality of the diet. Once the family's requirement for staple food has been met, the development of the homestead area is the next step in improving farmer welfare. For a subsistence farmer the homestead is as important as his cultivated field area. The development of homestead areas is most advanced on the small, low-income farms of Indonesia and Nepal. Those farms are characterized by a diversity of economic plant species, which number 50 to 60 in the more advanced systems. The plant components of the system may include: 5 or 6 tall-growing tree species [coconut (*Cocos nucifera*) or fruit], 5 or 6 medium-height tree species, 5 or 6 bush or shrub species, 4 or 5 root crops, and up to 30 shade-tolerant, short-statured or vine-type annuals.

These crops provide a wide diversity to the diet. They require no purchased inputs and only low management. Their growth is usually luxuriant because of the inflow and accumulation of nutrients in the homestead area from human and animal wastes. This use of accumulated nutrients in the homestead area is in fact an efficient recycling system which does much to offset the frequent lack of conscious recycling into the crop area. Hedgerows surrounding field plots can be considered an extension of the homestead area. Both areas having a high portion of perennial crops have relatively stable productivity.

The following factors limit the development of homestead areas on low income farms: (i) presence of untended forage animals which severely limit crop diversity (especially in India), (ii) clustered rural villages, (iii) seasonally deep water, (iv) a shifting village site, (v) high altitude, and (vi) location of the village in an estate crop area where space for alternate crops is not made available.

While little has been recorded concerning the content and importance of homestead areas, the effects of their presence or absence can be readily observed in rural households. Low income people who have to purchase all their dietary needs or who produce their own staple only will have a much lower dietary standard than those having access to a highly diversified and stable cropping system. This key component of the farming system has until now been overlooked in efforts to improve the lot of the low income farmer. The high management requiring vegetable crops of the often cited "kitchen garden" efforts are an ineffective substitute for a well-designed homestead area.

Large Farms (Above Five Hectares)

Because of their unique (for Asia) makeup, larger farms are briefly mentioned here as a separate category. They are characterized by a more "commercialized" system of management that has a source of mechanical power, market orientation (a relatively small portion of the produce being consumed on the farm), relatively high cash inputs, hired labor, and higher capital investment.

The cropping patterns are estate crops or simple crop sequences of a relatively few crops. In terms of number of farms, this type is of minor significance in most countries, but in terms of national economy and production they are much more prominent. Most of the so-called "modern" (capital, cash, and power intensive) technology is immediately relevant to this kind of farm. In most Asian countries, however, population pressure on land precludes the consolidation of smaller units into this easier type of system.

The crops grown on such farms are: estate crops—sugarcane, oilpalm (*Elaeis guineenis*), rubber (*Hevea brasiliensis*), coconut, tea (*Camellia sinensis*), etc.; timber; pineapple (*Ananas comosus*); corn (southeast Asia); wheat (India, Pakistan); and rice (to a limited extent).

Animal-Based Systems

Animal and crop production interact at several points. Crops and crop residue provide feed, and the animals provide power. Animal and crop enterprises usually compete for land, but they are complementary in the case where livestock are raised within crops, say coconut groves. Animals have uses which further complicate the analysis. They are used for meat, milk, as storers of value, for recreation, and are a source of status and pride. Bovine husbandry for the purpose of power would, in many cases, not be profitable were it not for the noncrop-related livestock uses.

The use of cattle for plowing in the east Java region around Probolinggo is an instructive example of some of the relationships involved. A surplus of cattle are raised here and shipped to other areas for slaughter. Many landless people work as caretakers for the small household herds. The animals are used for field work, even though the wage rate is one of the lowest in Asia, 0 to 20¢/day.

The simple interaction of bovines and crop cultivation, that is where bovines are fed on miscellaneous vegetation and crop residues and used mainly for power and later salvaged for meat, is a frequent component of cropping systems in southeast Asia. But in different areas even this simple type of interaction needs fine adjustment to special conditions that often are related to feed supply.

Farmers in Batangas, Philippines, intercrop a few rows of corn in upland rice fields to provide feed to draft animals during the growing season. This is perhaps necessary because crops cover the landscape almost throughout the year and the one crop of rice straw is not a year's feed supply.

Shifting Cultivation

Aside from the larger "capital intensive" farms, most other systems can best be viewed in terms of a dynamic process of change, with different stages of development in the same system seen through examples from different countries. There are three basic environment-dependent development patterns in Asian shifting cultivation systems. All are limited by a lack of natural production resources, some, by a lack of available market and input resources. All arise from the population pressure on the better agricultural land that has forced landless settlers onto land with marginal natural production capability.

These areas are: (i) low rainfall areas of flat to gently rolling topography with soils of low natural fertility, typified by the "Chaina" areas of Sri Lanka; (ii) low rainfall mountainous areas, typical of western Nepal; and (iii) high rainfall mountainous areas.

The population pressure that forced movement into the less suited agricultural areas often precludes planned movement out of them. Land often is simply not available. Shifting cultivation in Asia has been described in several major works (Barran, 1958; Conklin, 1954; Davis, 1973; Moerman, 1969; Spencer, 1966; Reed, 1965).

Nearly all workers remark on the ingenuity of peasant farmers and their propensity toward experimentation on at least a small portion of their farm, accounting for the evolution of efficient systems. Davis (1973) states: "If efficiency is measured in terms of the ratio between labor inputs and yields, rather than in terms of gross production per unit land, swidden (shifting cultivation) often is a remarkably efficient cultivation system, ingeniously adapted to low energy technologies in forested regions." We cannot, however, be satisfied with low productivity per unit of land area, and population pressure is rapidly forcing the slash-and-burn cultivator into a less stable system.

Development and stabilization of shifting areas takes several pathways. All include intensive development of the homestead areas.

The relatively dry, low fertility, gently rolling areas of Sri Lanka are stabilized as follows:

> Starting point: Shifting cultivation with 2 or 3 years of cropping and a 10-year fallow, no farm power.
> Development Phase 2
> > a. Construction of communal water catchment tanks with production of the staple crop below the tank. Low soil fertility makes paddy rice more productive in spite of limited water.
> > b. Addition of animal power.
> > c. Continued shifting cultivation above the tank. Farmers have cultivation rights in both areas.
> > d. Development of the homestead area with tree plantings.
> Phase 3
> > a. Markets and cash inputs available.
> > b. Cattle raising added as an enterprise.
> > c. Fertilizer inputs below the tank, making upland crop production possible using less water.
> > d. Pasture, low intensity annual tree interplant cultivation above the tank to stabilize the shifting portion.
> > e. Gradual entrance into a cash economy.

This process progresses by itself slowly, but research efforts now underway should hasten it. Technology for low intensity cropping on low fertility

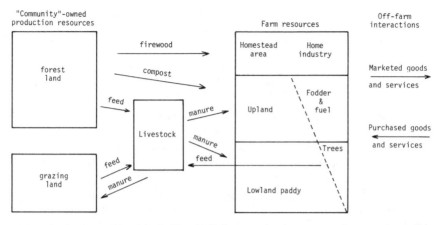

Figure 2. Conceptual model of a Nepal hill farm production system. (Harwood, 1974).

soils under conditions of low rainfall combined with animal production systems has been perfected in the dry portions of south central Java. Here a range of dry zone tree crops, some serving primarily as a fuel source, are combined with such drought-tolerant crops as sorghum, cassava (*Manihot esculenta*), and crotalaria (*Crotalaria* spp.) in intercrop and relay combinations.

We suggest, then, that to stabilize this kind of shifting system, proven traditional methods from similar areas in a more advanced stage of development be combined with new varieties and modern inputs to give more efficient use of available resources, higher productivity, and a more varied and stable source of food for the farm family. We suggest for this, as for other systems, "The use of new inputs in combination with traditional production factors in a new technical relationship—a movement to a new production response surface" (Hopper, 1975).

Shifting systems in the high rainfall mountainous areas can be stabilized following the pattern in the Himalayan foothills of eastern Nepal:

> Starting point: Slash and burn with no farm power. Two or 3 years cultivation in a 7 or 8 year cycle.
>
> Development Phase 1
>
> Establishment of terraced rice paddies in the lower regions. Addition of forage draft animals.
>
> Development Phase 2
>
> Limited cropping of nonterraced upland areas. Extensive development of the homestead area.
>
> Development Phase 3
>
> Labor intensive cycling of nutrients is begun if the system has no access to markets (Fig. 2). This eastern Nepal system represents the most advanced stage of purely traditional technology yet found in Asia. With market and cash availability, purchased fertilizer inputs partially substitute for the nutrient cycling. The extremely intensive but completely subsistence-oriented systems of the eastern Nepal foothills represent the ultimate in this development without market

availability. With markets available, a stable and highly productive (but labor intensive) system is possible. This system would afford the farmer who has no more than 2 ha of land, a high quality diet, stable production, and modest (by Asian standards) cash income that would enable him to obtain the few necessities for existence. It would not provide large marketable surpluses of food nor anything approaching a western standard of living.

Shifting cultivation in the drier mountainous areas, such as western Nepal, can move only toward an extensive tree-oriented homestead area and controlled cattle grazing with some pasture improvement.

None of these systems can afford the capital and cash input requirements of mechanical power. The forage capacity of draft and slaughter animals not only adds considerably to the productive efficiency of these systems but also minimizes cash output for power. The limited cash resources can be used for fertilizer inputs to correct the primary limitation to higher productivity in a shifting system.

Homestead crop technology is critical, as is a knowledge of tree and annual crop relay and intercrop techniques.

Rolling Upland Areas

In southeast Asia the low rainfall upland areas that have less than 3 months of rainfall above 200 mm/month are devoted primarily to corn production. On farms of around 2 ha, draft animals are used. A well-developed upland corn farm will supplement animal with tractor power for primary tillage. It will have an extensive homestead area, and fencerows planted on the contour for control of seasonally heavy rains. It will combine animal fattening and sale with its draft animal source and will use fertilizer inputs.

With higher rainfall (5 to 6 months with 200 mm/month or more), the system will be based on upland rice.

A time profile of such a system can be seen in the following:

Initial stage
Settling and initial land clearing with no animal component or power source. Intensive intercropping of annuals having different growth stages is used based on cassava, rice, and corn mixtures. This gives an 11 month growing period requiring a single primary tillage operation. No fertilizer inputs are used. This is typical of the transmigration areas of south Sumatra in Indonesia.
Stage 2
Draft and slaughter animals are introduced which utilize available feed and provide power. The cropping pattern changes to the use of several different crop sequences. This spreads the power requirement but uses power available for primary tillage. This is the shift toward a power-based system. The homestead and fencerow areas are then developed.
Stage 3
Contract tractor operations begin to handle some of the primary tillage, with animal power providing seedbed preparation and weed control as well as primary tillage of small plots and wet fields during

high rainfall. Intensive use of chemical fertilizer becomes common. Cropping patterns on a given farm will be varied from field to field to optimize labor and market resources (Grimble, 1973). Field and then garden vegetable culture are introduced as labor availability increases and markets appear. Intercropping corn with upland rice or other crops is practiced in intensive cropping. The IRRI outreach research location in Batangas, Philippines is typical of this latter stage as reported by de Ocampo et al. (1969).

The well-developed homestead area, the mixtures of upland crops, the intercropping of trees (coconuts) with annuals, and the integration of animal enterprises into the system are critical aspects of this system. Ready markets for field crops and an available source of fertilizer are absolutely essential. Improved crop varieties of suitable plant type and precise maturity requirements, along with rather complex pest management practices are also necessary. This has all been put together by the Filipino farmer in Batangas Province into one of the most effective combinations of traditional patterns and modern technology yet found in Asia.

This system follows the same patterns as those found in the drier upland areas, but uses shorter duration crops in intensive sequences and has far greater diversity of crop and animal enterprises. Similar intensive integrated animal crop systems exist in Taiwan (C. S. Lee, C. Y. Lee, and C. H. Tseng, 1973. Impact of multiple cropping diversification on farm income in Taiwan. Seminar on Multiple Crop Diversification in Taiwan and Its Relevance to Southeast Asian Countries. 29 Oct.-4 Nov. 1973. Taipei, Taiwan) and in Malaysia (Ho, 1962).

Fully Irrigated Systems

With adequate water for year-round irrigation, the farming system in east and southeast Asia on small farms will be based either on continuous rice (five crops in 2 years) or on continuous high value crops. Continuous rice is most commonly grown for several reasons. Most Asian irrigation systems have been constructed in the low-lying areas that tend to have heavier soils and a high water table, simply because water is easy to get into the system, less water is lost, and construction costs are cheaper. The systems are designed for irrigating paddy rice, with low cost paddy-to-paddy field distribution and surface drainage only. Below-ground-level drainage is not needed for paddy rice. It is, therefore, much easier to continuously puddle the soil for sequential plantings of lowland rice. Land preparation in the paddy requires low power inputs, and irrigation to achieve standing water in the paddy requires far less precision than the more exacting irrigation demands of an upland crop on clay soil. It may be true in the dry season that less water would be needed for an upland crop, but the conversion of puddled clay soil to an upland condition, the construction of ridges and furrows for in-paddy drainage, and the higher fertilizer inputs required for the upland crop all make continuous lowland rice more attractive unless water availability becomes the primary limiting factor.

Sugarcane is irrigated in Indonesia and in other countries, mainly on large farms. On the small farms (less than 1 ha) that have access to markets, continuous vegetable production will be followed as a third use of continuous irrigation facilities. This will often be through the use of raised beds. The ditch and dike system of Thailand is typical. It is designed around the water control needs of vegetables in low-lying, high water table areas in the alluvial plains around the large coastal cities of Asia.[4] The sorjan system of Indonesia is a modification of this method designed for areas with a seasonally high water table. This method uses a broad ditch for growing rice between the raised beds on which upland crops are grown.

Rain-fed and Partially Irrigated Rice-Based Systems

The system accounts for the bulk of Asia's rice and the great majority of small farms in east and southeast Asia. Annual rainfall is generally above 1,500 mm per year, the soils are heavy, farm size is about 1.5 ha, and the farmers sell about half of what they produce. Irrigation is supplemental during the rainy season, sometimes extending 1 or 2 months beyond the end of the rains. Much of this category of rice-based system is found in rainfall zones where the monthly rainfall is 200 mm/month for 5 to 6 months a year. In most instances, a single crop only is harvested, even with partial irrigation. Because these water-limiting situations offer great potential for more intensive cropping, they are the major focus of IRRI cropping systems research. In most years two crops of rice, or at least rice followed by an upland crop, are possible. Currently, in experiments early maturing rice varieties are being direct-seeded in nonpuddled soil at the start of the rains in areas where the monsoon starts gradually after a dry period. This method works only where the soil can be prepared at least a month before the rains begin, and where weed populations are not too dense. If the rains begin suddenly rather than gradually (climatic subzones 3.2 rather than 3.1, Table 5), the soil must be puddled and pregerminated seed sown on the soil surface rather than dry sowing. This is because rice will not emerge in soil if oxygen is limiting. These direct seeding methods replace the traditional long wait until the monsoon is well established as well as puddling and transplanting. This latter method uses the 5 months of good rainfall for a single rice crop. Direct seeding permits the growing of two short-season rice crops during the rainy period, with the second being transplanted in the normal fashion.

Upland crops after rice depend on soil texture, water status, and tillage capability (Harwood, 1975). Change in soil bulk density with puddling and tillage capability under upland conditions are closely related to multiple cropping potential (Fig. 3). Low tillage management following paddy rice offers a wide range of options for several crops.

---

[4]S. Sritunya, 1975. The intensive ditch and dike method of vegetable production in Thailand. M.S. Thesis. Central Luzon State University, Munoz, Nueva Ecija, Philippines. 1081, illus., maps.

Partially irrigated areas normally have a somewhat more dependable water source during the monsoon but nevertheless still run out of water shortly after the rains end. Two crops of rice followed by a short-season drought-tolerant crop like mungbean (*Vigna reticulata*) are often possible.

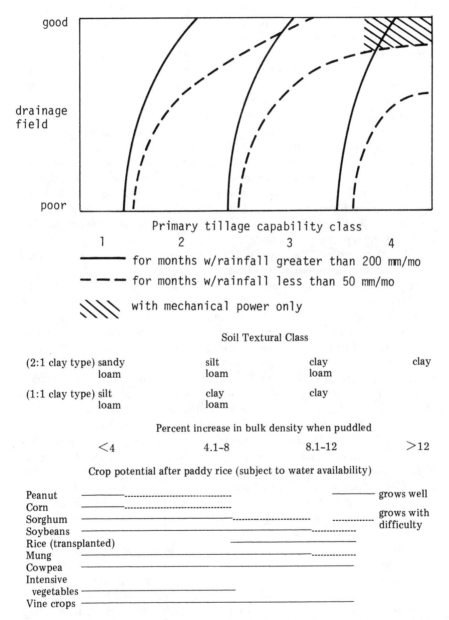

Figure 3. Soil classification categories which indicate multiple cropping potential in puddled rice soils having limited water (March 1975 estimate).

KINDS OF MULTIPLE CROPPING PATTERNS

Sequential Cropping

Sequences of crops grown in pure stands are by far the most common form of multiple cropping. In areas with a cool winter, paddy rice-wheat (in the high rainfall areas) is grown. This includes such areas as the low hills of Nepal, northern India, Pakistan, northwestern Bangladesh, Korea, and portions of the People's Republic of China. Most of these areas have soils that are coarser in texture and easier to till than those of southeast Asia, making the paddy rice-wheat conversion much easier. Maize-wheat rotations are used where summer rainfall is moderately intensive. The drier regions of India have multiple crop sequences as reported in several comprehensive summaries (IARI, 1967, 1970; Nair et al., 1973). Similar summaries are available for Sri Lanka (S. E. Upasena and G. W. E. Fernando, 1973. The cropping patterns in Sri Lanka. Paper presented at the Seminar on the Economic and Social Consequences of the Improved Seeds. Hotel Swisse, Kandy); Bangladesh, (Carolus & Kazi, 1958); and Taiwan (Iso, 1954; Cheng, 1972). Little attempt has been made to relate these crop sequences to physical or socioeconomic conditions of their respective areas, so generalizations are difficult from existing reports.

For the puddled, heavy clay soils following rice, where tillage is difficult or impossible, the soybean is probably the most well-adapted crop. For these same conditions the vine crops such as watermelon (*Citrullus vulgaris*), cucumber (*Cucumis sativus*), squash (*Cucurbita maxima*), ampalaya (*Momordica balsamina*), or the viny type of legume are well suited, since plants are spaced at wide intervals and a suitable seedbed can be prepared by digging holes at spaced intervals for hill planting. With zero tillage after paddy rice, these vine crops cover the soil before weeds emerge. The moisture requirements of various crops also determine their places in the pattern. In a typical monsoon rainfall pattern there may be a 4-month dry period with less than 50 mm of monthly rain, than 1 or 2 months of 100 to 200 mm/month, 5 months of 200 to 300 mm/month, one month of 100 to 200, then the dry season again. In such a pattern dry-seeded upland rice fits only at the start of the rains, since it must germinate before the soil becomes saturated by heavy rains. Rice can be harvested wet, so heavy rains at harvest time are less damaging to rice than to most other crops. Corn can likewise be planted early, as it can be harvested in wet weather, especially if it is for green "cooking" corn. The legumes and sorghum cannot be harvested in wet weather and fit better as a second crop at the end of the rains when their drought-tolerance is also at maximum. Crop selection is thus based on both crop growth and management requirements.

For paddy rice-growing areas now producing a single crop of rice a year with 5 to 6 months of high rainfall, direct-seeding followed by a second crop of transplanted rice can then be followed by a low-tillage broadcast mungbean or cowpea (*Vigna* sp.) in a larger portion of the rainfed rice area. Potentials for increase in cropping intensity in rainfed and partially irrigated areas by growing an additional crop in sequence are thus highly promising. Where that crop is either paddy rice or a legume, additional fertilizer requirements are well within reason (Nair & Singh, 1971).

In upland rice areas, a single crop is now normally grown, but most areas have the potential for at least a second crop. Here a wide range of field or vegetable crops is feasible. Unlike for second crop paddy, however, high levels of fertilizer must be used with intensive upland crop sequences. If productivity is to be maintained, the only alternative is the Nepal system of labor-intensive nutrient cycling.

Tree Crops Intercropped with Annuals

Coconut, oilpalm, and young rubber trees are often intercropped, in the early years of plantation, to a range of annual crops. Cassava, soybeans, peanuts (*Arachis hypogaea* L.), corn, and other crops may be used (Blencowe, 1969). Smallholder tree intercropping in the Philippines is done mostly in young mango (*Mangifera* sp.) or coconut plantations, where upland rice and corn are frequently used. In other plantings the more shade-tolerant cassava, ginger (*Zinqiber* sp.), and other minor root crops are used.

Tree Intercropping

Complex mixtures of trees of different canopy heights and shapes, characteristic of homestead areas, are also found in more extensive plantings, especially at altitudes of 300 to 500 m where coffee (*Coffea* sp.) grows well. Such mixtures may include two or three fruits, *Gliricidia sepium* for firewood, and a range of lower-growing trees and shrubs.

Similar patterns are found in dry areas of southeast Asia using kapok (*Ceiba pentandra*) and other drought-tolerant species. These plantings are characterized by stability of both production and management. They require low power and chemical input and a modest but continuous labor input. They are thus ideally suited to the resource pattern of the small farmer. Because of the long establishment time, however, these crop patterns are usually heavily intercropped with short-season annual cash crops in the early years.

Intensive Vegetable Production

The highland vegetable production, the ditch and dike, and the sorjan system all utilize intensive vegetable relay and intercropping techniques, separating them from most other types of patterns. These are situated near to markets and are high cash-flow systems. High levels of insecticides, fertilizers, and compost are used in extremely labor-intensive systems.[5] The in-

---

[5] S. Sritunya, 1975. The intensive ditch and dike method.

tensive vegetable trellis system in the Philippines is similar in resource requirements. Here, permanent horizontal wire trellis is supported 1.8 m above the ground on wood or concrete posts such that draft animals can be used for cultivation underneath. A year-round sequence of climbing legumes, squash, pumpkins (*Cururbita pepo melopepo*), and gourds (*Lagenaria* spp.) is grown.

Complex Intercropping of Annual Field Crops

These patterns outlined as follows are highly developed in Asia (IRRI, 1974, 1975).

A. Crops of similar plant type but of different maturity
Nigeria (Andrews, 1972)

| Millet, corn (3 months) /
| Sorghum (6 months)   /

B. Tall crops with shorter crops below them to establish different levels of leaf canopy.
1. Short season crops under permanent (tree) crops.

                          Time————————>
        Coconut, rubber, banana (*Musa paradisiaca sapientum*)   >
        /   Annual crops/

                   ————————————————
                        rainy season

2. Short-season crops planted at the start of the growing period of long duration crops.

/   sugarcane   (more than 1 year)
/Short-season crops /
(corn, soybeans)

3. Annual crops (less than 1 year duration)
   a. Major (tall) crop harvested first

   |Corn (3 months)   /
   |Cassava (10 months)   /
   |Corn (2½–3 months)   /
   |Peanut, rice,   /

   sweet potato (*Ipomoea batatus* Lam.) (4 months)
   b. Minor (short crop harvested first

   |Mung (2 months) /
   |Corn (3–4 months)   /

Two types of planting arrangements are used, depending on the permanence of the system and on the degree of organization.

1. Mixed planting—a random arrangement of each species in a given proportion (mixed intercropping).
2. Alternate row planting or (row intercropping), the confinement of each species to a uniform row.

POSSIBLE REASONS FOR INTERCROPPING

Labor use efficiency is high when power for primary tillage is not available (Norman, 1968). With no power, long duration intercrop sequences (usually based on cassava) are used, producing three or four crops in a 10-month period and requiring only one primary tillage operation per year. The rice-corn-cassava pattern of Indonesia is an excellent example.

IRRI data (1974) show that in specific cases both insect and weed management may be easier in intercrop combinations (Litsinger & Moody, 1976).

Theoretical productivity of the patterns seems to be significantly higher only if there is a major difference in maturity among the component crops. Rice-corn, corn-peanut, and mung-corn are examples (IRRI, 1974). The commonly used corn-soybean pattern is as productive as the sole crop plantings. It seems probable that in an area where corn is the dominant crop and downy mildew the major limiting factor in its yield, the wide (2-m) row spacing of corn in the intercrop combination may be a major factor in reducing mildew incidence.

The nonlegume combinations such as rice and corn have repeatedly shown higher efficiency of uptake of applied nitrogen than has either crop alone (IRRI, 1975).

The question of "harvest insurance" from intercropping arises in almost every report on the subject. A careful review of the literature, however, reveals no evidence to support this hypothesis. Our experience at IRRI shows that if a crop in a mixture is to be differentially eliminated or reduced in yield by some factor, it will normally happen after considerable vegetative growth has occurred (for instance corn downy mildew infestation in the corn-rice combination). The nonyielding crop will exert its competitive effect without producing anything, resulting in a lower productivity of the mixture than from the separate monoculture plantings. Our data show that with a single crop failure, individual monoculture plantings are better. The desire for stability of production and "crop insurance" is a strong argument for crop diversity but not necessarily for crop mixtures. The burden of proof lies with the advocates of the "insurance" hypothesis. Traditional patterns and systems have arisen for positive, not for negative reasons.

RELEVANT RESEARCH NEEDS OF SMALL FARMER AGRICULTURE IN ASIA

There is no question that continued institutional and infrastructure development to enlarge the resource base of the Asian farmer is critical. At the same time, however, technology is needed to make more efficient use of present and planned farmer resources. Countless small farmers in Asia, in the foreseeable future, will not have access to irrigation, to nearby markets, to mechanical power, or even to easily obtainable cash inputs. Our efforts at providing technology must, of course, be largely directed toward that highly productive and more easily reached segment that accounts for the bulk of Asia's food production. Social pressures, however, are forcing a mandate to help the heretofore "bypassed" sector, those small farmers with more limited resources. The clamor for "peasant-biased" technology (Griffin, 1972) has thus far resulted in little action. Norman (1970) suggests that increased productivity is possible within traditional systems. Earlier in our discussion the pathway of development was indicated for several of the more "backward" types of farming systems in Asia. The question now seems to arise: Can change (development) take place for these bypassed farmers without the complete realization of Mosher's "progressive rural structure" (Mosher, 1969)?

Evidence is beginning to accumulate suggesting that elements and patterns of traditional systems may be quite efficient. Some suggest that in nations where, because of high population pressure, production resources are limiting, high efficiency is critical (G. Conway and J. Romm, 1972. Ecology and resource development in southeast Asia. The Ford Foundation, Office for southeast Asia. Unpublished). This has been illustrated graphically (Fig. 4), showing the higher efficiency of resource use with contributions of traditional patterns with modern varieties and inputs typical of the N response data for corn-rice intercropping (IRRI, 1974). This also illustrates Hopper's "new response surface—a combination of new and old."

A major thrust in reaching small farmers remains in the hands of plant breeders. It is essential, however, that at least some varieties be developed to fit the low cash input situations of our target group of low resource farmers. Disease and insect resistance may not be as important in traditional settings

Farm productivity

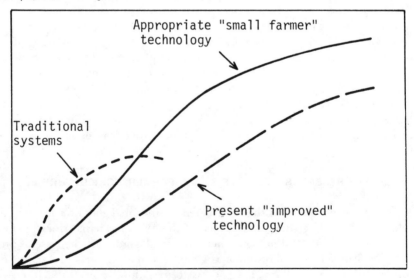

Quantity of inputs

Figure 4.   Comparative efficiencies of different farming systems with respect to use of inputs.

as are drought tolerance, shade tolerance, vigorous plant type, and proper maturity. Most traditional rice and corn varieties in southeast Asia do not have much resistance to any of the major pests and diseases. Plant breeders have a big challenge and can contribute significantly by developing improved varieties to fit into the low resource environment.

Secondly, if plant materials could be made available that would expand and improve the diversity of homestead areas, major improvements would be made in the diets of rural landed peoples. In the high rainfall areas of southeast Asia, there is little excuse for the persistence of Vitamin A deficiency. It will not be corrected, however, by importation of carrot seeds. High management crops are not readily accepted into low management systems.

This argument points to several needs and approaches which only recently have come into use. Heady and Agrawal (E. O. Heady and R. C. Agrawal. 1970. Prospects and problems in multiple cropping. *In* unpublished Report of the National Seminar of Multiple Cropping, New Delhi, India.) suggested the farming systems analysis approach to multiple cropping. Spedding (1971) furthers the notion that the approach should be based on an ecological awareness and a framework that makes optimum use of available resources. It should be realized, however, that where cash and capital intensive technology has failed, systems models based on these same principles can hardly be expected to do much better.

The approach being used at IRRI is to come to an understanding of the existing system before trying to determine how to change it. This is especially critical with traditional systems that are completely alien to our "western"

Figure 5. Asian cropping systems network present and planned sites.

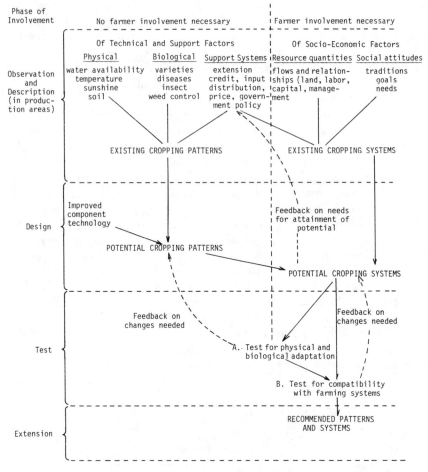

Figure 6. A framework for cropping systems research and extension. (Palacpac, Adelita C. 1976. World rice statistics. Mimeo. Int. Rice Res. Inst., Department of Agricultural Economics. 1976:95.)

mentality and education. The systems approach is critical, since in traditional systems the components are closely integrated.

A further example of this "relevant" technology is the low cost power tillers designed to better fit the resource pattern and needs of the small farmer with intensive cropping systems. Small multipurpose threshers and small planters are other examples. Such power units may be critical to the efficient use of production resources in intensive cropping systems (Banta, 1973; R. Bradfield, 1970. Concept of multiple cropping on paddy soils. Paper presented at FAO/Ceylon National Agricultural Extension workshop, In-Service Training Institute, Gannoruwa, Peradeniya, Ceylon).

An Asian cropping systems network is being established to provide a series of research sites (Fig. 5) to investigate possible increases in crop intensity in likely target areas (Carangal, 1975). On these sites a farmer-oriented research approach is being implemented to achieve data on relevant and potential cropping systems (Harwood, 1975a). IRRI proposed a research model to be followed (Fig. 6). It was recognized that comprehensive studies of all the suggested parameters are not feasible, but that, at the minimum, an intuitive knowledge of interacting factors is essential. It was stated that a single researcher, working alone, can follow this method. The farmer involvement in research is based on Johnson's (1972) hypothesis that "experimentation is as natural as conformity in traditional communities." To date our experience supports this hypothesis.

LITERATURE CITED

Amed, K. 1965. Agriculture in East Pakistan. M/S Amed Brothers Publications, Dacca.

Andrews, D. J. 1972. Intercropping with guineacorn—a biological cooperative: Part I. Samaru Agric. Newsl. 14(2):20-22.

Banta, G. R. 1973. Mechanization, labor, and time in multiple cropping. Agric. Mechan. Asia IV(1):27-30.

Barren, J. 1958. Subsistence agriculture in Melanesia: Honolulu. B. P. Bishop Mus. Bull. No. 219.

Blencowe, J. W. 1969. Crop diversification in Malaysia. Incorporated Society of Planters, Kuala Lumpur. 300 p.

Boyce, J. K., and R. E. Evenson. 1975. Agricultural research and extension systems. Dep. of Agric. Economics, Univ. of the Philippines at Los Banos and The Agricultural Development Council, Inc.

Carangal, V. R. 1975. The International Rice Research Institute Cropping Systems network, p. 261-266. In Proceedings of the Cropping Systems Workshop. IRRI, Los Banos, Philippines.

Chao, C. 1975. Improvements for increasing cropping intensity of paddy fields in Taiwan in the past five years, p. 219-230. In Proceedings of the Cropping Systems Workshop, IRRI, Los Banos, Philippines.

Carolus, R. L., and Q. H. Kazi. 1968. Observations and trials with various crops during the Boro season in Comilla (1967-1968). Pakistan Academy for Rural Development, Comilla.

Cheng, C. 1972. Multiple cropping in Taiwan. ASPAC—Food and Fert. Technology Center. Ext. Bull. No. 15.

Conklin, H. C. 1954. An ethnoecological approach to shifting agriculture. Trans. New York Acad. Sci. 17:133-142.

Coulter, J. K., J. F. Derting, L. R. Oldeman, M. M. Obradovich, and T. B. Slattery. 1974. An agro-climatic classification for evaluating cropping systems potentials in southeast Asian rice growing regions. IRRI Los Banos, Philippines.

Davis, W. G. 1973. Social Relations in a Philippine Market. Univ. of California Press, Berkeley and Los Angeles.

Food and Agriculture Organization. 1950. World Census of Agriculture: Report. United Nations, FAO, Rome.

Food and Agriculture Organization. 1962, 1971, 1972. Production Yearbook. United Nations, FAO, Rome.

Geertz, C. 1963. Agricultural involution. The process of ecological change in Indonesia. Univ. of California Press, Berkeley and Los Angeles.

Griffin, K. 1972. Economic aspects of technological change in the rural area of monsoon Asia. Geneva, United Nations Research Institute for Social Development. 69 p.

Grimble, R. J. 1973. The central highlands of Thailand: A study of farming systems. Overseas Dev. Adm. Special Report. Wye College, University of London.

Harwood, R. R. 1974. Farming systems in hill agriculture. p. 93-119. In A. H. Moseman (ed.) A study of hill agriculture in Nepal. The Rockefeller Foundation, New York.

Harwood, R. R. 1975. Farmer-oriented research aimed at crop intensification. p. 12–32. *In* Proceedings of the Cropping Systems Workshop, IRRI, Los Banos, Philippines.

Ho. R. 1962. Mixed farming and multiple cropping in Malaya. Trop. Geogr. 16:1–17.

Hopper, W. D. 1975. To conquer hunger: Opportunity and potential will. John A. Hanna International Development Lecture Series, Michigan State Univeristy, East Lansing, Michigan.

Indian Agricultural Research Institute. 1967. Symposium on new cropping patterns. IARI, New Delhi, India.

Indian Agricultural Research Institute. 1970. Report of the National Seminar on Multiple Cropping. IARI, New Delhi, India. 260 p.

International Rice Research Institute. (Undated). World Rice Statistics. Dep. of Agric. Econ., IRRI, Los Banos, Philippines.

International Rice Research Institute. 1974. IRRI Annual Report for 1973. Los Banos, Philippines.

International Rice Research Institute. 1975. IRRI Annual Report for 1974. Los Banos, Philippines. (In press).

Iso, E. 1954. Rice and crops in its rotation in subtropical zones. Japan FAO Association. Tokyo. 611 p.

Johnson, A. W. 1972. Individuality and experimentation in traditional agriculture. Hum. Ecol. 1:149–159.

Litsinger, J. A., and K. Moody. 1976. Pest management in multiple cropping. p. 293–316. *In* R. I. Papendick (ed.) Multiple cropping. Spec. Pub. No. 27. Am. Soc. of Agron., Madison, Wis.

Manu, S. 1975. Maximizing utilization of rice areas in the Chiang Mai Valley. p. 126–143. *In* Proceedings of the Cropping Systems Workshop, IRRI, Los Banos, Philippines.

Mears, L. A. 1974. Rice economy of the Philippines. University of the Philippines Press, Quezon City.

Menegay, M. R. 1975. Socio-economic factors affecting cropping systems for selected Taiwan farmers. p. 231–251. *In* Proceedings of the Cropping Systems Workshop. IRRI, Los Banos, Philippines.

Moerman, M. 1969. Agricultural Change in Peasant Choice in a Thai Village. Univ. of California Press, Berkeley and Los Angeles. 227 p.

Mosher, A. T. 1969. Creating a Progressive Rural Structure. Agric. Dev. Council, Inc., New York.

Munsoon, F. P., chairman. 1963. Area handbook of Cambodia. Foreign Area Studies, American University, Washington, D. C. 415 p.

Nair, P. K. R., and A. Singh. 1971. Production potential, economic possibilities and input requirements of five high intensity rotations with rice (*Oryza sativa* L.). Indian J. Agric. Sci. 41:807.

Nair, P. K. R., A. Singh, and S. C. Modgal. 1973. Cropping patterns involving rice and their management. Indian J. Agric. Sci. 43(1):70.

National Economic and Development Authority. 1974. NEDA Statistical Yearbook. NEDA, Manila, Philippines.

National Statistical Office. 1971. Statisitcal Yearbook, 1970–71. Thailand.

Norman, D. W. 1968. Why practice intercropping. Samaru Agric. Newsl. 10:6.

Norman, D. W. 1970. Initiating change in traditional agriculture. Agric. Soc. Nigeria (7):6–14.

Ocampo, N. R., de., E. V. Gaon, and E. M. Albano. 1969. The effects of cropping patterns on farm earning capacity in Malvar, Batangas. Philipp. Agric. 53(1):17–27.

Oshima, Harry T. 1975. Multiple cropping in Asian development: summary and further research. Philipp. Econ. J. 14(1,2):7–29.

Rao, M. V. 1975. Cropping systems in Southern India—Problems and Prospects. p. 170–181. *In* Proceedings of the Cropping Systems Workshop. IRRI, Los Banos, Philippines.

Reed, R. R. 1965. Swidden in Southeast Asia. Lipunan 1(1):24–52.

Spedding, C. R. W. 1971. Agricultural ecosystems. Outlook Agric. 6(6):242–247.

Spencer, J. E. 1966. Shifting cultivation in southeastern Asia. Univ. California Press, Berkeley and Los Angeles. 247 p.

Thodey, A. R., and W. Aree. 1974. The Chiang Mai central crop market: Structure conduct and performance. Fac. of Agric. Chiang Mai University, Chiang Mai, Thailand.

Double Cropping in the Eastern United States[1]

W. M. Lewis and J. A. Phillips[2]

Multiple cropping systems can maximize total production per hectare. They may include double cropping, three crops in 2 years, or five crops in 4 years. In a sense multiple cropping helps growers increase crop hectarage thereby helping to meet the ever expanding need for food and feed. At the same time the systems demand careful management for success. They encourage more intensive land use and also more efficient utilization of machinery, labor, and capital investment. This discussion will concentrate on double cropping of agronomic crops in the eastern U. S. Double cropping may be defined as growing two successive crops on the same field during 1 year.

Double cropping has proven successful under the longer growing seasons in the southeastern U. S. In recent years double cropped hectarage has increased in Delaware and Maryland and the southern part of the Corn Belt, Kentucky, Illinois, Indiana, and Ohio. Interest has been stimulated in double cropping by recent developments in herbicides, newer shorter season cultivars particularly soybeans [*Glycine max* (L.) Merr.] and small grains, favorable crop prices, and especially the development of no-tillage planting techniques.

No-tillage planting contributes to the success of double cropping by enabling a second crop to be established with the least delay. Additional advantages of no-tillage planting, which are influenced by the individual grower's situation, are: reduced labor and fuel requirements, increased flexibility in timing of farm operations, elimination of tillage to conserve moisture for critical planting and growth of the summer-planted crop, and control of water and wind erosion.

---

[1]Paper No. 148 of the Journal Series of the North Carolina State Univ. Agric. Ext. Ser., Raleigh.
[2]Professor of crop science and professor of soil science, North Carolina State University.

TYPES OF DOUBLE CROPPING SYSTEMS

The potential for double cropping systems is great when one considers the many possible agronomic crops and their utilization (Table 1). These examples of double cropping systems involve a winter small grain followed by a summer crop.

The choice of a double cropping system may depend upon several interrelated considerations: crop utilization, farm type, and length of the growing season. The selection of the particular small grain depends upon the intended utilization. Wheat (*Triticum aestivum* L.) can be grown for either silage or grain. Harvesting wheat for grain will delay planting of the summer crop until mid to late June in the southeast and as late as 10 July in the southern Corn Belt. On the other hand, barley (*Hordeum vulgare* L.) matures earlier allowing earlier planting of the crop to follow. For example, 'Barsoy' barley matures 2 weeks earlier than wheat. By far the most popular double cropping system is wheat or barley harvested for grain followed by soybeans for grain. Large growers may spread out their harvesting and planting season by using both barley and wheat, thereby utilizing their labor and equipment more efficiently. Rye (*Secale cereale* L.) makes a good grazing crop as does a mixture of rye, oats (*Avena sativa* L.), and barley. Early harvest, artificial drying, and selection of early maturing cultivars of small grains aid early planting of the summer crop.

What type of farm? Cash crop, dairy, beef cattle, or a combination of types influences the selection of a particular double cropping system. A dairy farmer may consider wheat for silage followed by no-tillage planted corn (*Zea mays* L.) or sorghum [*Sorghum bicolor* (L.) Moench.] for silage. On the other hand, a cash grain farmer may grow barley followed by no-tillage soybeans.

Length of growing season also plays an important role by affecting crop cultivar and crop utilization. Under a shorter growing season the grower might select a double cropping system of a small grain for hay followed by no-tillage corn for grain or a small grain for grain followed by corn or sorghum for silage.

Table 1. Double cropping systems practiced in southeastern U. S.

Winter crop	Summer crop
Small grain for:	corn (grain or silage)
grain	soybeans
silage	sorghum (grain or silage)
hay	sorghum-sudangrass*
grazing	millet†
green chop	

* sudangrass (*Sorghum vulgare sudanense*).
† millet [*Setaria italica* (L.) Beauv].

EXAMPLES OF DOUBLE CROPPING

A few examples of double cropping have been selected to illustrate both research and farmer experience in multiple cropping in the eastern U. S. Systems involving conventionally planted and no-tillage planted crops will be discussed.

Conventional Tillage Planting

Earlier trials support the success of double cropping soybeans planted in a conventionally prepared seedbed after winter wheat. In a 3-year Alabama study (Rogers et al., 1971) at the Black Belt Substation on a Houston clay, soybeans grown as a single crop yielded an average of 2,124 kg/ha. Soybeans grown in a double cropping system following wheat harvested for grain (2,533 kg/ha) yielded an average of 1,808 kg/ha. The straw was baled and the land plowed and disked before the soybeans were planted. On a Norfolk sandy loam soil near Raleigh, North Carolina, the 6-year average yields of 'Ogden' and 'Roanoke' soybean cultivars double cropped after wheat were 1,714 kg/ha (Brim et al., 1955). Yields from the same varieties planted earlier but not preceded by wheat were 1,841 kg/ha. Wheat yielded 2,029 kg/ha. In both cases double cropping improved the net income per hectare. These researchers, as well as others, emphasized that soil moisture in late June is often a critical factor in the success of late-planted soybeans after wheat. The usual practices of preparing a seedbed results in a rapid loss of moisture in the top few centimeters of soil.

Corn and sorghum for grain or silage and soybeans for grain have been successfully double crop planted in June following winter barley harvest in eastern Virginia (Camper et al., 1972). When the June plantings were harvested for grain, corn produced the greatest net dollar returns. However, when planted in July soybeans were more dependable for grain than corn or sorghum. At each planting date net returns from both corn and sorghum silage were consistently greater than from any grain crop and returns and yields from sorghum silage were greater than corn silage.

No-Tillage Planting

Mississippi studies on a Black Belt soil compared no-tillage and conventional tillage methods for soybeans and grain sorghum following wheat planted by conventional methods (Sanford et al., 1973). In 2 of the 3 years both soybeans and grain sorghum yields were significantly greater for conventional tillage than no-tillage. However, when the weeds were adequately controlled in the soybeans during the third year, no yield difference occurred due to tillage methods. Wheat grown after soybeans yielded significantly more than wheat grown after grain sorghum. The wheat-soybean double cropping system produced significantly higher net returns over production costs than the wheat-grain sorghum sequence. Again double cropping was shown to be an efficient way of increasing grain production per unit of land and the need for careful weed control management in no-tillage production was demonstrated.

Double cropping research in Georgia has emphasized systems for silage and grain production (Gallaher, 1975). These included wheat for silage or grain followed by no-tillage corn or sorghum for silage or grain or by no-tillage soybeans for grain. The potential for double cropping throughout Georgia was illustrated particularly for two silage crops in 1 year or a silage crop plus a grain crop. Yields of no-tillage summer grain and silage crops following wheat silage were similar to those from these crops planted conventionally and at customary times. Triple cropping systems were also successful, for example, barley-corn (relay intercropped in barley)-soybeans and barley-corn-snapbeans (*Phaseolus vulgaris* L.). Herbicide selection taking into account crop tolerance would be critical in a triple cropping system.

Many observations in the southern Corn Belt support the double cropping system of no-tillage planted soybeans following conventionally planted wheat. Studies conducted in 1967 demonstrated the feasibility of double cropping soybeans using the no-tillage planting technique in southern Illinois (McKibben & Pendleton, 1968). No-tillage double cropped soybean yields are generally equal or superior to yields of the same varieties grown by conventional methods in Kentucky experiences (Phillips & Young, 1973). Five tests conducted in southern Indiana and as far north as Lafayette during 1971-72 support the potential of no-tillage double cropped soybeans in that state following winter wheat or barley (Swearingin, 1973). No-tillage soybeans have been produced successfully following small grain as far north as Wooster, Ohio (Triplett et al., 1971).

An Alabama farmer is double cropping cotton (*Gossypium hirsutum* L.) following wheat harvested for grain (Ehmke, 1975). Yields of no-tillage planted cotton have exceeded his conventionally planted cotton which he attributes to conservation of moisture by the mulch. Furthermore, because of the mulch he has extended production to hilly land without erosion problems using no-tillage planting techniques. Double cropping also stretches out his planting season and use of equipment.

LONG-TERM TEST INVOLVING MULTIPLE CROPPING

In North Carolina we have examined in a 4-year study (1971-74) no-tillage planting of corn, soybeans, and grain sorghum in different multiple cropping systems (Table 2). Each year of the 3-year system was represented yearly. Therefore, comparisons could also be made on the basis of double cropping systems. The wheat-corn systems represented the most severe test because, if such a double cropping system proved profitable, we would know

Table 2. Double cropping systems in long-term test (North Carolina)

1st year		2nd year		3rd year	
Winter	Summer	Winter	Summer	Winter	Summer
	Corn CS		Same		Same
	Corn NT‡		Same		Same
Wheat CS*	Corn CS		Same		Same
Wheat CS	Corn NT		Same		Same
Wheat OS†	Corn NT		Same		Same
Wheat CS	Corn NT	Wheat CS	Soybean NT	Wheat CS	Grain sorghum NT
Wheat OS	Corn NT	Wheat OS	Soybean NT	Wheat OS	Grain sorghum NT

* CS = conventional seedbed
† OS = overseeded in previous crop
‡ NT = no-tillage planted

that other systems which involve earlier maturing crops, for example barley, and earlier cultivars would also work. The no-tillage planted crops followed wheat planted in a conventionally prepared seedbed versus overseeded in the previous crop. All crops were harvested for grain. Observations were made on yield, weed control, shifts in weed populations, herbicide soil residues, effects of herbicides on succeeding crops, and fertility levels at different soil depths.

One test location was on a Piedmont soil, an Appling sandy loam (Typic Hapludult; clayey, kaolinitic, thermic), and the second on a Coastal Plains soil, a Norfolk fine sandy loam (Typic Paleudult; fine loamy, siliceous, thermic). The average growing season is 10 days longer at the Coastal Plains location. Each test had four replications. Continuous corn was planted by both conventional and no-tillage methods at the normal corn planting time for the area (9 April–12 May). In the multiple-cropping systems the summer row crops were planted following wheat harvest (17 June–5 July). The no-tillage planter consisted of a fluted coulter followed by a double-disk seed opener. Conventional seedbed preparation involved moldboard plowing followed by disking. The herbicide applied preemergence in grain sorghum was atrazine [2-chloro-4-(ethylamino)-6-(isopropylamino)-s-triazine] at 2.24 kg/ha and in soybeans linuron [3-(3,4-dichlorophenyl)-1-methoxy-1-methylurea] at 1.12 kg/ha. The herbicide treatments on the corn plots were subdivided with one-half receiving atrazine at 2.24 kg/ha and the other half cyanazine [2-[[4-chloro-6-(ethylamino)-s-triazin-2-yl]amino]-2-methylpropionitrile] at 2.24 kg/ha. To each of these treatments were added paraquat (1,1'-dimethyl-4,4'-bipyridinium dichloride) at 0.42 kg/ha and X-77 surfactant. In 1973 and 1974 it was necessary to apply a layby treatment of linuron at 1.12 kg/ha to the corn plots for additional grass and broadleaf weed control.

At both locations the early-planted continuous corn yielded similarly whether planted in a conventionally prepared seedbed or no-tillage planted

(Table 3). These treatments were the basis for comparing the double crop-ping systems in the study. No-tillage corn yielded more than conventionally planted corn following winter wheat planted in a conventionally prepared seedbed. For the two locations the average yield increase was 49%. Appar-ently moisture reserves were depleted by seedbed preparation following wheat harvest in the latter part of June. The no-tillage planted corn follow-ing wheat harvest yielded from 7 to 44% less than the early-planted continu-ous no-tillage corn. Yield reductions were greater at the Coastal Plain loca-tion.

Wheat overseeded into the previous crop yielded from 40 to 78% less than when seeded in a conventionally prepared seedbed. Overseeding into soybeans when the first leaves begin to drop was more successful than seed-ing at the same time into corn or grain sorghum. The overseeded wheat was winter-killed in 1972.

Wheat was not adversely affected by herbicide residues. Even after 4 continuous years of herbicide applications under no-tillage and conventional planting systems, atrazine residues in the soil were < 0.05 to 0.08 ppm and cyanazine < 0.03 ppm prior to planting corn the fifth year. Therefore, seed-ing method was the cause of small grain yield differences.

Whether or not the seedbed had been tilled for the previous crop of wheat had little influence on no-tillage double cropped corn. However, no-tillage soybeans following wheat planted in a conventionally prepared seed-bed produced 336 kg/ha more in the Piedmont and 471 kg/ha more in the Coastal Plains (20% and 32%, respectively) than following wheat overseeded directly into the previous corn crop. Perhaps the residual surface broadcast fertilizer applied to the preceeding corn crop benefited the soybeans when it was mixed into the soil during seedbed preparation. At the Piedmont loca-tion, no-tillage double-cropped grain sorghum also yielded more following conventionally planted wheat.

Table 3. Four-year average yields in long-term test (North Carolina)

Cropping system		Piedmont		Coastal plains	
Winter	Summer	Winter wheat	Summer crop	Winter wheat	Summer crop
			———kg/ha———		
	Corn CS		5,143		5,582
	Corn NT‡		5,268		5,268
Wheat CS*	Corn CS	2,486	2,822	1,747	2,383
Wheat CS	Corn NT	2,486	4,641	1,613	3,136
Wheat OS†	Corn NT	1,008	4,892	470	2,948
Wheat CS	Soybean NT	2,453	2,016	1,882	1,949
Wheat OS	Soybean NT	991	1,680	403	1,478
Wheat CS	Grain sorghum NT	2,234	3,450	1,781	2,697
Wheat OS	Grain sorghum NT	1,331	2,885	988	2,634

* CS = conventional seedbed
† OS = overseeded in previous crop
‡ NT = no-tillage planted

Table 4. Four-year average net return to land and management (North Carolina)*

	Location	
Cropping system†	Piedmont	Coastal Plains
	———— $/ha ————	
Corn	230	161
Wheat-Corn	91	–54
Wheat-Soybeans	237	165
Wheat-Grain sorghum	119	10

* Based on average annual price (1971–74) in North Carolina for each crop and variable production costs per year. All production charges were included except land and management.
† Wheat planted in conventionally prepared seedbed. Summer crop no-tillage planted.

The largest net return to land and management was obtained with a double cropping system of no-tillage soybeans following conventionally planted winter wheat (Table 4). These returns, however, only slightly exceed continuous no-tillage corn. Greater corn yields and higher prices in 1974 helped to increase the average returns for continuous corn. Also on the basis of this measure of net return, a 3-year sequence of wheat-corn, wheat-grain sorghum, and wheat-soybeans would be less profitable than double cropping wheat and soybeans for 3 years. However, a 2-year sequence of wheat followed by no-tillage soybeans the first year and no-tillage corn the 2nd year would be nearly as profitable as double cropping wheat and soybeans for 2 years.

Control of annual grass weeds in the summer crop was influenced by the planting methods. Poor control was obtained in the double cropping system involving conventionally prepared seedbeds for both wheat and corn. On the other hand, weed control in corn improved when corn was no-tillage planted following wheat planted in a conventional seedbed. In the double cropping systems of wheat-corn, wheat-soybeans, and wheat-grain sorghum, annual grass control in the summer no-tillage crops was more favorable following wheat conventionally seeded than overseeded in the previous crop at the Piedmont location.

In the atrazine-treated corn plots the crabgrass population gradually shifted from large crabgrass [Digitaria sanquinalis (L.) Scop.] to smooth crabgrass [D. ischaemum (Schreb.) Muhl.]. In the cyanazine plots goosegrass [Eleusine indica (L.) Gaertn.] increased as well as the broadleaf weeds, redroot pigweed (Amaranthus retroflexus L.) and horsenettle (Solanum carolinese L.).

MANAGEMENT STUDIES

A number of management studies have been conducted concerning double cropping. Two tests have been selected to illustrate the effects of

Table 5. Soybean yields in a soybean-small grain double cropping system.
Princeton, Kentucky (Herbek, 1974)

Cropping system	Planting date	Cultivar	
		'Calland' (III)	'Essex' (V)
		—————kg/ha —————	
Single-crop	6 June	3,313	3,636
After barley	15 June	3,300	3,501
After wheat	2 July	2,473	3,064

cultivar selection and row width in small grain-soybean double cropping systems.

Cultivar selection is related to timeliness of the harvesting and planting operations for successful double cropping. It is essential to use early maturing small grain cultivars which permit planting of the double cropped soybeans before the planting date which would be expected to result in reduced yields. Barley is an excellent small grain for double cropping because of its earlier maturity. Barsoy barley has a 2-week advantage over wheat in maturity and this advantage shows up in higher soybean yields following barley as compared to wheat in Kentucky (Table 5) (Herbek, 1974).

However, most of the double cropped soybean hectarage follows wheat harvested for grain. For most sections, this means soybeans are planted from 15 June to 10 July which results in yield loss for the soybeans. Generally yields of midseason and full season soybean cultivars begin to drop when planted after mid-June. However, yield reductions are less with a later cultivar ('Essex', Maturity Group V) than with an earlier cultivar ('Calland', Maturity Group III) when planted late after wheat harvest (Table 5).

Narrow rows contribute to increased yields for double cropped soybeans. Since late-planted soybeans produce shorter and narrower plants, narrow rows help achieve a crop canopy for maximum sunlight interception and quick ground cover which aids in weed control. For no-tillage double cropped soybeans, narrow rows are usually in the range of 38 to 51 cm.

Soybean yields were increased by 403 to 672 kg/ha when planted in 38-cm rows rather than 76-cm rows in an Ohio study (Table 6) (Jeffers et al., 1973). In addition, these data support the planting of late-maturing soybean cultivars ('Harsoy-63', Maturity Group II versus 'Chippewa-64', Group I) in a double cropping system.

Relay Intercropping

Farmers and researchers have attempted to relay plant corn into wheat. In a 2-year study at Dixon Springs, Illinois, wheat was planted in three 18-cm rows with a 76-cm space between which allowed the corn to be planted prior to combining the wheat (McKibben, 1970). This was compared to solid drilled wheat followed by no-tillage corn planted after wheat harvest.

Table 6. Double crop soybeans yields from two-row widths. Data are averages of
soybeans planted 2 and 8 July 1971, Northwestern Branch in Ohio
(Jeffers et al., 1973)

Tillage	'Chippewa-64' (I)		'Harosoy-64' (II)		Average*
	38 cm	76 cm	38 cm	76 cm	
			kg/ha		
No-till	2,150	1,478	2,419	1,949	2,016
Disk	2,150	1,478	2,419	2,150	2,882
Plow-disk	1,747	1,008	2,016	1,546	1,613
Average†	2,016	1,344	2,285	1,882	

* Least significant difference at the 5% level is 202 kg/ha.
† Least significant difference at the 5% level is 269 kg/ha.

Wheat yields were 50% less in the relay intercropped system than the double
cropping system. Corn yields were similar in both systems. In North Carolina studies, wheat yields were approximately 25% less in the relay-intercrop-
ping system (A. D. Worsham, 1968. Unpublished data, Crop Science Department, North Carolina State University, Raleigh). Yields of relay intercropped
corn did not compare favorably to no-tillage double cropped corn. Barley
yields in Georgia were 50% less and corn yields 25% less in relay intercropping compared to double cropping (Gallaher, 1975). These results from three
states question, at least to date, the advisability of relay planting corn into
wheat or barley when compared to double cropping.

Relay planting of no-tillage soybeans into standing wheat can be successful according to an Indiana farmer's experience and preliminary research
results in Illinois (Lassiter, 1973).

SUMMARY

Double cropping soybeans after wheat or barley is the most successful
multiple cropping system for grain production in the southeastern states and
the southern Corn Belt. A forage producer may grow one or two silage crops
in a small grain-corn or sorghum system. The systems demand timely and
careful management; including early harvest, use of short-season cultivars,
narrow rows for double cropped soybeans, selection of herbicides based on
planting method and crop sequence, and consideration of no-tillage planting
of the summer row crops.

LITERATURE CITED

Brim, C. A., H. W. Johnson, and H. D. Bowen. 1955. Two crops a year. Crops Soils.
    December:18,21.
Camper, H. M., Jr., C. F. Genter, and K. E. Loope. 1972. Double cropping following
    winter barley harvest in Eastern Virginia. Agron. J. 64:1–3.
Ehmke, V. 1975. Double-cropping wheat and cotton works! Prog. Farmer April:29.

Gallaher, R. N. 1975. All out feed production by multiple cropping. Proceedings Feeds and Feeding Research Day. Georgia Exp. Station, Experiment, GA. 1:29–36.

Herbek, J. Double Cropping. 1974. Proceedings No-Tillage Research Conference. Univ. of Kentucky. 70–75.

Jeffers, D. L., G. B. Triplett, and J. E. Beuerlein. 1973. Double-cropped soybeans. Ohio Report 58(4):67–69.

Lassiter, F. 1973. Plant beans into standing grain. No-Till Farmer. June:1,19.

McKibben, G. E. 1970. Double-cropping. Proceedings National Conference on No-Tillage Crop Production. Univ. of Kentucky.

McKibben, G. E., and J. W. Pendleton. 1968. Double cropping in Illinois. Illinois Report. Summer:6–7.

Phillips, S. H., and H. M. Young, Jr. 1973. No-tillage farming. Reiman Associates, Milwaukee, Wis.

Rogers, H. T., D. L. Thurlow, and G. A. Buchanan. 1971. Cropping systems and other cultural practices. Soybean Production—Recent Research Findings. Agric. Exp. Stn., Auburn Univ. Bull. 413:31–38.

Sanford, J. E., D. L. Myhre, and N. C. Merwine. 1973. Double cropping systems involving no-tillage and conventional tillage. Agron. J. 65:978–982.

Swearington, M. L. 1973. Double cropping in the Corn Belt. Better Crops Plant Food 2:20–23.

Triplett, G. B., D. L. Jeffers, D. M. Van Doren, Jr., and C. R. Weaver. 1971. Double cropping wheat and soybeans. Ohio Report 56(2):24–27.

Multiple Cropping in Tropical America

A. M. Pinchinat, J. Soria, and R. Bazan[1]

In tropical America, as in most other parts of the developing world, improving agricultural production is viewed as an immediate goal to avert severe food shortage and, in the process, to contribute to the betterment of rural life. A possible way to achieve this goal is the development and adoption of more efficient systems of crop production.

This paper focuses on multiple cropping, in practice and research, as a means of increasing food production in tropical America, especially at the small farmer level. Implicit in this objective is the improvement of rural life through balanced nutrition, higher and more even distribution of income, fuller utilization of hand labor, protection of the environment, and upgrading of general well-being.

DEFINITION AND CHARACTERISTICS OF TROPICAL AMERICA

Tropical America is defined as the geographical area between the Tropic of Cancer and the Tropic of Capricorn ($23°30'$ lat. N and $23°30'$ lat. S). Argentina, Uruguay, Paraguay, and Chile are the only Latin American countries not considered as part of the tropical area. The ecological background of the American Tropics was summarized by Duckham and Masefield (1971, p. 432-455).

[1]Members, Farming Systems Team, Department of Tropical Crops and Soils, Tropical Agricultural Research and Training Center (CATIE), Turrialba, Costa Rica.

On the basis of farming systems, tropical America can be divided into three zones according to elevation (Hardy, 1970).

1. *The lowlands*—the area from sea level to 1,000 m elevation having a mean annual temperature of 24 to 30C and mean annual rainfall > 2,000 mm distributed in three major patterns: (a) near continuous wet season throughout the year; (b) a definite 6 to 7 month wet period alternating with a 5 to 6 month dry season; and (c) a limited rainfall in desert and semidesert areas.

2. *The middle or temperate lands*—the area from 1,000 m to 2,000 m elevation, with a mean annual temperature of 18 to 24C and a mean annual rainfall of 1,200 mm, most of which has a marked 3 to 6 month dry season a year.

3. *The highlands*—the area above 2,000 m elevation, with a mean annual temperature below 18C and variable rainfall most of which is characterized by a marked but longer (6 to 8 month) dry season during the year.

Contrary to what may occur in other tropical regions of the world, the areas of high rural population, comprised mainly of small farmers, are primarily located in the middleland and highland regions such as the Central tablelands in Central America and the Andean Plateau in South America. Small farming systems are common in the lowlands of Brazil and the Caribbean. Agriculture in Latin America originated in the middle or highland areas through the rise of the Maya Civilization in Mexico and Guatemala (Patino, 1965) and the Inca Civilization in Peru and Bolivia (Bukasov, 1963). In turn, the development of these civilizations and consequent high concentration of population in the middlelands and highlands was encouraged by the milder climate and higher and more stable fertility of the soils there compared with the lowlands. Competition from high population density has forced more intensive use of available agricultural land. Under such conditions, multiple cropping tends to be practiced more widely. In the lowlands, mainly in South America, many variants of shifting cultivation systems still occur where population pressure on agricultural land is light.

THE SMALL FARMER AND CROP PRODUCTION

A small farmer is defined as one who operates a production unit of less than 7 ha and practices traditional crop husbandry methods.[2] The vast majority of small farmers may be classified as the poorest group in rural tropical America. Since the small farmers are so numerous, they play an important role in the economy of tropical America. This large contribution occurs even though their crop yields are much lower than those of local agricultural experiment stations or of large commercial holdings dealing mainly with monoculture systems.

---

[2]Regional Office for Central American Programs, 1974. A preliminary assessment of rural economic development in Central America. AID, Guatemala, Mimeo. 81 p.

Generally, industrial or large market-oriented crops such as coffee (*Coffea* sp.), bananas (*Musa paradisiaca sapientum*), cacao (*Theobroma cacao*), sugarcane (*Saccharum* sp.), cotton (*Gossypium* sp.), and rice (*Oryza sativa* L.) are produced on large to medium (> 10 ha) farms under advanced technology, which includes the use of machinery, fertilizers, pesticides, and other high cost inputs. On the other hand, traditional basic food crops such as maize (*Zea mays* L.), bean (*Phaseolus* sp.), cassava (*Manihot esculenta*), quinoa (*Chenopodium quinoa*) and others are produced on small (< 10 ha) holdings, following traditional farming practices, in which fertilizers and other expensive inputs are scarcely or not used at all.

Eighty percent of the farms in Guatemala, 85% in El Salvador, 60% in Honduras, 43% in Nicaragua, and 46% in Costa Rica, belong to the small farm category (SIECA, 1972). In Columbia, about 70% of the food consumed in the country is produced by small farmers, and 65% of the farms measure less than 10 ha each.[3] The percentage of small farmers may be even higher in the Andean plateau. For example, in Bolivia the rural sector comprises approximately 3.8 million people or about 70% of the entire population; the larger portion, approximately 85% of the rural population, is concentrated in the "Altiplano" or Andean plateau and in the valley (middle-lands), under marked small farming conditions or "minifundio"; the remaining 15% is located in the lowlands, also under conditions of small scale farming (Pereira, 1975).

MULTIPLE CROPPING IN PRACTICE

One of the features that characterize the small farmer in tropical America is intensive land use. He normally grows more than one crop a year under a wide range of multiple cropping systems. These encompass sequential cropping and intercropping. These two systems are often combined in many ways.

It is well known that the Maya Indians in Central America and the Incas in South America grew their maize and beans either sequentially or in intercropping systems, as is still being done in several areas in tropical America.

Where sequential cropping is practiced, usually two to three different basic food crops are grown during the year. With short season crops included in the system, e.g., vegetables, the number of croppings per year may be higher than three. Also some grain crops, such as field bean and maize, are often harvested in the green stage to make room for subsequent croppings. Sequential cropping tends to apply more to the large and medium farmers than to the small farmer.

In the intercropping system, the central or primary crop can be fairly typical of a region. Thus, in Central America it may be maize (Castillo, 1974), whereas in the Amazon Basin and the lowlands of Colombia and Venezuela it may be cassava (Soria, 1975).

---

[3] Regional Office for Central American Programs, 1974. Mimeo.

The contribution of intercropping in bean production alone was found to be 50% in El Salvador, 85% in Colombia, 58% in Mexico, and 80% in Brazil (Scobie et al., 1974). Also in El Salvador, sorghum (*Sorghum* sp.) is almost exclusively produced intercropped with maize (Alas, 1974).

Intercropping of a food crop such as beans and an industrial crop such as sugarcane has been practiced or is receiving more attention in tropical America. Also in fields of slow-growing perennial species, such as cacao, coffee, rubber (*Hevea brasiliensis*), timber, or fruit trees, many annual food crops may be interplanted, to provide subsistence food along with weed control and shade to the young seedling of the perennial crop. For example, a study made in the coffee growing area of Colombia in 1955 to 1956 demonstrated that 33% of the coffee farms were intercropped (Valdes et al., 1961). The more frequently intercropped food plants were plantains (*Musa* sp.) and other edible bananas, followed in importance by sugarcane, cacao, vegetables, and fruits.

We have noticed that the diversity and number of species intercropped by the small farmer on his plot tend to increase from the lowlands to the highlands. Thus in the lowlands, maize, sorghum, upland rice, cassava, cowpea (*Vigna* sp.), and pigeon pea (*Cajanus cajan*) are often the principal crops. In the middlelands and highlands, besides the ubiquitous maize and beans, one finds yams (*Dioscorea* sp.), sweet potato (*Ipomoea batatas*), Irish potato (*Solanum tuberosum*), various cucurbits and other vegetables among the most important crops. Especially in the Andean regions, quinoa, ulluco (*Ullucus tuberosus*), oca (*Oxalis tuberosa*), chili pepper (*Capsicum* sp.), broad bean, wheat (*Triticum aestivum* L.), and barley (*Hordeum vulgare* L.) are frequently found in the farming systems (Adams, 1959, p. 113–128).

MULTIPLE CROPPING RESEARCH

Only limited systematic research has been carried out in Latin America to improve or develop agricultural production systems which are adjusted to the specific ecological, social, and economic conditions of a region. Until recently, attention has rarely been given to the working conditions of the small farmer.

At the beginning of the 1970s, the diffusion of multiple cropping research results from other parts of the world, especially the Philippines (Bradfield, 1969, 1970, 1972) stirred interest in the study of multiple cropping in tropical America, with emphasis on small scale farming. Such interest has received institutional endorsement at several national and international centers. The results of research carried out at these centers, in the area of production agrosystems, are now being published. We will review some of the multiple cropping studies that directly relate to the production of annual food crops, especially those that are basic components of traditional diets in tropical America.

Annuals with Annuals

Experimentally, 14 cropping systems were practiced over a 9-year period in Palmira, Colombia (Gomez, 1968). Of particular relevance here were four that spanned a 1-year cycle. These were: (i) sequential maize (M-M), (ii) continuous soybean, *Glycine max* (L.) Merr., (S-S), (iii) maize followed by soybean (M-S), and (iv) soybean followed by maize (S-M). Maize in rotation with soybean maintained high yields, similar to those of sequential maize fertilized with nitrogen, in the high base status soil of the Cauca Valley.

Data from an experiment on sequential cropping without fertilizers, with upland rice or with sugarcane, for 5 consecutive years, on an alluvial soil near Santa Cruz, Bolivia, indicated that there was no important reduction in yield during the period (Sanchez, 1973). The highest yield of rice was obtained in the fourth year, and of sugarcane in the first. A report of an experiment in Yurimaguas, Peru, (North Carolina State University, 1973) showed also that there was no major yield reduction in the first three continuous crops of upland rice. The third crop was greater than the previous ones, perhaps due to a better rainfall distribution. In order to increase yields from 1 to 3 metric tons/ha, fertilization was necessary in this acid Ultisol from the Amazon Jungle.

An experiment was established at Turrialba in a soil of volcanic origin to test five cropping systems at three soil fertility levels (North Carolina State University, 1973). Food crops were included in three of the systems. The first was a rotation of bean, rice, and maize; the second, maize intercropped with bean, followed by two additional maize crops; and the third, an intercropping of cassava and bean, followed by rice. Rice failed from blast disease caused by *Pericularia orizae,* making it difficult to evaluate the systems as originally planned. However, yield comparison between bean grown alone and bean intercropped with cassava or maize indicated that the cassava crop had no effect on bean yield, while maize reduced it to nearly one-third.

Lepiz (1971) reported data from an intercropping trial of maize and bean, conducted for 3 consecutive years at Chapingo, Mexico. He used a single fertilizer level (80-40-0) and different population densities for each crop, including the density of the traditional maize-bean system of the small farmer (20,000 maize plants and 20,000 bean plants per hectare). Intercropping at various seeding densities, including those traditionally adopted by the local small farmers, resulted in grain yields and income superior to those of the respective single crop grown under optimum densities for the area.

A scheme based on intensive relay planting of dry bean and vegetables in maize was tested by Hildebrand and French (1974) in El Salvador. Agronomically as well as socio-economically it was shown to be, on balance, a potential improvement of the traditional systems practiced by the small farmer in that country.

Flor and Francis (1975) presented results from agronomic and economic experiments of bean (F) and maize (M) row intercropping in Palmira, Colombia, under different spatial or chronological arrangements. Using as reference the monocrops of maize (44,000 plants/ha = 100% M) and bean (222,000 plants/ha = 100% F), we calculated that, in one experiment, the land equivalent ratio (LER) values for agronomic production associated with 100% M + 50% F (in two distinct spatial arrangements) or 100% M + 100% F ranged from 1.63 to 1.89. The association involving a full plant stand of maize and bean (100% M + 100% F) was the best. In another experiment any one of four ways of row intercropping 44,000 plants/ha of maize and 222,000 plants/ha of bean, produced about twice as much gross income as the bean monocropping at 222,000 plants/ha; there was no maize monocropping. In the last experiment reported, a calculation of LER values showed that maize relay-planted 5 to 15 days after the sowing of bean (F/M) was a better practice than bean relay-planted 5 to 15 days after the sowing of maize (M/F) or than bean-maize row intercropping (F + M); both relay and row intercropping were better than monocropping with either crop. Similar results were obtained in intercropping studies on pole bean and maize carried out in Palmillas within the scope of the Puebla Plan, Mexico (Moreno et al., 1973).

A more comprehensive study of farming systems for the American tropics has been initiated by the Tropical Crops and Soils Department of CATIE at Turrialba, Costa Rice, in which various crops and cropping systems are compared agronomically and socio-economically. In one field experiment established in November 1973, in Turrialba, 54 crop patterns based on maize, bean, rice, cassava, and sweet potato were tested at up to four levels of technology, thus forming a total of 216 different "cropping systems". In all the systems, sowing density per crop was maintained uniform: 100,000 plants/ha of beans; 40,000 of corn; 50,000 of sweet potatoes and 20,000 of cassava.

Data of 25 systems, selected as representative of the different cropping patterns, with maize (M), bean (F), cassava (Y), and sweet potato (C) were reported (Soria et al., 1975). Systems with rice were not included in the report because this crop was completely lost due to adverse climatic conditions and damage by disease and soil insects. Moreover, the report considered only two levels of technology, low and high, differing in the amount of inputs used, such as fertilizers and pesticides.

As rated by their LER value, the majority of multiple cropping systems were more efficient than their monocrop analogues in producing food and total biomass. The most outstanding were: (i) the rotation of bean with two subsequent crops of maize (F–M–M), (ii) the intercropping of bean with maize followed by a crop of maize (F+M–M), (iii) the intercropping of bean with cassava followed by maize (F+Y–M), and (iv) the intercropping of maize with cassava followed by sweet potato (M+Y–C). Food and total biomass production, both in monocropping as well as in multiple cropping, were greater at the higher technology level. At the same time, within each technology level, multiple crops yielded more than monocrops and utilization of solar radiation was increased by multiple cropping and a high level of technology.

Fertilizer use was perhaps the most important factor determining the best yields in high technology. In decreasing order, the efficiency of the major nutrient elements, measured as the ratio of amount of nutrient applied to amount of food produced was $K > N > S > P$.

The multiple cropping systems were also more efficient than monocropping in suppressing weeds.

Airborne diseases were more evident and their consequences more serious in monocrops than in multiple crops, where some species acted as natural barriers against spore dispersal. On the other hand, some multiple crop patterns favored a microenvironment with high relative humidity and shade, leading to the development of other types of diseases.

The multiple cropping systems in general permitted a broader utilization of hand labor and were more profitable than monocropping.

Annuals with Perennials

In his textbook on cacao, Hardy (1961, p. 25-34) stresses that in the early stages of field establishment, cacao needs the protection of temporary shade plants, row intercropped with the cacao seedlings. For this purpose, many food crops such as maize, pigeon pea, cassava, malanga (*Xanthosoma* sp.) and especially bananas and plantains, can be utilized.

Among various food crops intercropped in a young rubber plantation on the Atlantic Coast of Costa Rica (Morales et al., 1949), maize or cassava gave the best economic and agronomic results. Besides producing food for local consumption, intercropping saved an average of $24/ha in hand labor, particularly for weeding, during the first 2 years of establishment of the rubber plantation.

Experiments on intercropping sugarcane with various crops in Puerto Rico (Lopez et al., 1953) showed that planting distances influenced the production of sugar, regardless of whether the cane was grown alone or intercropped. Yields of intercropped legume species, such as soybeans, red or white beans, and cowpea were satisfactory. Intercropped cucumber (*Cucumis sativus* L.), melon (*C. melo* sp.), or tomato (*Lycopersicon esculentum*) did not reduce sugarcane yields. However, the intercropping of cane with maize reduced sugarcane production.

Two other trials of intercropping sugarcane with common beans and cowpeas were conducted in Pernambuco, Brazil (Krutman, 1968). Results were inconclusive as to the best distance of rows in the intercroppings. Pulse yields in the intercropping treatments were lower than in the corresponding monocroppings, but there was no reduction in sugarcane production.

In Pernambuco, Mangueira et al. (1970) conducted two experiments for 5 years in Terra Talhada Station, to review previous inconclusive experimental results reported by other researchers on the relative efficiency of the traditional system of cotton (*Gossypium hirsutum*) production in the northeast region of Brazil. The system involves intercropping of cotton with common bean, maize, forage *Opuntia,* or sesame (*Sesamum indicum*). In the first experiment were tested cotton as a monocrop, cotton intercropped with *Opuntia* and cotton intercropped with maize and beans; in the second, the treatments were cotton as a monocrop, intercropping of cotton with maize and beans in two row patterns of the maize and bean crops, intercropping of cotton with sesame, and intercropping of cotton with maize and forage *Opuntia.* During the 5-year period, cotton yields in general were higher in the intercropping than in the monocropping systems, excepting intercropping with sesame.

Taungya system experiments with eucalyptus (*Eucalyptus* sp.) in Brazil (Gurgel Filho, 1965) with *Cordia alliodora, Cupressus lusitanica, Swietenia humilis,* and teak (*Tectona grandis*) in Turrialba (Aguirre, 1963) have shown that intercropping the timber species with food crops during the first years of establishment of the plantation yielded many economic advantages, including the saving of labor in weed control.

PROPOSED TRENDS IN MULTIPLE CROPPING RESEARCH AND PROMOTION

At present, the majority of Latin American governments are giving top priority to the improvement of the standard of living of their rural populations, particularly at the small farmer level. However, only limited information is available about the small farmer's real situation.

In traditional scientific spheres there is a general belief that the small farmer is a subsistence group, producing only for home consumption. In Latin America, however, although a good portion of the small farmer's crop production is consumed by his immediate family, a sizeable portion is sold for cash to satisfy other needs. Among many of the small farm products that find their way to the urban markets are beans, maize, cassava, sweet potatoes, vegetables, plantains, and yams which generally are not grown by the large- or medium-sized farmers.

On one hand a variety of traditional production systems, which have remained unchanged for decades or longer, are still practiced by a large number of small farmers in tropical America in spite of the existence of the much-heralded "modern technology." On the other hand, the local agricultural experiment stations are testing new technological packages, with resources and approaches totally different from those of the small farmer across the fence. Concern is expressed about the lack of adoption by the small farmers of the experimental results published by the stations, but in general only scant effort has been dedicated to the analysis and lessening of such discrepancy. A common *a priori* judgment has been that what the small farmer practices is primitive technology and should be eliminated.

However, experimental results from testing some of the small farmer's production systems show or imply several advantageous features.

Even with low technology, total production of an area under intercropping in conditions of tropical America is more profitable than under monocropping. The use of intercropping ensures food production against abrupt climate, pest, and price fluctuations. Multiple cropping systems are better adjusted to the small farmer's available resources, such as abundant hand labor, lack of capital for buying inputs, permanent availability of solar energy, and limited land area. Intercropping or rotation systems involving different species that often present differential reactions to diseases and insects and provide better ground cover, allow a more efficient management of diseases, insects, weeds, and soil and better use of solar energy. Also, the growing of a large array of different crops in the year offers broader diversification of food products.

From these and other considerations, it seems urgent that a new research approach be adopted to produce technology more useful to and acceptable by the small farmer.

The development of new technology on farming systems needs a team approach with specialists in areas of ecology, biology, agriculture, economics, and sociology, all engaged in the development of sound agricultural systems, adjusted to the tropical climate and to the socio-economic conditions of the farmer.

Plant breeders should develop earlier varieties with plant architectures adapted so as to complement and not to compete for resources when grown in multiple cropping schemes. Special attention should be given to the selection of genotypes that are more productive and less dependent on large amounts of fertilizers and water and are insensitive to day length. New types and formulae of fertilizers best suited for intercropping and rotation under the climatic conditions of tropical America need to be developed. Special emphasis should be placed on the economic use of fertilizer along with consideration of methods and times of application. Moreover, the mineralization of crop residues should be considered to cut down still further the amount of commercial fertilizers required.

Integrated control methods of diseases, insects, and other pests (including weeds), with a minimum use of chemicals, should be developed; the outlook appears promising through the combined practice of intercropping, rotation, and use of resistant varieties, along with appropriate timing of planting. More research should be done on planting densities and planting chronology.

In developing farming systems for small producers, testing for yield stability through crop management should be of foremost importance as its lack has been the main cause of shifting cultivation in the tropics. Other studies should evaluate income stability of the farming systems involving crops (annual and perennial, and food and nonfood species) and animals.

Because the small farmer in tropical America ordinarily respects traditions and possesses a low level of literacy, patience must be taken in transferring to him research results. Considerable and direct technical assistance, especially in the early phases of the process of technology transfer, will be required. Adoption by the small farmer of new techniques is likely to be easier the more he directly participates in the development of such techniques, is convinced of their practical value, and finds them compatible with his beliefs.

In tropical America like elsewhere multiple cropping research and practice in itself will not substitute the need for profound social and political reforms to lessen social and economic disparities. However, from a broad perspective, multiple cropping is a most promising means of utilizing resources. It is an essential lever in engineering stepped-up food production programs to avert world famine and consequent social and political turmoils.

LITERATURE CITED

Adams, R. N. 1959. A community in the Andes. Problems and progress in Muquiyauyo. Univ. of Washington Press, Seattle.

Aguirre Corral, A. 1963. Estudio silvicultural y economico del sistema Taungya en condiciones de Turrialba. Inst. Interamer. de Ciencias Agric., Turrialba, Costa Rica, 103 p.

Alas, L., M. 1974. Breve descripcion del sistema de produccion del pequeno productor en El Salvador. Apendice F. *In* Conferencia sobre sistemas de produccion agricola para el tropico. Centro Agronomico Tropical de Investigacion y Ensenanza. Informe final. CATIE, Turrialba, Costa Rica.

Bradfield, R. 1969. Training agronomists for increasing food production in the humid tropics. p. 45-63. *In* J. R. Cowan and L. S. Robertson (ed.) International agronomy training and education. Spec. Pub. 15, Am. Soc. of Agron., Madison, Wis.

Bradfield, R. 1970. Increasing food production in the tropics by multiple cropping. p. 229-242. *In* D. G. Aldrich, Jr. (ed.) Research for the world food crisis. Pub. 92, Am. Assoc. Adv. of Sci., Washington, D. C.

Bradfield, R. 1972. Maximizing food production through multiple cropping systems centered on rice. p. 143-163. *In* Rice, science, and man. IRRI, Los Banos, Philippines.

Bukasov, S. M. 1963. Las plantas cultivadas de Mexico, Guatemala y Colombia. IICA–OEA, Zona Andina Pub. Misc. No. 20, Lima, Peru. 261 p.

Castillo, M. 1974. Algunos sistemas de produccion agricola en Guatemala. Apendice F. *In* Conferencia sobre sistemas de produccion agricola para el tropico. Centro Agronomico Tropical de Investigacion y Ensenanza. Informe final. CATIE, Turrialba, Costa Rica.

Duckham, A. M., and G. B. Masefield. 1971. Farming systems of the world. Chatto and Windus, London.

Flor, C. A., and C. A. Francis. 1975. Propuesta de estudio de algunos componentes de una metodologia para investigar los cultivos asociados en el tropico americano. Programa Cooperativo Centro-americano para el Mejoramiento de Cultivos Alimenticios, San Salvador, El Salvador. Memoria. XXI Reunion Ann. I:45-61.

Gomez, L., J. A. 1968. Rotacion y rendimiento en maiz. Informe sobre una rotacion con soya o alfalfa en la produccion del maiz. Agric. Trop. (Colombia) 24:204-220.

Gurgel Filho, O. A. 1965. Milho baixa custo do eucalipto. Coopercotia 22(186):39.

Hardy, F. (ed.). 1961. Manual de cacao. Inst. Interamericano de Ciencias Agricolas, Turrialba, Costa Rica.

Hardy, F. 1970. Suelos tropicales, pedologia tropical con enfasis en America. Herrero Hermanos Sucs., S. A., Mexico. 334 p.

Hildebrand, P. E., and E. C. French. 1974. Un sistema salvadoreno de multicultivos: Su potencial y sus problemas. Apendice F. *In* Conferencia sobre sistemas de produccion agricola para el tropico. Centro Agronomico Tropical de Investigacion y Ensenanza. Informe final. CATIE, Turrialba, Costa Rica.

Krutman, S. 1968. Cultura consorciada cana x feijoeiro. Primeiros resultados. Pesqui. Agropecu. Bras. 3:127-134.

Lepiz. I., R. 1971. Asociacion de cultivos maiz-frijol. Agric. Tec. Mex. 3:98–101.

Lopez, M. A., B. G. Capo, F. Aros Tegui, and A. Riollano. 1953. Intercropping sugar cane with food crops. J. Agric. Univ. P. R. 37(3):171–182.

Mangueira B., O., J. Pereira T., e A. Dantas P. 1970. Ventagems da consorciacao na cultura do algodoeiro "moco" (*Gossypium hirsutum* L. var. Marie-Galante Hutch). Inst. de Pesqui. Agro. Sceretaria de Agric. Estado de Pernambuco Bol. Tec. 48. 30 p.

Morales, O. J., W. N. Bangham, and F. M. Barrus. 1949. Cultivos intercalados en plantaciones de Hevea. Inst. Interamer. de Ciencias Agric. Bol. Tec. 2, Turrialba, Costa Rica. 26 p.

Moreno R., O., A. Turrent F., y R. Nunez E. 1973. Las asociaciones de maiz-frijol, una alternative en el uso de los recursos de los agricultores de Plan Puebla. Agrotecnia (Mexico) 14:103–117.

North Carolina State University. 1973. Agronomic economic research on tropical soils. Annual report 1973, Soil Science Department, Raleigh, N. C. 190 p.

Patino, V. M. 1965. Historia de la actividad agropecuaria en America equinoccial. Imprenta Departamental, Cali, Colombia. 601 p.

Pereira, F. 1975. La transferencia de tecnologia en el desarrollo agricola de Bolivia. *In* Reunion tecnica regional sobre transferencia de tecnologia agricola a los productores. Maracay, Venezuela, 1975. IICA-Zona Andina. 16 p.

Sanchez, P. A. 1973. Manejo de suelos bajo el sistema de roza. *In* R. A. Sanchez (ed.) Un resumen de las investigaciones edafologicas en America Latina tropical. North Carolina State Univ. Tech. Bull. 219:51–74.

Scobie, G. M., M. A. Infante, and U. Gutierrez P. 1974. Production and consumption of dry beans and their role in protein nutrition: A review (Preliminary). CIAT, Cali, Colombia. 53 p.

Secretaria de Integracion Economica de Centro America. 1972. El desarrollo integrado de Centroamerica en la presente decada. Bases y presupuesto para el perfeccionamiento y reestructura del Mercado Comun Centroamericano. Estudio No. 4. Programa de Desarrollo Integrado, Guatemala. 304 p.

Soria, J. 1976. Sistemas de produccion bajo varias condiciones ecologicas en America Latina, con enfasis en el majoramiento de la agricultura tradicional de pequenos productores. *In* Consulta de Expertos sobre Investigacion Agricola en America Latina organizada por FAO, Ciudad de Panama, 1975. 17 p.

Soria, J., R. Bazan A. M. Pinchinat, G. Paez, N. Mateo, R. Moreno, J. Fargas, y W. Forsythe. 1975. Investigacion en sistemas de produccion agricola para el pequeno productor del tropico. Turrialba 25:283–293.

Valdes, H., A. Machado S., y H. Uribe A. 1961. Diversificacion de la agricultura (con respecto al problema del cafe). Cafe (Costa Rica) 3(9):58–62.

Intercropping Systems in Tropical Africa

B. N. Okigbo and D. J. Greenland[1]

Tropical Africa lies south of the Sahara Desert bounded by imaginary lines both north and south of the equator. The northern line runs from Cape Blane on the Atlantic coast of Mauritania due east to the northern tip of Ethiopia on the Red Sea coast. The southern line traverses east from Mocamedes on the Atlantic coast of Angola to the southernmost tip of Mozambique on the east coast of Africa. It is a land 5,150 km long and 7,400 km wide with an area of about 22×10^6 km^2 (Kimble, 1962). The area extends over the entire equatorial belt of Africa and latitudinally to about 20°N and 26°S. This land mass which is about twice the area of the U. S. exhibits great diversity in relief, climate, vegetation, and crops grown (Fig. 1, 2, 3, 4).

Tropical Africa has a population of over 290 million people of many racial backgrounds and according to Grove (1970) up to 800 linguistic groups. There are 40 countries represented with widely different cultural, economic, colonial, and political backgrounds and experience. These factors in addition to the level of technological development and resource availability (Norman, 1974) constitute the basis of diversity in the number of crops grown and variations in cropping and farming systems. In this paper, characteristics of cropping systems in traditional farming practices are considered as a basis for a survey of multiple cropping systems in tropical Africa and a review of related research in relevant countries.

FARMING SYSTEMS AND ASSOCIATED CROPPING PATTERNS

Of the 13 major agricultural regions in Whittlesey's (1962) classification, only nomadic herding, shifting cultivation, rudimentary sedentary cultivation and nonrice based intensive agriculture, special horticulture, and plantation

---

[1]Assistant director, Farming Systems Program, and director of research, International Institute of Tropical Agriculture, Ibadan, Nigeria, respectively.

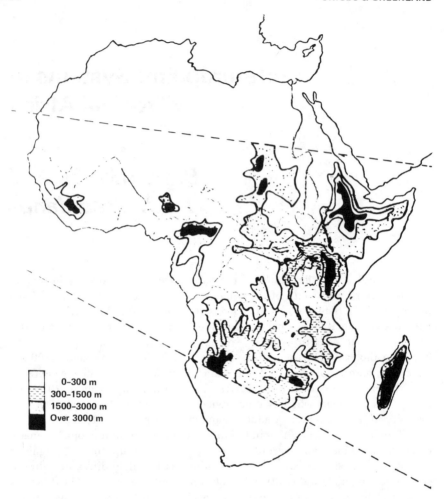

Figure 1. Major physical area of tropical Africa (Kimble & Steel, 1966).

0–300 m
300–1500 m
1500–3000 m
Over 3000 m

agriculture are found in tropical Africa. Since then, attempts have been made to develop more functional and acceptable classifications of the farming systems of the world (Dumont, 1970; Duckham & Masefield, 1971; Laut, 1971; Evenson et al., 1973; Grigg, 1974). Classifications of farming systems with emphasis on the agriculture of the tropics include those of Allan (1965), Miracle (1967), Morgan and Pugh (1969), Morgan (1959a, 1969), Floyd (1969), Boserup (1970), Ruthenberg (1971, 1974), Benneh (1972) and Greenland (1974). With the exception of Ruthenberg's classification which takes into account vegetation, migration, rotation, clearance, cropping, and tool systems, most methods of classifying farming systems of the tropics are based on differences in intensity of cropping and variations in the duration of the fallow period for the restoration of soil fertility.

Figure 2. Tropical Africa, mean annual rainfall (Kimble & Steel, 1966).

With the exception of some parts of Africa where farming methods are patterned after the modern systems of Europe and plantation agriculture, multiple cropping constitutes a major component of the existing farming systems. However, these systems are transitory stages in the evolution of either potentially permanent systems under proper management of resources and adjustment to change or degenerating systems that are subject to final collapse under poor management of resources and failure to adjust to change brought about by population pressure and other processes. Consequently, they are not necessarily in equilibrium with the biological and cultural environments of the farmer as might have existed centuries ago under low population pressure when adjustments to conditions came about naturally by providence or after long periods of gradual evolution.

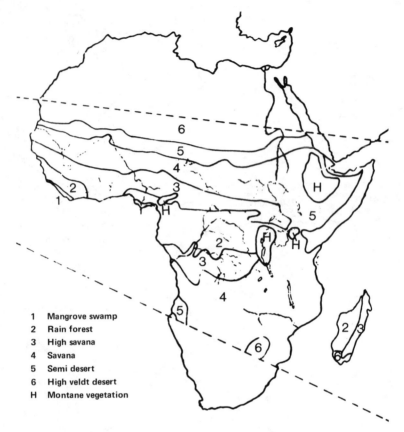

1   Mangrove swamp
2   Rain forest
3   High savana
4   Savana
5   Semi desert
6   High veldt desert
H   Montane vegetation

Figure 3. Africa, natural vegetation zones (Jarrett, 1966).

Classifications which provide a suitable background for the understanding of the developments that led to the existing cropping systems, their complexities, similarities, and contrasts are those of Porteres (1962) and Benneh (1972). Porteres, on the basis of his studies of origin of cultivated plants and agriculture in Africa, arrived at two main conclusions. First, Africa evolved two agricultural complexes—a *seed agricultural complex* characteristic of open unforested regions analagous to our savannas of today and a *vegecultural complex* peculiar to forested regions and involving cultivation of roots, tubers, and cuttings in gardens rather than fields. Second, differences between these two complexes have gradually disappeared as crops and techniques developed elsewhere were adopted within the traditional systems. Benneh's (1972) classification which covers the types of existing farming systems in West Africa is based on methods of soil fertility maintenance in fallow and permanent systems prevalent on farms of different sizes consisting of the following categories:

A. Traditional and transitional systems

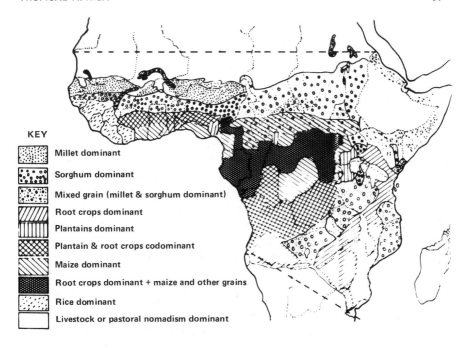

KEY

- ▨ Millet dominant
- ▨ Sorghum dominant
- ▨ Mixed grain (millet & sorghum dominant)
- ▨ Root crops dominant
- ▨ Plantains dominant
- ▨ Plantain & root crops codominant
- ▨ Maize dominant
- ▨ Root crops dominant + maize and other grains
- ▨ Rice dominant
- ▨ Livestock or pastoral nomadism dominant

Figure 4. Crop dominant regions (Johnston, 1958; Miracle, 1966; Morgan & Pugh, 1969; Morgan, 1969; Matheson & Bovril, 1950).

    1. Nomadic herding:
      shifting cultivation (Phase 1), $L > 10^2$
    2. Bush fallowing or land rotation:
      shifting cultivation (Phase II), $L = 5 - 10$
    3. Rudimentary sedentary agriculture:
      shifting cultivation (Phase III), $L = 2 - 4$
    4. Compound farming and extensive subsistence agriculture:
      shifting cultivation (Phase IV), $L < 2$
    5. Terrace farming and floodland agriculture
    6. Mediterranean agriculture (traditional)
  B. Modern farming systems and their local adaptations
    1. Mixed farming
    2. Livestock ranching
    3. Intensive livestock production (poultry, pigs, dairying)
    4. Large scale farms and plantations
      a. Large scale food and arable crop farms based on natural rainfall
      b. Irrigation projects involving crop production
      c. Large scale tree crop plantations
    5. Specialized horticulture
      a. Market gardening
      b. Truck gardening and fruit plantations
      c. Commercial fruit and vegetable production for processing.
    6. Mediterranean agriculture (modern)

[2] $L = C + F/C$ where C = Cropping Period, F = Fallow Period, L = Land Use Factor.

The groups of farming systems under A (1b-6) and B (1, 4, 5, and 6) are those under which multiple cropping is found in tropical Africa. The complexity of these systems may be illustrated by the fact that a farmer usually operates a much diversified agricultural enterprise, often including a combination of different systems listed by Benneh (1972). For example, a farmer on an upland well-drained soil may operate a compound farm close to this homestead while at the same time maintain two or more plots under cropping systems of different periods of forest, bush, or planted fallows at varying distances from his home. In addition to this, he may practice flood-land cultivation in the flood plain of a nearby river or stream. He may also raise goats, sheep and/or poultry for manure and other purposes. The cropping on the compound farm often involves major staples, vegetables and condiment plants grown in double, relay, and mixed intercropping patterns under the canopy of tree crops such as oilpalms (*Elaeis guineensis*), mangoes (*Mangifera* sp.), and oranges (*Citrus* sp.). The compound farm or homestead garden thus carries more species of cultivated plants than bush fallow farms since on the latter only major staples and a few protected trees may be grown.

SOME CHARACTERISTICS OF TRADITIONAL FARMING AND ASSOCIATED CROPPING SYSTEMS

A simplistic model of traditional farming would consist of a concentric pattern of fields on which are practiced various methods of fertility maintenance or fallowing, clearance systems, production of different numbers of species and varieties of crops and cropping patterns and sequences according to the prevailing customs and the needs of the farmer. Based on this concept, the following generalizations can be made of these systems:

1. There is a diversity of farming systems ranging from "true" shifting cultivation where the settlement is moved to permanent cultivation.
2. "True" shifting cultivation is rare and restricted to parts of Rhodesia (Allan, 1965), the Ivory Coast and the Cameroun Republic (Morgan, 1969; Grigg, 1974).
3. Permanent cultivation occurs in (i) compound farms, kitchen or homestead gardens, (ii) some soils of high fertility, (iii) confined sites (such as steep slopes of Maku in the East Central State of Nigeria where terrace farming is practiced and on islands such as the Ukara Island in Lake Victoria, and (iv) overcrowded areas of high population densities such as in the Ibo and Ibibio areas of the east central State of Nigeria, the eastern rice-growing slopes of the Malagasy Republic and Kano close-settled zone of the north central State of Nigeria (Morgan, 1969).
4. The compound farm system is the most widespread permanent cropping or farming system and often forms the center from which paths lead to other field systems. The largest number of crop species in mixtures are found in compound farms since the crops there are not only grown for food but also for oils and fats, condiments and spices, masticants and stimulants, drugs, fiber, struc-

tural materials, animal feed, demarcation of boundaries, firewood, ornamentals, shade, protection and privacy of the homestead, religious and social functions, and various other uses. Its development as a regular feature in the traditional farming systems is related to two phenomena: i) The division of labor between the sexes in which the women are responsible for cooking and the provision of soups and sauces. The main starchy staples are primarily produced by men. They are eaten with fresh condiment plants, spices, and vegetables at available close range through the year and ii) The fact that with frequent clearing of forests and bushes, useful trees harvested from the wild or protected in fallows are gradually disappearing and their cultivation in compound farms ensures that their products are readily available and that they do not become scarce or extinct.

5. Semipermanent long and short bush or planted fallow systems vary in cultivation period relative to length of fallow. Factors are the natural fertility of the land, distances from the homestead, methods of fertility maintenance, and population pressure. In semipermanent fields, major staples are predominant with a few subsidiary crops, all much less in number than in compound farms.

6. The most important staples and cash crops are usually grown the first year following clearance of forest, natural bush, planted fallow or grassland. The number of crop species decreases as the number of years of continuous cropping increases.

7. Intercropping is widespread with the highest complexity in the compound gardens, especially in the rainforest where annual staples, vegetables, and perennial fruit trees are intercropped. Tables 1, 2, and 3 show the extent to which intercropping is practiced in different ecological zones in Nigeria and Uganda. In farms or fields located at varying distances from the homestead, semiwild protected and selected wild tree crops, but rarely cultivated species, are found.

8. The growing of more than one crop on the same land in 1 year in traditional farming systems takes the form of mixed intercropping and relay intercropping more so than sequential cropping involv-

Table 1. Areas in important crops in Nigeria in relation to the system of production in 1970–1971

Crops	Hectarage sole	Hectarage mixed	Percentage mixed
	ha $\times 10^{-3}$		%
Yams	503.7	733.2	59.2
Cassava	307.2	112.6	26.8
Cocoyam	27.4	173.9	86.4
Rice	103.9	143.3	58.0
Maize	355.2	1092.8	75.5
Melon	25.9	334.3	92.8
Cowpeas	39.0	3777.1	99.0
Groundnut	19.8	419.7	95.5
Cotton	130.2	524.5	80.1
Guinea corn	1152.0	4557.0	79.8
Soya-bean	48.2	51.8	100.0
Benniseed	36.8	41.3	52.9
Millet	510.9	4411.1	89.6

Table 2. Area of crops grown in most of Uganda according to area and percentage of system of cropping in 1963–1964 (Jameson, 1970)

	Area in hectare		Percentage of crop grown in			Overall mixed cropping
Crop	Pure	Mixed	Pure	Mixed predominant	Mixed not predominant	
	ha (000)			%		
1. Beans	57.9	250.6	18.7	10.3	71.0	81.3
2. Cowpeas	29.6	47.8	38.2	6.3	55.5	61.8
3. Cassava	85.0	84.6	50.1	10.3	39.6	49.9
4. Robusta coffee	114.6	174.9	39.6	33.0	27.4	60.4
5. Arabica coffee	6.1	10.5	36.6	--	--	63.4
6. Cotton	367.6	130.4	73.8	21.2	5.0	26.2
7. Groundnuts	67.2	86.6	43.7	33.8	22.5	56.3
8. Maize	44.9	232.0	16.3	14.6	69.1	83.7
9. Sorghum	135.6	115.8	54.0	7.4	38.6	46.0
10. Finger millet	226.7	206.1	52.4	41.3	6.3	47.6
11. Peas	17.4	4.0	81.1	--	--	18.9
12. Pigeon peas	12.6	39.7	24.0	7.0	69.0	76.0
13. Bananas	268.8	195.5	57.9	20.9	21.2	42.1
14. Sesame	51.0	53.0	49.0	19.1	31.9	51.0
15. Sweet potatoes	73.7	11.7	86.3	4.7	9.0	13.7

ing monocultures. Row intercropping and alternate strip intercropping are not common except where animals or tractors are used in cultivation.

9. Classical crop rotations involving sequences of crops grown in monoculture are rare in traditional farming systems. More common are the "pseudo-rotations" in which mixed intercropping with different species are followed by different sets of dominant and subsidiary crops also in mixed intercropping (Allan, 1965). Some crops are relay intercropped with the preceding ones.

10. Farm sizes are usually small ranging from less than 1 ha up to 5 ha. Farm sizes tend to be greater but number of crops in mixtures lower in moving from the rainforest to savanna or drier areas.

11. Cash or export crops are more likely to be grown as sole crops or in association with fewer crops than noncash staples.

12. Farming involves simple tools and much human labor.

13. The most widespread land clearing systems involve the use of fire.

14. With the exception of irrigation, some locations in semiarid and arid areas, most cropping systems rely on rainfall. The cropping patterns and mixtures are related to the uncertainities in rainfall distribution and intensity.

FACTORS CONTRIBUTING TO CHANGES IN CROPPING SYSTEMS AND ADAPTATIONS TO PREVAILING CONDITIONS

Variations and changes in cropping systems have arisen from:

1. The introduction of Asian crops [taro (*Colocasia antiquorum* sp.), water yam (*Dioscorea alata*), bananas (*Musa* sp.), rice (*Oryza sativa*

Table 3. Food crops and other useful plants found in crop mixtures in compound and outlying farms in parts of southeastern Nigeria

	A* 0.003–0.45 Ha		B* 0.04 Ha		Area of sample C* 0.04–0.4 Ha		D* 0.04–0.5 Ha		E* 0.04–0.5 Ha		Mean percentage frequency
Crop plant group	Range	Mean	Range	Mean	Range	Mean	Range	Mean	Range	Mean	
1. Roots & tubers	1–12	5	4–6	5	5–8	7	1–8	4	7–9	8	47
2. Cereals & other starchy staples	0–3	1	1–2	1	2–3	2	0–4	2	2–3	2	38
3. Leaf vegetables	3–7	4	0–4	2	4–8	6	10–11	6	2–8	5	27
4. Fruit vegetables	4–6	4	1–3	2	5–6	5	0–6	2	3	3	44
5. Legumes	1–5	3	0–4	2	2–4	2	0–3	1	0–3	2	33
6. Fruits, nuts & oil plants	1–14	5	0–1	1	10–11	10	2–15	7	5–12	9	20
7. Spices & beverages	0–3	1	0–1	1	2–6	4	0–9	4	1–7	4	18
8. Miscellaneous useful plants	0–7	2	0–1	0	10–14	13	1–29	11	4–18	12	11
Range in total number of species or cultivars	6–52		4–19		40–48		6–62		25–52		

* A = Derived Savanna; B = Transition Zone—Derived Savanna-Oil Palm Bush; C = Oil Palm Bush—High Population Density; D = Oil Palm Bush—Medium-High Population Density; E = Oil Palm Bush—High Population Density.

L.)] starting from the first three centuries A.D. and American crops [maize (*Zea mays* L.), cassava (*Manihot esculenta*), sweet potatoes (*Ipomoea batatas*)] in the 16th century A.D. and later (Shaw, 1972).

2. Population growth following the introduction of Asian and American crops and modern advances in medicine, sanitation and public health which have resulted in increasing pressure on the land.
3. The development of markets for perennial crops (Morgan, 1959a).
4. Expansion of cassava production due to its adaptation to shorter periods of fallow resulting in lower soil fertility and demands for cheaper staple foods in urban centers (Morgan, 1959b). Moreover, in areas where the dry season ranges from 1 to 5 months, cassava is the only crop that can thrive without irrigation.
5. Development of commercial production of food crops and market gardening especially close to urban centers.
6. Development of railways, road systems, and markets and the growth of settlements and farms along roads and railways and close to markets (Morgan, 1959b).
7. Increased fruit and vegetable production for sale and in support of local canning industries.

Crop Diversity and Spatial Arrangement

A common feature of traditional farming systems is production of several species of crop plants and numerous varieties of each species by each farmer. In Zaire, the Medje grew as many as 80 varieties of the 30 species of food crops they cultivated in 1911 (Miracle, 1967). Of these, there were 27 varieties of bananas and plantains (*Musa* sp.) and 22 varieties of yams and related crops. The various varieties of each crop exhibit different characteristics, mature at different times, and may be adapted to different ecological situations and cultural practices. While crops are apparently established haphazardly in mixed culture, close study of planting patterns indicates that both on the macro and micro level of a given landscape, the pattern of land use or planting used in traditional cropping systems usually involves location and spacing of plants in such a way as to:

1. take advantage of local topographic features, toposequences, micro-relief and other related peculiarities,
2. disperse individual plant species at such wide spacing as to allow other crops to be grown in between without unnecessary overlapping of their canopies,
3. ensure that crop cover is adequate to effectively control soil erosion and weeds, and
4. ensure that heliophytes are grown more in open spaces while shade tolerant species such as cocoyams (*Colocasia esculenta* and *Xanthosoma sagittifolium*) are located under trees and along hedge rows.

Where annual staples are uniformly planted among tree crops in compound farms, heavy pruning of the tree crops is usually carried out to ensure that light reaches the ground level. Whether crops are grown on mounds, beds, ridges, or on the flat, their spatial arrangements and frequencies in mixtures are usually related to their importance in the diet and sometimes to their uses. Vegetable crops such as cucurbits (*Cucurbita* spp.), cowpeas (*Vigna* sp.), bitter leaf (*Vernonia amygdalina*), and peppers (*Capsicum* sp.) which are harvested for household use are usually planted along the edges of the garden or along fences surrounding gardens close to the homestead. The ingenuity involved in the utilization of various parts of the large mounds on which different crops are grown in a hydromorphic soil of the Abakaliki area of the east central State of Nigeria is illustrated in Figure 5. The crops are located on the mounds according to their root systems and in relation to their tolerance to high water tables.

Various methods of utilizing special topographic and other features include: the concentration of sugarcane (*Saccharum officinarum* L.), rice and off-season vegetable crops in depressions and valley bottoms, the location of pineapples (*Ananas comosus*) and fruit trees along pathways in compound gardens, the growing of climbing crop plants such as lima beans (*Phaseolus lunatus*), climbing cowpeas and yams close to trees, shrubs, fences, hedges, and other structures which act as supports or stakes. Related to this is the location of condiment plants, fruit trees, and vegetables where they can be protected, watered, and harvested with ease. Various compound farm land use and cropping arrangements in parts of tropical Africa have been reported by Allan (1965), de Schlippe (1956), and Miracle (1967).

In addition to these intercropping patterns, small patches of pure stands of certain crops in adjacent plots are prevalent in many areas. Similarly, in smallholder market gardens close to urban centers, vegetables are grown either in pure stands or in mixtures on small adjacent beds.

REGIONAL AND COUNTRY SURVEY OF MULTIPLE CROPPING SYSTEMS

Nigeria

Nigeria stretches from 5°N to 15°N latitude and 2.5°E to almost 15°E longitudes. It has physical and climatic features which have resulted in parallel vegetation and ecological zones. These range from mangrove swamps of coastal areas, with almost no dry season in the extreme south, to the Sahel savanna zone in the extreme north with over 5 dry months. The elevation varies from sea level to over 1,000 m. A diversity of crops can be grown including roots and tubers of the tropical rainforest, crops of semiarid areas such as sorghum (*Sorghum bicolor*) and millet (*Pennisetum typhoides*) and subtropical crops such as potatoes (*Solanum tuberosum* L.) and vegetables. Unlike the countries of east, central, and south Africa, there has been no European settlement. Consequently, with the exception of a few tree crop plantations and some large-scale irrigation projects under development, the agricultural and cropping systems have been restricted to traditional smallholdings. About 55% of the farms in Nigeria are less than 1 ha and about 90% are less than 4 ha (FOS, 1972). Farm sizes are smallest in the southern states where over 86% are below 1 ha.

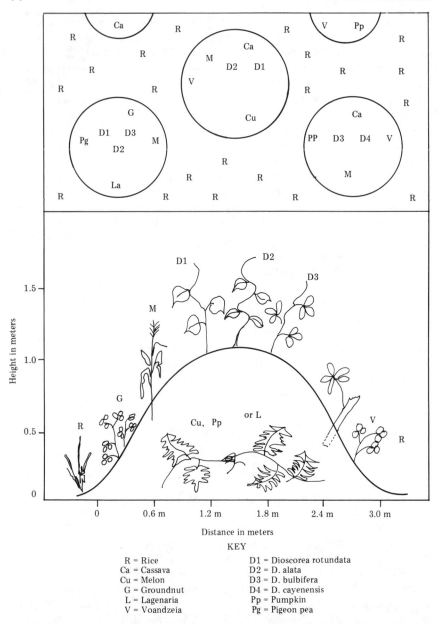

Figure 5. Spatial distribution of crops on mounds in Abakaliki, East Central State, Nigeria.

Mixed intercropping is the predominant practice for both major staples and cash crops. The number of crops involved in the mixtures may exceed 50 species and consequently many more varieties since several strains of a single crop may be grown in a field. The practice of mixed intercropping is a long standing tradition to the extent that it sometimes militates against adoption of new varieties (Faulkner & Mackie, 1933). For example, farmers in certain parts of Nigeria could not be persuaded to grow an improved introduced and superior American cotton (*Gossypium hirsutum* L.) variety because it did not perform as well when intercropped as did the local variety.

The predominant practice of maintaining soil fertility is bush fallowing involving consecutive cropping periods of 1 to 5 years alternating with fallow periods of 2 to over 15 years, depending on the population pressure. In the densely populated areas of the East Central and Southeastern States, planted fallows of *Acioa barteri* and *Anthonotha macrophylla*, respectively, are used. Similarly, *Gliricidia sepium* is grown for the same purpose in the western State of Nigeria. Permanent cultivation with no fallow or short fallow periods is practiced in the compound farms on floodland terraces of southeastern Nigeria and the Kano close-settled areas (Morgan, 1969). Shifting cultivation proper (Phase I shifting cultivation, Greenland, 1974) is restricted to some parts of Ogoja province adjacent to the Cameroun Republic.

The most widespread multiple cropping systems consist of mixed intercropping and relay intercropping. Double cropping is limited to the growing of two crops of maize. Sometimes a double cropping, triple cropping, and alternate strip cropping systems are practiced in market gardens and with certain vegetable crops. In the southeastern states of Nigeria the dominant staples are yams, cassava, cocoyams, bananas, plantains and some maize. These crops are usually grown with subsidiary crops such as groundnuts (*Arachis hypogaea*), okra (*Hibiscus esculantus*), pumpkins (*Cucubita pepo*), melons (*Colocynthis vulgaris* and *Cucumeropsis* spp.), and leaf vegetables (*Amaranthus hybridus, Celosia argentia, Corchorus olitorus, Telfairia occidentalis*). Yams, cassava, cocoyams, bananas and plantains are also grown in western Nigeria but the bananas, plantains and cocoyams are not important in the eastern parts of the country. Tree crops grow in association with the annual and biannual staples. For example in much of southeastern and midwestern Nigeria, oilpalm constitutes part of the climax vegetation and is an important cash crop. Semiwild groves and plantations of oilpalms exist in monoculture but many palms are found in compound farms or scattered in outlying fields where they are protected. Similarly, rubber (*Hevea brasiliensis*) in the Midwest State and cocoa (*Theobroma cacao*) and kola (*Cola nitida*) in the Western State are also found in association with annual staples. The "Middle Belt" of Nigeria which consists of much of the Benue Plateau, Kwara, and northwest states grows some of the important crops of the tropical rainforest such as yams in the southern half of the area and sorghum and millet in the northern half.

Clearance systems involve slash and burn techniques. Planting on mounds or heaps and sometimes ridges is a general practice except in areas with deep alluvial or sandy soils where planting on the flat is common. The mounds attain their most impressive development in the hydromorphic soils of Abakaliki Division of the East Central State of Nigeria. Here, mounds up to 2.5 m in height and over 3 m in basal diameter are found.

SOUTHEASTERN NIGERIA

    Traditional cropping systems range from shifting cultivation in isolated areas near the Cameroun border to intensive sedentary cultivation (Floyd, 1969; Uzozie, 1971). Figure 6 shows the key to cropping schedules and combinations followed in this discussion.

    No systematized rotations are in regular use. Crops are grown in sequence according to the number of compatible species in the mixture that can produce reasonable yields at the existing soil fertility level. Examples of crop rotations used in bush fallow and rudimentary sedentary cultivation fields at Nnewi in Onitsha Province reported by Floyd (1969) are shown in Figure 7.

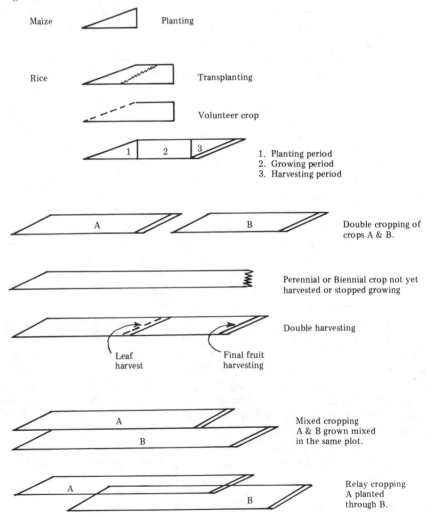

Figure 6. Key to cropping schedules and combinations.

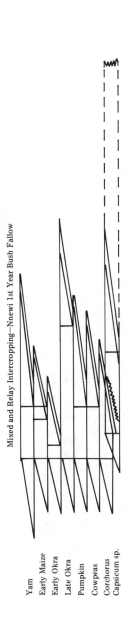

Mixed and Relay Intercropping—Nnewi 1st Year Bush Fallow

Yam
Early Maize
Early Okra
Late Okra
Pumpkin
Cowpeas
Corchorus
Capsicum sp.

Mixed Intercropping—Nnewi Rudimentary Sedentary Cultivation 1st & 2nd Years

Yams
Corchorus

Cowpea
Amaranthus
Early Maize
Early Cassava

Note: Okra, pumpkin, cowpeas and vegetables are planted on sides or bases of mounds. Maize sometimes planted on flat between mounds.

J F M A M J J A S O N D   J F M A M J J A S O N D
First Year   Second Year

Figure 7. Schedule of planting, combinations and harvesting at Nwewi, Onitsha Province, southwest Nigeria.

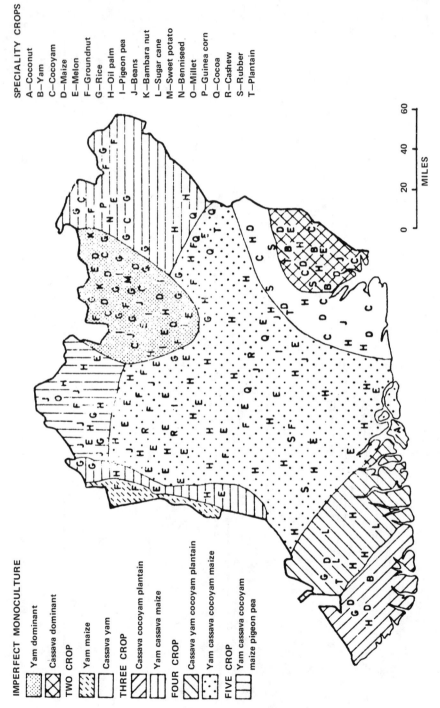

Figure 8. Crop combination areas in southeastern Nigeria (Uzozie, 1971).

SPECIALITY CROPS

A—Coconut
B—Yam
C—Cocoyam
D—Maize
E—Melon
F—Groundnut
G—Rice
H—Oil palm
I—Pigeon pea
J—Beans
K—Bambara nut
L—Sugar cane
M—Sweet potato
N—Benniseed
O—Millet
P—Guinea corn
Q—Cocoa
R—Cashew
S—Rubber
T—Plantain

IMPERFECT MONOCULTURE

Yam dominant
Cassava dominant

TWO CROP

Yam maize
Cassava yam

THREE CROP

Cassava cocoyam plantain
Yam cassava maize

FOUR CROP

Cassava yam cocoyam plantain
Yam cassava cocoyam maize

FIVE CROP

Yam cassava cocoyam maize pigeon pea

MILES

0   20   40   60

Uzozie (1971) identified the following crop combination regions which are illustrated in Figure 8:

a) imperfectly developed monoculture based on yams
b) imperfectly developed monoculture based on cassava
c) yam-maize
d) cassava-yam
e) yam-cassava-maize
f) plantain-cocoyam-cassava
g) cocoyam-plantain-cassava-yam
h) cassava-yam-cocoyam-maize
i) yam-cassava-cocoyam-maize-pigeon peas (*Cajanus cajan*)

WESTERN AND MIDWESTERN NIGERIA

The dominant food crops in the Midwest and Western States are yams, cassava, maize, cocoyams, plantains and bananas, and subsidiary vegetable and other minor crops. The most important cash crops in the Midwest State are rubber and oilpalm while in the Western State cocoa and kola are the important tree crops. There are subsidiary fruit trees and perennials, nuts and oil plants which include the African pear (*Dacryodes edulis*) in the Midwest State and conophor (*Tetriacarpedium concophorum*), coconuts (*Cocos nucifera*), avocado pears (*Persea americana*), citrus fruits, pineapple, castor beans (*Ricinus communis* sp.), guava (*Psidium* sp.), etc. in both states.

Cropping sequences observed in the vicinity of Ibadan are shown in Figure 9 (Faulkner & Mackie, 1933).

In both midwestern and western Nigeria small plots of tree crops such as cocoa and rubber may be grown in semiwild groves or carefully established plantations. Otherwise, most tree crops are scattered about the farms at different spacings from each other. More of the perennial fruit trees are located nearer the homestead than nonfruit trees such as rubber. In his studies of some villages in midwestern and western Nigeria, Upton (1967) observed the following numbers of trees owned per farm family: oilpalms, 39–106; plantains and bananas, 0–83; kola trees, 0–64; and citrus trees, 0–38.

In southern Nigeria, the number of species and individual tree crops per unit area decreases with increasing distance inland until in the derived savanna belt in the northernmost parts of the rainforest zone there are intrusions of savanna cereals and other crops that thrive best in moderate to low rainfall areas. These crops include sorghum, millet, cotton, and various grain legumes. In Oyo, north of Ibadan, sorghum usually precedes yams, and the broken culms of the sorghum are used as stakes or trellises for yams.

MIDDLE BELT OF NIGERIA

The Middle Belt of Nigeria is a transition zone between the root crops-oilpalm-cocoa belt of the south and the sorghum-millet-cotton-groundnut belt of the northern states. This area is the mixed grain and root crops belt sometimes designated as the benniseed (*Sesamum indicum*) belt. This belt

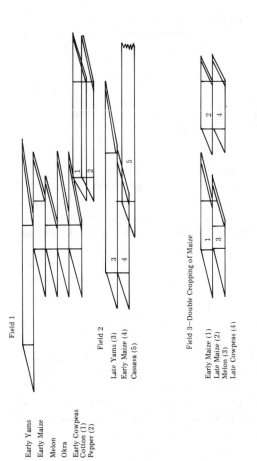

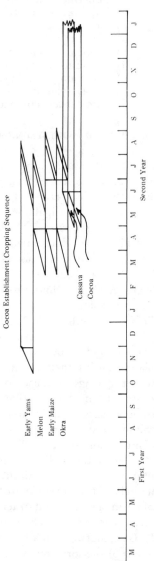

Figure 9. Cropping schedules in Ibadan Area, western Nigeria.

also contains the Jos Plateau with terrace farms and where recently there has developed significant increases in large scale production of subtropical and temperate crops and vegetables for the urban centers of the south. These crops include tomatoes (*Lycopersicon esculentum*), Irish potatoes, and carrots (*Daucus carota* L.). The region is noted for its multiplicity of crops including sorghum, pearl millet (*Pennisetum typhoides*), and two indigenous African grain crops, the hungry rice or acha (*Digitaria exilis* and *D. iburua*) and finger millet (*Eleusine corocana*), yams, cassava and cocoyams in addition to the ancient root and tuber crops risga (*Plectranthus esculentus*) and tumuku (*Solenostemon rotundiflorus*), cotton, sesame (*Sesamum indicum*), indigo (*Indigofera* sp.), soybeans (*Glycine max* L. Merr.), groundnuts, and cowpeas. Other crops include onions (*Allium cepa* L.), rice, sweet potatoes, tobacco (*Nicotiana tabacum* L.), *Capsicum* peppers and henna (*Lawsonia inermis*). Intercropping is a widespread practice.

Netting (1968) studied the Kofyar of the Benue Plateau and details of their cropping systems (Fig. 10). The Kofyar grow at least 30 species of crops in (i) farms, (ii) village gardens close to the continuously farmed homestead gardens, (iii) bush farms lying just outside the settled village perimeter, and (iv) "migrant bush" farms which may be located several hours walk from the village. The homestead farms are permanently cultivated with maize, cocoyams and cowpeas in addition to various subsidiary crops and vegetables. Early millet is often interplanted with sorghum and cowpeas and pumpkins, okra, some maize plants and roselle (*Hibiscus sabdariffa*). Several subsidiary crops such as tobacco, groundnuts, Bambara groundnuts (*Voandzeia subter-*

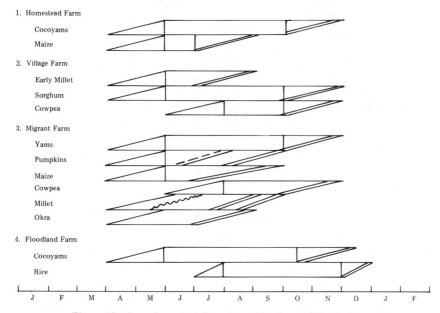

Figure 10. Cropping schedule and combinations of the Kofyar.

ranea) and sweet potatoes are planted on separate plots in different parts of the homestead or village farms. Tree crops such as mangoes, African elemi (*Canarium schweinfurthii*) and papaya (*Carica* sp.) are located near the homestead entrance and may also be dotted about the farms. Details of the planting schedule and patterns of the Bong who live in this area are presented in Figure 11. Average size of farms is about 1 ha, but many are less than 0.5 ha.

NORTHERN NIGERIA

Northern Nigeria stretches from about 10°N to almost 14°N latitude and lies in the semiarid zone of west Africa where the duration of the dry season is over 5 months and the growing season less than 200 days. The major food crops are sorghum and millet while the minor crops are rice, ginger (*Zingiber* sp.), cowpeas, maize, sweet potatoes, yams, pepper, and onions. The main cash crops are groundnuts and cotton.

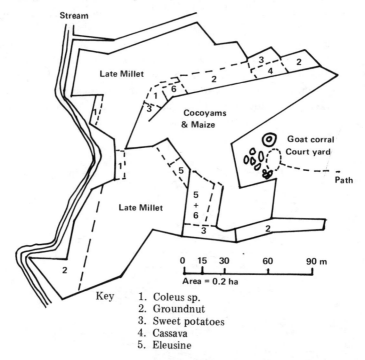

Key   1. Coleus sp.
       2. Groundnut
       3. Sweet potatoes
       4. Cassava
       5. Eleusine

MIGRANT BUSH FARM ROTATION

1st Year	2nd Year	3rd–8th Year	9th–11th Year	12th Year
Yam	Millet Sorghum Cowpea	Millet Sorghum Cowpea	Cotton or Groundnut	Fallow

Figure 11. Homestead and bush field land use and cropping pattern at Dalung, Bong, Benue Plateau (Netting, 1968).

Intercropping is widely practiced. Norman (1974) in a study of inter-cropping combinations in Zaria Province of the North Central State of Nigeria reported up to 156 different crop mixtures consisting of sole crops, two, three, four, five and six crop mixtures accounting for 16, 42, 23, 12, and 5% of the mixtures, respectively. The seven most frequent mixtures were:

Millet-sorghum (25%)
Millet-sorghum-groundnut-cowpeas (5%)
Millet-sorghum-groundnuts (5%)
Cotton-cowpeas-sweet potatoes (4%)
Cotton-cowpeas (3%)
Millet-sorghum-cowpeas (3%)
Sorghum-groundnuts (2%)

These seven crop combinations covered 61% of the area under the crop mixtures. The areas under sole crops covered 8.4, 3.1, 1.8, and 3.3% of sorghum, cotton, groundnuts, and other crops respectively. Sorghum is the most important food crop and cotton and groundnuts are the most important cash crops.

With the exception of the Kano area and other mixed farm or high population density areas of northern Nigeria, bush fallowing is the common practice with fallow periods ranging from 4 to over 8 years in areas of low population density. Compound farms are common to all areas and are cropped every year with such crops as maize, okra, pepper, roselle, pump-kins, tobacco, and various vegetables. In addition to compound farms and bush fallow fields, there are fadama[3] fields (hydromorphic areas) where bananas, rice, sugarcane, and vegetables are grown. In the flood plains of streams, rice and sugarcane are grown with irrigation. Apart from fruit trees such as mangoes and oranges which are grown in compound gardens, pro-tected plants such as tamarind (*Tamarindus* sp.), locust beans (*Parkia* spp.) and baobab (*Adansonia digitata*) are found dotted about the outlying fields. Where ridges are used, there is usually a definite spatial arrangement of crops with millet occupying the furrow areas while sorghum and cotton are grown on the ridges. Some of the southern crops such as yams and cassava are grown on ridges or mounds. The cassava farms or gardens are usually fenced from other crops for protection against livestock. Some of the mixed crop-ping schedules used in the area are presented in Figure 12.

Other Countries of West Africa

Various aspects of the cropping systems of west Africa have been re-ported by Faulkner & Mackie (1933), Allison (1941), Irvine (1969), Porteres (1952, 1955), Johnston (1958), Hardcastle (1959), Guinard (1961), Wills (1962), Bourke (1963), Anyane (1963), Catherinet (1965), De Sapir (1969),

---

[3]Valley Bottom lands or depressions that are subject to flooding or high water-table in the savanna areas of northern Nigeria. These are often used for the growing of off-season vegetables, bananas and sugarcane.

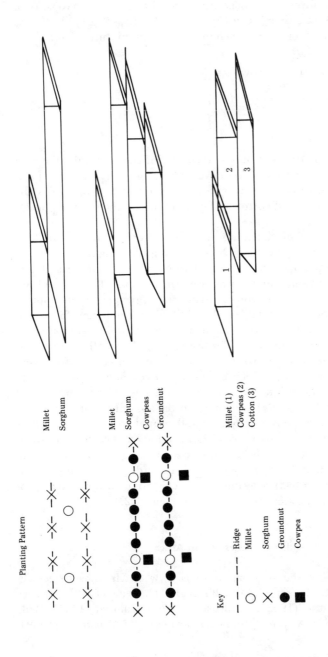

Figure 12. Cropping schedules and pattern of planting for some crop combinations in northern Nigeria (Norman, 1973).

Hartoungh (1969), Kline et al. (1969), Morgan (1969), Morgan & Pugh (1969), Weil (1969), Donald (1970), Grove (1970), Muckle (1971), Thornton (1973), Spencer (1973), Charreau (1974), and Van Santen (1974). Porteres (1955) reported changes in crops grown in parts of Senegal as a result of emergence of groundnuts as a commercial crop. He noted the absence of groundnuts in cropping systems and rotations of Senegal in 1850 and the replacement of seed cotton and sesame by groundnuts in the cropping systems of northern, central, and southern zones of Senegal by 1950, in addition to the inroad made by cassava into the cropping systems of southern Senegal. Charreau (1974) observed that mixed intercropping is widely practiced in the peasant cropping systems in the Francophone countries of west Africa.

Wills (1962) listed various crops grown in compound and outlying farms in parts of Ghana and stressed the increasing importance of market gardening close to urban areas. All the works cited in the preceding paragraph emphasize the widespread practice of mixed intercropping of the kinds found in similar ecological and vegetation zones of Nigeria. Examples of cropping systems which differ somewhat from those of Nigeria include the intensive shallot (*Allium escalonicum*) and vegetable cropping systems of Angola in Ghana (Irvine, 1969, Grove, 1970) and the upland rice intercropping systems of Liberia and Sierra Leone (Fig. 13).

At the edge of the Keta Lagoon, in the Anloga area of Ghana there is an intensive shallot industry involving three crops of shallot in 1 year. The shallot is grown in small patches on beds and vegetables are grown as sole crops or mixtures between the harvesting of one and planting of another shallot crop. The duration of each crop is 6 weeks and tomatoes, okra, maize, and pepper are intercropped with shallot the third crop. The fertility of the alluvial soils on which they are grown is maintained with bat and cow dung, crop residues, fish manure, and household refuse. The shallot farmers usually divide themselves into three groups each of which plants his own shallots 2 weeks after the other to avoid glut in the shallot market. Most of the shallot is sold in Accra.

Van Santen (1974) reported that in the Foya area of Upper Lofa in Liberia upland rice which is planted in May to July is usually intercropped with pepper, bitterball (*Solanum* sp.), beans, maize, bananas, plantains, and cassava. Similarly, Spencer (1973) observed that 91% of the upland rice crop of Sierra Leone is intercropped with cassava, maize, cotton, pigeon peas and/ or okra (see examples in Fig. 13).

Central and Southern Africa

Several complex forms of shifting cultivation, bush fallow and semi-permanent farming systems are found in the Congo, northern Rhodesia and adjacent regions in central and southern Africa.

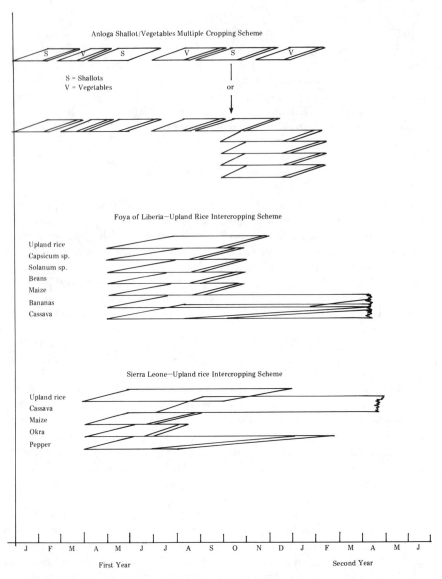

Figure 13. Some multiple cropping schedules of Ghana, Liberia, and Sierra Leone.

THE CONGO

The farming systems of the Congo include bush fallow systems and field types as encountered in west Africa but lower population densities in some areas have resulted in longer periods of fallow than in west Africa. Miracle (1967) identified four major groups of cropping systems in the Congo: classic tropical long fallows, ash fertilizer dependent long fallow systems, compost dependent fallow systems, and short fallow systems. Each of these exhibit variations in terms of sequences of field operations associated with planting.

The Bemba who practice the *chitemene* system clear woodlands 5 to 20 times the area to be cropped, pile the wood and burn it to obtain the ash which is used as fertilizer (Ruthenberg, 1971). Bemba field systems include typical bush fallow field cultivation, anthill cultivation, coleus potato gardens, river gardens, and hutsite gardens (Miracle, 1967; Richards, 1939; Trapnell, 1953). Crop sequences on fields, gardens, and old hutsites are presented in Figure 14. Some of the striking characteristics of these cropping systems include (i) the use of volunteer self-propagated sorghum and groundnuts as components of traditional crop mixtures, (ii) elaborate piling up of wood and trash for burning to obtain ash fertilizer in a system designated as *chitemene* or *citemene*, and (iii) movement of homesteads to facilitate cropping of fertile hutsites. In west Africa, volunteer crops involved in traditional agriculture do not involve major staples but are limited to protected useful tree crops such as the oilpalm and semiwild and indigenous vegetables such as *Corchorus olitorus, Ocimum viride* and several species of *Amaranthus*. Reasons for movement of homesteads other than restoration of soil fertility include superstition and witchcraft and reduction of distance between homesteads and fields (Miracle, 1967).

The Azande Cropping System—De Schlippe (1956) and Reining (1970) investigated the agricultural systems of the Azande, the third largest tribe in Congo Kinshasha and small sections of which are also found in the southern Sudan and the Central African Republic. The Azande tackled the short-run problems of decreasing soil fertility by alternation of crops and the long-term by shifting homesteads. As with the Bemba, other reasons given for shifting of homesteads included death of a wife, crop failure due to pest and disease epidemics, and repeated illness suspected to be due to witchcraft. Whenever homesteads were moved, the courtyard gardens were first cultivated before being left to revert to bush by which time the fertility that had been built up during years of human habitation had been almost exhausted. De Schlippe (1956) identified several field types, i.e., (i) the main Eleusine (finger millet) association, (ii) the groundnut Eleusine (finger millet) succession, (iii) Eleusine through grass, (iv) bean patch, (v) ridge cultivation, (vi) maize through sweet potato or sweet potato strip, (vii) maize and oilseed gourd association, and (viii) cassava fallow. In addition to the main field types which are located outside the ridge which defines the outer perimeter of the compound farm or courtyard, there were 11 specialized environments with their special crops. These were: (i) the courtyard on which vegetables, condiment plants, fruit trees, medicinal plants and other useful plants are grown, (ii) the minor ridge in the courtyard on which are grown okra, yams, groundnuts (vegetable), and other vegetables; (iii) old refuse heaps with rice, bananas, cowpea, sesame, maize, etc.; (iv) thatch overhang under the shade of which tobacco nurseries were located; (v) ash accumulations on which tobacco, vegetables, cowpeas, and climbing plants are grown; (vi) living trees used as supports for yams; (vii) termitaria (termite mounds) which were flattened for the produc-

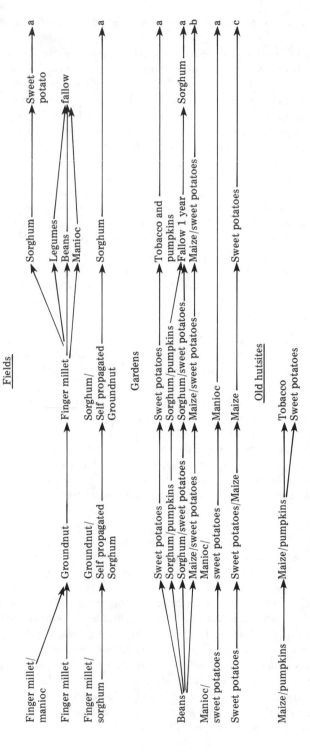

Figure 14. Bemba crop sequences (Richards, 1939 according to Miracle, 1967).

* Source: Richards (1939) according to Miracle (1967).
a. No information given on what follows
b. Maize and sweet potatoes planted year after year until soil is exhausted, then sweet potato alone as last crop.
c. Maize and pumpkins sown so long as soil is fertile, then tobacco or sweet potatoes.

tion of sorghum, rice, and cowpeas; (viii) satellite cultivations located in patches or strips on the borders of fields of main staples; (ix) rubbish heaps in fields on which grow crops requiring higher fertility; (x) spontaneous or volunteer crops; and (xi) valley cultivation beside streams or inside the forest gallery on silt deposited by erosive floods. Some of the above field types, cropping schedules, and associations of the common field types are presented in Figures 15, 16, and 17.

It may be concluded that the cropping systems of the Congo are similar to those of west Africa. Although intercropping is as widespread in the Congo as in west Africa, there is greater dominance of single crops in some of the initial and terminal crop associations. Thus, in the forest zone of the Congo, most crop sequences begin with bananas-plantains and their associations are 44 and 9% of the sequences, respectively, followed by maize (11%) and maize associations (21%). The terminal associations are dominated by cassava (41%), cassava associations (25%), and bananas-plantains associations (16%). In the savanna, initial crop sequences consist of millet-sorghum (16%),

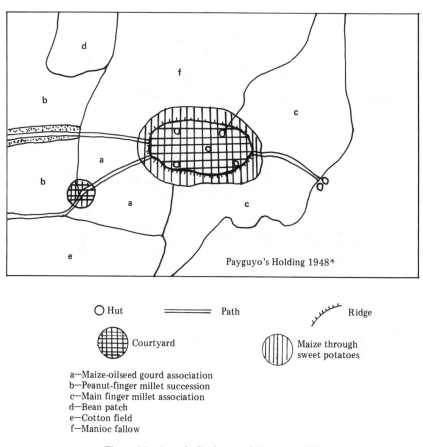

Payguyo's Holding 1948*

○ Hut   ═══════ Path   Ridge

⊞ Courtyard   Maize through
                               sweet potatoes

a—Maize-oilseed gourd association
b—Peanut-finger millet succession
c—Main finger millet association
d—Bean patch
e—Cotton field
f—Manioc fallow

Figure 15. Azande field types (Miracle, 1967).

groundnuts (14%), beans (10%), sweet potato (7%), and cassava associations (19%) as compared to the terminal sequences dominated by cassava (36%) and cassava associations (15%), followed by beans and peas (*Pisum* sp.) (14%) and millet-sorghum (7%). The dominance of cassava in terminal crop sequences in forest areas is similar to the forest zone of west Africa where cassava is usually the last crop before fallow. In most areas of west Africa, annual starchy staples (e.g., maize, yams, and rice) are more likely to dominate the initial crop association than bananas-plantains and their associations

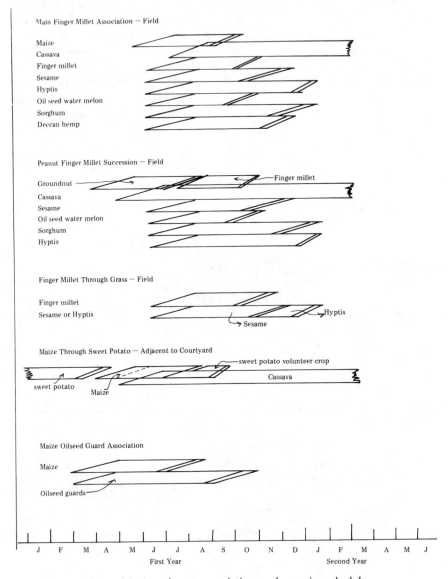

Figure 16. Azande crop associations and cropping schedule.

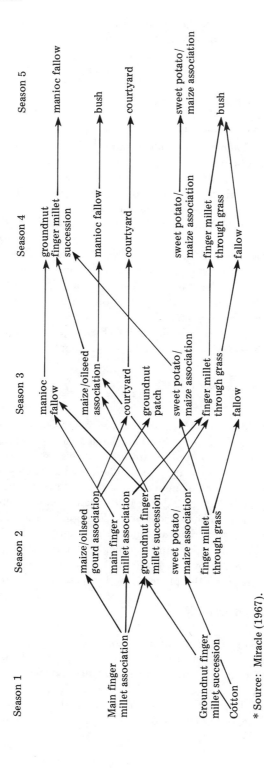

Figure 17. Azande crop sequences (Miracle, 1967).

* Source: Miracle (1967).

as in the Congo basin. In the savanna areas of west Africa, cassava does not attain such dominance of terminal crop associations as in the Congo. However, in both areas there are fewer choices of crops to be grown at the terminal stage of the cropping cycle with its declining soil fertility.

NORTHERN AND SOUTHERN RHODESIA

Allan (1965), Miracle (1967) and Morgan (1969) described the agricultural systems of Zambia, and Yudelman (1964) the agriculture of southern Rhodesia. The agriculture of this area consists of two main systems, i.e., the European and the African systems. The European system involves mechanized large scale farming, with sole cropping and crop rotations. Alienation and reservation of land for Europeans in southern and east Africa prior to recent political developments in Kenya and Tanzania made available to Europeans proportionately more land per capita than for Africans.

African agriculture in this area involves the same *chitemene* shifting cultivation system of the Bemba. Unlike the Bemba who use large ash circles each covering over 0.4 ha, the Lala, Lamba, and Ndembu of northern Rhodesia (Allan, 1965; Miracle, 1967) and some tribes of southern Rhodesia (Yudelman, 1964) employ several small circles (each about 7-11 m in diameter) in place of each large ash circle. Field systems of the small circle *chitemene* are, however, similar to those of the Bemba.

East Africa

East Africa consists of Mozambique, Tanzania, Kenya, Uganda, Ethiopia, and Somalia. Most of these states have large areas of savanna with pastoral peoples who are nomadic and regard crop cultivation as secondary to livestock raising. Consequently, crop production is adapted to a way of life, and it is often the business of women and children. Prior to the advent of land reforms in Kenya and independence of Tanzania and Mozambique, agriculture in this region with the exception of Ethiopia was a dualistic economy consisting of European agriculture and African agriculture. In most of east Africa a wide range of crops can be grown as a result of the prevailing range of elevation from below 500 to 4,000 m. Examples of some of the elevation range of certain crops in Ethiopia reported by Westphal (1975) are in Table 4.

KENYA, UGANDA AND TANZANIA

Acland (1971) reported that although any crop grown in east Africa may be grown in pure culture especially in commercial farms, most have been observed in mixed culture. Examples of mixtures include (i) bananas interplanted with coffee (*Coffea* sp.) in the central province of Kenya, high rainfall areas of Tanzania and with robusta coffee in Uganda; (ii) bananas grown with maize, potatoes, cowpeas, or sugarcane in the central province of

Table 4. Crop adaptation to elevation ranges in Ethiopia (Westphal, 1975)

Crop	Range	Most suitable range
	m above sea level	
Maize	500–2500	500–2000
Finger millet	500–2000	1000–1800
Bullrush millet	500–1600	500–1500
Sorghum	500–2500	500–2000
Tref (Eragrastistef)	1500–2500	1700–2300
Wheat	1500–2500	1700–2400
Groundnut	500–1600	1000–1500
Sesame	500–1500	1000–1300
Cassava	500–2000	1500–1800
Sweet potato	500–2100	1250–2000
Cowpeas	500–2000	1250–1700
Okra	500–1800	1200–1700
Sugar cane	500–2000	1000–1500
Coffee	1200–2400	1500–2000
Banana	500–2000	1500–1700
Mango	500–1700	1100–1600

Kenya; (iii) beans intercropped with maize or cassava; (iv) hyacinth bean (*Dolichos lablab*) intercropped with maize, beans, potatoes, peas, or bananas; (v) bullrush millet (*Pennisetum typhoides*) intercropped with Bambara groundnuts on Ukara Island in Tanzania and with cowpeas, pigeon peas, beans, or maize in the Machakos district of Kenya; (vi) cashew (*Anacardium* sp.) along the southern Kenya coast of east Africa planted at random between coconuts, mango trees, bananas, or cassava; (vii) cassava which is usually the last crop before fallow inter- or relay cropped with sweet potatoes, maize, and beans or sometimes with bananas, yams, and sugarcane on the coastal strip of east Africa; (viii) coconuts intersown with pastures along the coast or planted at wide spacing with bananas, cashew, and mango; (ix) interplanting of coffee with shade trees, e.g., *Albizzia* sp. in Tanzania and *Cordia abyssinica* in Kenya; (x) cowpeas intersown with other food crops or grown for their leaves in patches of pure stands near homesteads; (xi) grams (*Cicer arietinum*) intercropped with cereals, root crops, and other legumes; (xii) pigeon pea relay cropped with finger millet and after millet harvest, intersown with sesame or cowpeas, or intercropped with maize and beans; and (xiii) sisal (*Agava sisalana*) intercropped with beans, maize, cotton, pineapple, or cover crops.

The farming systems of Kenya have undergone changes due to European settlement and introduction of European farming techniques. As a result, traditional cropping systems in Kenya have undergone greater transformation than those of Tanzania and Uganda.

Von Rotenham (1968) reported that mixed cropping was originally widespread in Sukumaland in Tanzania. However, the cultivation of cotton led to considerable amount of sole cropping despite the fact that it was recommended to be grown as a mixed crop in German colonial times. Although sole cropping is common with crops such as rice, only one-third of the area is under mixed cropping. The Wasukuma, for example, practice relay cropping of maize, beans, groundnuts and sweet potatoes. The maize is first planted, and after about 2 weeks, groundnuts and beans are sown in between the maize. After the first weeding, sweet potatoes are added. Crop rotations in several parts of Sukumaland carry both pure cotton and mixed cropping of various kinds according to location and soil type (Table 5).

Ludwig (1968) studied the Wukara permanent cropping system on Ukara Island on Lake Victoria in Tanzania. The first year in a 3-year rotation, bullrush millet is relay intercropped with a late manure crop, *Crotolaria striata*, which is used as green manure for a record crop of early bullrush millet during the second year. The second year bullrush millet is again relay intercropped with late groundnuts and in the third year following harvesting of groundnuts, another early bullrush millet crop is followed by a late crop of sorghum which ends the 3-year cycle. In addition to these crops, the Wukara have developed several permanent cropping systems for different contours or catenas for the valleys on the island and fertility is maintained by the use of organic manures, crop residues, and household refuse.

ETHIOPIA

Westphal (1975) recognized 14 systems of agriculture. Some examples of mixed or intercropping systems are: (i) seed farming complex with absence of vegetables, fruit trees, and shrubs; (ii) seed farming complex where sorghum is dominant with field cropping, home gardening and growing of fruit trees and shrubs; (iii) seed farming complex with sorghum dominant but farming is carried out in well-constructed terraces; (iv) ensat (*Ensete ventricosum*) planting complex with ensat as staple food; and (v) ensat planting complex with ensat as co-staple with cereals and tubers.

Table 5. Examples of crop rotations in Sukumaland (von Rotenham, 1968)

Shinyanga	Black cotton soils and Alluvial soils
1963 Cotton	Maize-sorghum-legume
1962 Cotton	Maize-sorghum-legume
1961 Maize-sorghum-legume	Fallow
1960 Maize-sorghum-legume	Cotton
1954 Cotton	Maize-sorghum-legume
1958 Cotton	Maize-sorghum-legume
Ukerewe	
Sandy to partly loamy soils	Alluvial soils
1963 Cassava	Rice-sweet potato
1962 Cassava	Rice-sweet potato-maize
1961 Cassava	Rice-sweet potato
1960 Cotton	Rice-sweet potato
1959 Cotton	Rice-sweet potato
1958 Cassava	Rice-sweet potato-maize

In the Begemdir and Simen area where vegetables and fruits are absent, the common practice is to grow two successive crops in the same field each year (double cropping) with emer (*Triticum dicocum*), barley (*Hordeum vulgare* L.) or lentil (*Lens culinaris*) used as the late crop. Mixed cropping is also practiced with barley and wheat as the most common mixture. Other mixtures include pea and horsebean (*Vicia faba equina*), t'ef (*Eragrostis tef*) and garden cress (*Lepidium sativum*), sorghum and finger millet, sorghum and chick pea, safflower (*Carthamus tinctorius*), and t'ef, sesame and common bean, and maize and gourds (Westphal, 1975).

In Hararge area where field systems, home gardening, and cultivation of shrubs are widely practiced (Westphal, 1975) three cropping zones are encountered, (i) the coffee zone (1,400–1,700 m) with bowl-shaped valleys where there are irrigated banana groves and extensive gardens with mixtures of crops such as coffee, sugarcane, ch'at (*Catha edulis*), maize, sweet potato and t'ef; (ii) durra zone (1,600–2,000 m) where sorghum is the dominant crop with ch'at and coffee at valley bottoms; and (iii) the barley zone (2,000–2,400 m) where barley, wheat, horsebean and peas are grown. In the durra zone 'Gooseneck' sorghum is the most widely grown and is usually planted in mixtures with maize and sometimes, bullrush millet, finger millet, and sesame, with groundnuts and maize or with maize and beans in between. Hararge is the center for ch'at which is usually found between 1,500 and 2,000 m elevation and is commonly intercropped with sorghum, maize, bean, sweet potato, pepper, or coffee. Around the city of Harar, there are orchards of ch'at, coffee, and citrus.

In the sorghum-hoe-terrace complex in Konso area, there are well-constructed terraces supporting an intensive agriculture involving permanently cultivated and regularly manured land surrounding the villages. Away from the villages a fallow system without cultivation is used to maintain soil fertility. Crops grown in this area in mixed culture include maize, pulses, tuber crops, linseed (*Linum* sp.), sunflower (*Helianthus* sp.) and cotton. Pure cotton occurs in periphery of settlements and yams are grown as single plants in gardens near terrace walls. Sorghum is nearly always broadcast with finger millet. Usually the first crop in the mixture to be planted are cormels of *Araceae* which are then followed by cotton, cereals, and pulses before the seeds are covered with soil. Wheat and barley in the zone between 1,700 and 2,000 m are sown in mixed stands. To minimize competition, sowing is done when other crops are about 10 cm high.

The ensat planting complex in which ensat is the main food source is found among the Gurage, Sidamo, and other peoples in the southeastern part of the Ethiopia highlands in the Rift Valley and in the eastern Sidamo Highlands (Westphal, 1975). The Sidamo, who live south of Lake Awasa, grow large plantations of ensat in addition to coffee gardens. Ensat is planted in age classes on previously cropped land near the homestead and only near huts are age classes mixed. The ensat is often mixed with coffee and sometimes interplanted with a legume (*Erythrina sp.*). Part of the homestead garden carries small irregular patches of wheat, barley, t'ef, and pea. Outside the homestead gardens, maize, sorghum, and t'ef and sometimes wheat and barley are grown during the cropping cycle after the fallow. In the ensat area, there are different elevation zones for (i) coffee (1,800–2,000 m), where small patches of t'ef, wheat, taro, beans (in mixed culture), sweet potatoes, and tobacco are grown; (ii) wheat-pulse (2,000–2,500 m) where maize, sorghum, and coffee decrease and wheat, barley, and horsebean appear; and (iii) in the upper ensat and barley (2,400–2,500 to 3,000 m), where barley, cabbage (*Brassica* sp.) and ensat near huts are important.

In the ensat co-staple area with cereals and tubers, the Wollamo inhabit the area north of Lake Abaya. There is a regular planting pattern and patch intercropping is common. There is an almost fixed pattern around the homestead especially in eastern Wollamo. The exit to huts always leads to an ensat plantation. Planted on both sides of the entrance are cabbage, tobacco, pepper, and other spices. Behind the hut, is the first semicircle of coffee shrubs and in areas above 1,600 m a small ensat plantation. Then the field with mixtures of maize, sorghum, beans, and cabbage follow. Various remote parts are occupied by pure stands of wheat, barley, pulses, and tuber crops.

REVIEW OF RESEARCH ON INTERCROPPING IN AFRICA

As far back as 1934 Leakey (L. S. B. Leakey and C. L. A. Leakey, 1970. Science and the African. Re-edition of a paper by L. S. B. Leakey, 1934.) emphasized that more priority should be given to research in the indigenous methods of food production than to cash crops because of advantages of mixed cropping. Although several studies in east Africa were devoted to intercropping and relay cropping as reported by Chaundy (1939), Sturdy (1939), Briant and Johns (1940), Nye (1940), Robertson (1941), Edwards (1941), Watson (1941), Evans (1960, 1962), and Grimes (1963). Interest lagged until Osiru and Willey (1972), Willey and Osiru (1972), and Enyi (1972, 1973) reported results of recent work. In Nigeria, Faulkner and Mackie (1933) reported the widespread practice of intercropping and the reluctance of farmers to abandon the practice. Some of the early rotations started on students' farm in Moor Plantation involved intercropping and double cropping (F. A. Dada, 1974. Agronomics analysis of crop rotation management in the School of Agriculture. Moor Plantation, Ibadan. IRAT, Unife, M. P. Ibadan. Mimeo, p. 1–11). Favorable results of temporary intercropping of oilpalms for the first few years during plantation establishment were reported by Sparnaaij (1957). Since 1964 socio-economic studies of traditional farming systems were initiated at the Institute of Agricultural Research in Samaru later followed by intercropping agronomic investigations (Norman, 1968, 1973a, b, 1974; Baker, 1974; Andrews, 1974, 1975; Kassam & Stockinger, 1973; D. W. Norman, 1973. Incorporating the time dimension: The case of crop mixtures in N. Nigeria. Multiple Cropping Workshop, IRDC and IRRI, Philippines. Mimeo; B. J. Buntjer, 1970. Aspects of the Hausa system of cultivation. IAR, Samaru. Mimeo; D. J. Andrews, 1970.

Relay and intercropping with sorghum at Samaru. Ford Foundation/IITA/ IRAT Conference on mixed cropping, Ibadan, Nov. 1970. Mimeo, p. 1-12).

CONCLUSIONS

The above review of traditional cropping systems in Africa indicate that:

1. Multiple cropping systems are part of traditional farming in Africa.
2. The most widespread cropping system in Africa consists of mixed intercropping in compound farms which forms a complex but stable agroecosystem.
3. Intercropping involving small patches of a few pure stands of crops at varying distances from each other in addition to relay cropping are also more common than successive cropping sequences.
4. Traditional cropping systems involve many field types and elaborate compound farm system components which are designed to take advantage of various environmental situations or topographic features on the farms.

Research and observations on mixed cropping, patch intercropping and relay cropping systems in Africa indicate that:

1. The traditional farmer practices intercropping because it gives higher total yields and greater returns than the same crops grown in pure culture.
2. Because of minimized pest and disease losses and losses due to adverse environmental conditions, risk is lower in intercropping than sole cropping.
3. Investigations in intercropping should include:
   a. plant populations of the component crops
   b. length of the cropping season
   c. plant structure (height, canopy structure, rooting systems)
   d. relative duration of the life cycles of the component crops
   e. nutrient requirements
   f. planting patterns
   g. soil fertility
4. According to Wrigley (1969) and other research, the overall advantages of intercropping include:
   a. increased erosion protection
   b. insurance against crop failure
   c. labor and harvesting are spread more evenly during the cropping season and storage problems may be minimized
   d. locations are found for crops required in small quantities, for a range of products, and facilitating production of many commodities in a limited area
   e. it results in efficient utilization of resources by plants of different heights, rooting systems, and nutrient requirements
   f. where legumes are grown with grasses, grasses may benefit from the nitrogen fixed by the companion crop
   g. diseases and pests do not spread rapidly in mixed culture as in pure culture since all crops involved are not susceptible to the same extent

5. Disadvantages of intercropping include:
   a. Mechanization planting and harvesting is difficult
   b. It is more difficult to apply improved inputs, e.g., fertilizers and herbicides as in sole cropping
   c. Experimentation with intercropping is more complex and difficult to manage than with sole cropping.

At present, increased priority is being given to research on multiple cropping in tropical Africa at the Institute of Agricultural Research (IAR), Samaru, Zaria; the International Institute of Tropical Agriculture at Ibadan (IITA); and various institutions of higher learning, especially at the Universities of Tanzania (Morogoro), Makerere, Ibadan, Ife, Ile-Ife, and Nigeria.

LITERATURE CITED

Acland, J. D. 1971. East African Crops, Longmans Group, London.

Allan, W. 1965. The African Husbandman, Oliver & Boyd, Edinburg.

Allison, P. A. 1941. From Farm to Forest. Farm Forest 2(2):95-98.

Andrews, D. J. 1974. Responses of sorghum to intercropping. Exp. Agric. 10:57-63.

Andrews, D. J. 1975. Intercropping with sorghum. In N. G. P. Rao and L. R. House (ed.) Sorghum in the 70's. Oxford & IBH Publishing Co., New Delhi.

Anyane, S. L. 1963. Ghana Agriculture, Oxford University Press, London.

Baker, E. F. I. 1974. Research into intercropping aspects of farming systems in Nigeria. Mixed cropping with cereals: A system for improvement. p. 287-301. In Proceedings of the Farming Systems Workshop. ICRISAT, Hyderabad, India.

Benneh, G. 1972. Systems of agriculture in tropical agriculture. Econ. Geogr. 48(3): 245-257.

Boserup, T. P. 1970. The conditions of agricultural growth. Allen and Unwin, London.

Bourke, O. O. D. 1963. The West African millet crop. Afr. Soils VIII(I):121-132.

Briant, A. R., and R. Johns. 1940. Cassava investigations in Zanzibar. E. Afr. Agric. For. J. 5:404-412.

Catherinet, M. 1965. Note Sur la Culture du Macabo et du taro an Cameroun. Agronomie Tropicale 20(8):717-724.

Charreau, C. 1974. Systems of cropping in the dry tropical zone of west Africa with special reference to Senegal. p. 443-468. In Proceedings of the Farming Systems Workshop. ICRISAT, Hyderabad, India.

Chaundy, G. N. 1939. Primitive agricultural methods of the West Suk Tribe and some improvements. E. Afr. Agric. For. J. 5:23-30.

De Sapir, O. L. 1969. Agriculture and Diola society. p. 192-227. In P. F. M. McLoughlin (ed.) African food production systems: cases and theory. The Johns Hopkins University Press, Baltimore.

Donald, Leland. 1970. Food production by the Yalunka household Sierra Leone. p. 165-191. In P. F. M. McLoughlin (ed.) African food production systems cases and theory. The John Hopkins Univ. Press, Baltimore.

Duckham, A. N., and G. B. Masefield. 1971. Farming systems of the world. Chatto and Windus, London.

Dumont, R. 1970. Types of rural economy: Studies in world agriculture. Methuen and Co., Ltd., London.

Edwards, D. C. 1941. Possibility of establishment of grass under maize. E. Afr. Agric. For. J. 6:233-235.

Enyi, B. A. C. 1972. Effects of intercropping maize or sorghum with cowpeas, pigeon peas or beans. Exp. Agric. 9:83-90.

Enyi, B. A. C. 1973. Effects of intercropping maize or sorghum with cowpeas, pigeon peas or beans. Exp. Agric. 9(1):83-90.

Evans, A. C. 1960. Studies in intercropping. E. Afr. Agric. For. J. 26:1-10.

Evans, A. C. 1962. Soil fertility studies in Tanganyika III: On the Kikuyu and Lusoni soil types of the lake and western regions. E. Afr. Agric. For. J. 28:231-239.

Evenson, J. P., D. L. Plucknett, and I. Horton. 1973. A proposed classification for agricultural systems. p. 63–69. *In* Proceedings Second International Symposium on Tropical Root and Tuber Crops. 23–30 Aug. 1970. Honolulu. Vol. II.

Faulkner, O. J., and J. R. Mackie. 1933. West African agriculture. Cambridge University Press, London.

Federal Office of Statistics. 1972. Nigeria rural economic survey consolidated report of crop estimation 1968/69 to 1970/71, Agriculture Statistic Unit. FOS, Lagos.

Floyd, B. 1969. Eastern Nigeria. A geographical review. MacMillan, London.

Greenland, D. J. 1974. Evolution and development of different types of shifting cultivation. Regional Seminar on Shifting Cultivation and Soil Conservation. W. Africa. Soils Bull. No. 24. p. 5–13. FAO, Rome.

Grigg, D. B. 1974. The agricultural systems of the world: An evolutionary approach. Cambridge University Press, London.

Grimes, R. C. 1963. Intercropping and alternate cropping of cotton and maize. E. Afr. Agric. For. J. 28:161–163.

Grove, A. T. 1970. Africa south of the Sahara. Oxford University Press, London.

Guinard, A. 1961. Le Systeme Cultural de la region de Man (Cote d'Ivoire) Agronomie Tropicale XVI(2):148–178.

Hardcastle, J. E. Y. 1959. Development of rice production and research in Nigeria Trop. Agriculture Trin. 36(2):79–95.

Hartoungh, Ir J. C. C. 1969. Problems of development in Ogoni. World Crops 21(3): 182–185.

Irvine, F. R. 1969. West African agriculture. Vol. 2. Oxford University Press, London.

Jameson, J. D. (ed.). 1970. Agriculture in Uganda. Uganda Government Min. of Agriculture and Forestry. Oxford University Press, London.

Jarret, H. R. 1966. An outline geography of Africa, 2nd Edition. Methuen and Co., Ltd., London.

Johnston, B. F. 1958. The staple food economics of western tropical Africa. Stanford University Press, Stanford.

Jones, W. O. 1965. Environment, technical knowledge and economic development in Tropical Africa. p. 29–48. *In* D. Brokensha (ed.) Ecology and economic development in Tropical Africa. Institute of International Studies. Res. Series No. 9, University of California, Berkeley.

Kassam, A. H., and K. R. Stockinger. 1973. Growth and nitrogen uptake of sorghum and millet in mixed cropping. Samaru Agric. Newsl. 15(1):28–32.

Kimble, G. H. T. 1962. Tropical Africa Vol. I: Land and Livelihood. Doubleday & Co. Inc. Garden City, New York.

Kimble, G. H. T., and R. Steel. 1966. Tropical Africa today. Webster Division, McGraw Hall Book Co., St. Louis.

Kline, C. K., D. A. G. Green, R. L. Donahue, and B. A. Stout. 1969. Agricultural mechanization in equatorial Africa. Institute of International Agriculture Research Report No. 6, Michigan State University, East Lansing.

Laut, P. 1971. Agricultural geography. Vol. 1. Thomas Nelson, Sydney, Aust.

Ludwig, H. D. 1968. Permanent cropping on Ukara: The impact of land shortage on husbandry practices. p. 87–135. *In* H. Ruthenberg (ed.) Smallholder farming and smallholder development in Tanzania, Munich: IFO Institute for Economic Studies. African Studies No. 24.

Matheson, J. K., and E. W. Bovril (ed.). 1950. East African agriculture: A short survey of the agriculture of Kenya. Uganda, etc. Oxford University Press, London.

Miracle, M. P. 1967. Agriculture in the Congo Basin. University of Wisconsin Press, Madison.

Morgan, W. B. 1959a. Agriculture in southern Nigeria. Econ. Geogr. 35:138–150.

Morgan, W. B. 1959b. The influence of European contact on the landscape of southern Nigeria. Geogr. J. 125:48–64.

Morgan, W. B. 1969. Peasant agriculture in tropical Africa. p. 241–272. *In* M. F. Thomas and G. W. Whittington (ed.) Environment and land use in Africa. Methuen and Co., Ltd., London.

Morgan, W. B., and J. C. Pugh. 1969. West Africa. Methuen and Co., Ltd., London.

Muckle, T. B. 1971. Farming in Sierra Leone. Agriculture, Vol. 78(4):171–174.

Netting, R. McC. 1968. Hill farms of Nigeria. University of Washington Press, Seattle.

Norman, D. W. 1968. Why practice intercropping? Samaru Agric. Newsl. 10(4):107–116.

Norman, D. W. 1973a. Crop mixtures under indigenous conditions in northern part of Nigeria. p. 130–144. *In* I. M. Ofori (ed.) Factors of agricultural growth in West Africa. Proceeding of the International Conferences, Legon April 1971, Accra. Institute of Social and Economic Research, University of Ghana.

Norman, D. W. 1973b. Economic analysis of agricultural production and labour utilization among the Hausa in the north of Nigeria. Samaru Research Bulletin 191, IAR, Ahmadu Bello University, Zaria.

Norman, D. W. 1974. Rationalizing mixed cropping under indigenous conditions: The example of northern Nigeria. J. Development Studies II(I):3–21.

Nye, G. W. 1940. Some results from Bukalasa Experiment Station Uganda. Part 1: General. E. Afr. Agric. J. 5:460–465.

Osiru, D. S. O., and R. W. Willey. 1972. Studies on mixtures of dwarf sorghum and beans. J. Agric. Sci. Camb. 79:531–540.

Porteres, R. 1952. Linear cultural sequences in primitive systems of agriculture in Africa and their significance. Afr. Soils II(I):15–29.

Porteres, R. 1955. Agricultural crisis in Senegal. Afr. Soils III(I):41–51.

Porteres, R. 1962. Primary cradles of agriculture in the African continent. p. 43–58. *In* J. D. Fage and R. A. Oliver (ed.). 1970. Papers in African Prehistory, Cambridge University Press, London.

Reining, P. 1970. Social factors and food production in an east African peasant society: The Haya. p. 41–89. *In* P. F. M. McLoughlin (ed.) African food production systems: cases and theory. The John Hopkins Press, Baltimore.

Richards, A. 1939. Land, labour and diet in northern Rhodesia. Oxford University Press, London.

Robertson, J. K. 1941. Mixed or multiple cropping in native agricultural practice. E. Afr. Agric. For. J. 6:228.

Ruthenberg, Hans. 1971. Farming systems of the tropics. Oxford University Press, London.

Ruthenberg, Hans. 1974. Agricultural aspects of shifting cultivation. FAO, Regional Seminar on Shifting Cultivation in Africa, Ibadan. FAO/SIDE/ARCN Soil Bull. No. 24. p. 99–112, FAO, Rome.

Schlippe, P., de. 1956. Shifting cultivation in Africa. The Land Systems, Routoledge and Kegan, London.

Shaw, T. 1972. Early agriculture in Africa. J. Historical Soc. of Nigeria VI(2):144–192.

Sparnaaij, L. D. 1957. Mixed cropping in palm cultivation. J. West Afr. Inst. Oil Palm Research 2(7):244–264.

Spencer, D. S. C. 1973. Rice production and marketing in Sierra Leone. p. 130–144. *In* I. M. Ofori (ed.) Factors of agricultural growth in west Africa. Proceeding of the International Conference, Legon April 1971. Accra. Institute of Social and Economic Research, University of Ghana.

Sturdy, D. 1939. Leguminous crops in native agricultural practice. E. Afr. Agric. For. J. 5:31–32.

Thornton, D. S. 1973. Agriculture in southeast Ghana. Vol. 1. Summary Report, Development Study No. 12, University of Reading, Dep. of Agric. Econ. and Management, Reading.

Trapnell, C. G. 1953. The soils, vegetation and agriculture of northeastern Rhodesia, Report of the Ecological Survey, Lusaka.

Upton, M. 1967. Agriculture in southwestern Nigeria. Development Studies No. 3, University of Reading, Dep. of Agric. Economics, Reading.

Uzozie, I. C. 1971. Patterns of crop combination in the three eastern states of Nigeria. J. of Tropic. Geogr. 33:62–67.

Van Santen, C. E. 1974. Farm management and production economy. Papers I–VI Republic of Liberia, Ministry of Agricultural Development of Rice Cultivation Project in Liberia UNDP/SF/FAO/LIR/70/505.

Von Rotenham, D. 1968. Cash cropping in Sukumaland. p. 87–135. *In* H. Ruthenberg (ed.) Smallholder farming and smallholder development in Tanzania. Munich. IFO Institute for Economic Studies. African Studies No. 24.

Watson, J. M. 1941. Some aspects of Teso agriculture. Afr. Agric. J. 6:207–212.

Weil, P. M. 1969. The introduction of the ox plow in central Gambai. p. 229–263. *In* P. F. M. McLoughlin (ed.) African food production systems: cases and theory. Johns Hopkins University Press, Baltimore.

Westphal, E. 1975. Agricultural systems in Ethiopia. Agricultural Research Report No. 826 College of Agriculture Hail Sellassie I University and Agriculture University of Wagenengen, Centre for Agric. Publishing and Documentation.

Whittlesey, D. 1962. Major agricultural regions of the earth. p. 416–444. *In* P. L. Wagner and M. V. Mikesell (ed.). 1962. Readings in cultural geography. The University of Chicago Press, Chicago.

Wills, J. B. 1962. The general pattern of land use. p. 210-225. *In* J. B. Wills (ed.) Agriculture and land use in Ghana, Oxford University Press, London.

Willey, R. W., and D. S. O. Osiru. 1972. Studies on mixtures of maize and beans (*Phaseolus vulgaris*) with particular reference to plant population. J. Agric. Sci. Camb. 79:517-529.

Wrigley, G. 1969. Tropical agriculture: the development of production. Faber and Faber, London.

Yudelman, M. 1964. Africans on the land economic problem of African agricultural development in southern, central and east Africa with special reference to southern Rhodesia. Harvard University Press, Cambridge Mass.

Multiple Cropping in the Western United States[1]

F. B. Gomm, F. A. Sneva, and R. J. Lorenz[2]

The land area of the 17 western states totals approximately 468.7 million hectares (61% of the contiguous states). Agricultural censuses have placed this area into four regions, Pacific, Mountain, Northern Plains, and Southern Plains (Fig. 1). About 65% of the area is used for grazing, 15% for crops not including pastures, and an additional 10% is in nongrazed timbered land exclusive of parks, reservations, etc. (Frey, 1973).

When considering the cropping systems of the western U. S., it must be recognized that the native grasslands and mixed timber-grass ranges are important intercropping systems. Range management, silviculture, and wildlife management are specialized sciences that deal with the management of these important natural resources. It should be recognized that approximately one-third of the nation's land is federally owned, most of which is in multiple-use multiple-cropping management to provide forage, meat, timber, and water to the agricultural economy of the region.

Land used for crop production remains about constant in the Pacific and Mountain states, but declined from 1949 to 1972 in the Plains states, especially in the Southern Plains (Frey, 1973). Much of the land taken out of crops was put into pasture and timber-pasture production. In 1974, the trend was reversed and land went back into crop production. This indicates that land use in the Plains depends on economic conditions.

AGRICULTURAL AREAS

The land of the western states has been placed into 14 cropping areas (Austin, 1965) based on general environmental conditions and the major crops or type of farming (Fig. 2).

[1]Contribution of the Agricultural Research Service, USDA. Grateful acknowledgment is given to those providing information through correspondence.

[2]Research agronomist and range scientist, Eastern Oregon Agricultural Research Center, Burns, Oregon; and director, Northern Great Plains Research Center, Mandan, North Dakota.

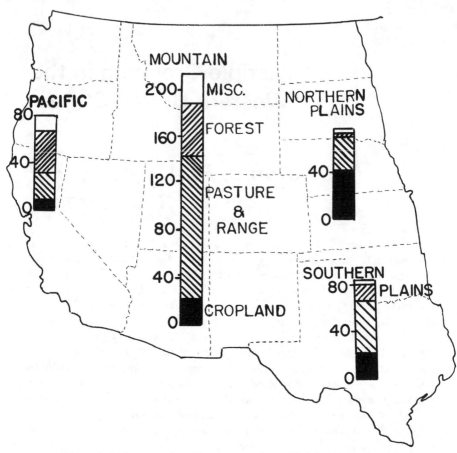

Figure 1. Major uses of land by census regions, 1969 (millions of hectares).

Northwestern Forest, Forage, and Specialty Crop Region

This region, west of the Cascade Range, is humid with cool summers and mild winters, but July and August are dry which makes irrigation advantageous.

The largest multiple cropping practice in the region is intercropping of oats (*Avena sativa* L.) with red clover (*Trifolium pratense*). The oats and clover are planted in the fall. The oats are then harvested as grain or hay. Adverse weather during harvesting can result in killing a large proportion of the clover where windrows remain on the field too long.

In the fruit and nut orchards, small grains or annual forage crops are grown between rows of newly established trees.

A new intercropping practice in southern Oregon is that of planting wheat (*Triticum aestivum* L.) in areas previously in subclover pastures. Short-

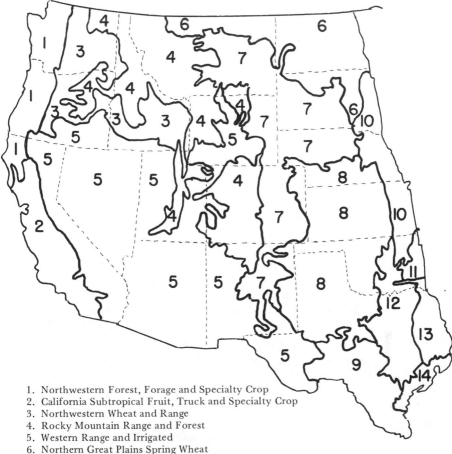

1. Northwestern Forest, Forage and Specialty Crop
2. California Subtropical Fruit, Truck and Specialty Crop
3. Northwestern Wheat and Range
4. Rocky Mountain Range and Forest
5. Western Range and Irrigated
6. Northern Great Plains Spring Wheat
7. Western Great Plains Range and Irrigated
8. Central Great Plains Winter Wheat and Range
9. Southern Plateaus and Plains Range and Cotton
10. Central Feed Grains and Livestock
11. East and Central General Farming and Forest
12. Southwestern Prairies Cotton and Forage
13. Gulf Slope Cash Crop, Forest and Livestock
14. Gulf Coast Lowland Forest and Truck Crop

Figure 2. Land resource areas of the western U. S., adapted from *U. S. Department of Agriculture Handbook 296, 1965* (Austin, 1965).

ly after the wheat is planted, a volunteer stand of subclover appears because of its hard seed characteristic. After the wheat is harvested, a good crop of dry forage remains for summer pasture.

Double cropping is practiced where vegetable crops, bush beans (*Phaseolus vulgaris* L.) or sweet corn (*Zea mays* L.) follow early maturing annual crops.

California Subtropical Fruit, Truck, and Specialty Crop Region

Except for the coastal mountains, the climate is generally dry with mild winters and frost-free periods of 200 to more than 330 days.

Because of the long growing season and generally favorable climate, multiple cropping is practiced with a wide variety of cash crops being used in double cropping systems. Cotton (*Gossypium hirsutum* L.) and sugar beets (*Beta vulgaris* L.) are frequently double cropped with cereal grains, but where markets are favorable, double and triple cropping with a wide variety of vegetables is practiced.

Northwest Wheat and Range Area

Because of the high, cold semidesert climate of this region, little multiple cropping is done in Washington and Oregon. Where precipitation is adequate, however, winter wheat is planted in the fall following a pea (*Pisum sativum* L.) or lentil (*Lens culinaris*) crop. In irrigated areas, a winter cover crop of cereal grain or vetch (*Vicia* sp.) is grown to improve soil and prevent wind erosion. It is then plowed under in the spring before the summer crop. Where center pivot sprinkler irrigation is being used, potatoes (*Solanum tuberosum* L.) or peas are harvested early, and summer annual grasses, sudan (*Sorghum vulgare sudanense*) or sorghum (*Sorghum bicolor*)-sudan are used for forage or wind protection, or sweet corn may be grown as a vegetable crop. In recent years, soybeans (*Glycine max* L. Merr.) following peas have been grown in limited amounts. Also soybeans planted with peas have been followed by winter wheat.

In southern Idaho, dry peas grown as a cash crop are usually harvested about 1 August which leaves the land bare and unproductive for 2.5 more months. Experiments with sudangrass and sorghum following peas have been disappointing, but corn with 16,000 plants/ha produced nearly 7 metric tons/ha of dry matter. Although corn is not a reliable second crop because of early frost danger, it is considered as an emergency crop if the pea crop fails due to an unseasonable freeze or severe hailstorm.

Alfalfa (*Medicago sativa* L.) planted with peas is practiced on the Snake River Plains of Idaho. Turnips (*Brassica rapa*) have also been planted with peas but it is not considered to be a good practice. Occasionally, alfalfa is planted with a crop of canning peas in northern Utah. After the peas are harvested in June or July, the alfalfa may make a crop later in the year.

Rocky Mountain Range and Forest Region

High rugged mountain peaks and ranges dominate this region and influence the climate accordingly. The annual precipitation and length of growing season varies with latitude and elevation.

Multiple cropping is limited to growing multiple species grass-legume pastures, or is used as a relay-companion crop in which perennial pastures or alfalfa are started with a cereal grain. Frequently, a legume companion crop is plowed as green manure. The merits of the companion crop pattern have been debated, and it is generally recommended only for those areas where rainfall is adequate or where irrigation is practical.

Western Range and Irrigated Region

Most of this region is semidesert to desert in nature, and cultivated agriculture is dependent on irrigation.

Except for intercropping of companion grain and forage crops, multiple cropping is largely restricted to double cropping in southern Nevada, Arizona, and New Mexico.

In southern Nevada, cereal grains are planted in the fall for winter and spring use and harvested as green chop, grazed, or as seed. The land is then freed for growing other summer crops. Harvesting small grains in May allows planting of sorghum or corn for silage.

Overseeding of dormant bermudagrass (*Cynodon dactylon* L.) with small grains produces forage nearly the year around. Alfalfa is frequently planted in bermudagrass in October. The next season the grass is crowded out.

Approximately 70% of Arizona's farmed land is located where double cropping might be considered. At the lower elevation in southeastern Arizona, barley (*Hordeum vulgare* L.) and wheat are harvested in May or June. Sorghum is planted as the second crop to be harvested in the fall when cereal grains are again planted. Full season hybrid sorghums are planted in April and May without double cropping. Safflower (*Carthamus tinctorius*) which is planted on dates similar to the cereal grains, is harvested in July and August, depending on elevation. Using conventional crops, double cropping with safflower has not been popular, but double cropping with winter season vegetables has good potential, especially at low elevations.

Double cropping in central Arizona is practiced on a small scale with sorghum following sugar beets. Sugar beets are grown for 6 to 10 months depending on elevations. The growing season at higher elevations is too short to recommend double cropping.

The feasibility of using cotton in double cropping with cereal grains is being studied (Scott Hathorn, Jr., and B. Brooks Taylor. University of Arizona, Agric. File Q-131). It appears that late-planted cotton and narrow-row cotton are more profitable crops than sorghum grain in a double cropping system.

Photoperiodic sorghum varieties have been used to essentially grow two crops of sorghum from a single seeding. The photoperiod sensitive varieties, growing under short day lengths, mature grain when 1.25 to 1.50 m high. Combining is easy. Later, under the long day period, the same plant will grow to 2.5 to 3 m tall before maturing grain. It can then be cut for silage (Stith & Voight, 1962).

As in Arizona, New Mexico producers are double cropping the lower irrigated valleys, and researchers are attempting to develop earlier maturing cottons and barleys in an attempt to grow these two crops in a 12-month period (Arden A. Baltensperger, New Mexico State University, personal correspondence). This is being done using a semidwarf cotton strain, 'Acala', that is 12 days earlier but fully equivalent to standard varieties in fiber quality; also being used is a barley variety that matures extremely early and is quite frost resistant.

Northern Great Plains Spring Wheat Region

The growing season is too short and precipitation is insufficient for much double cropping in this region. It is possible, however, to produce a crop of early barley and then an oat crop for hay, silage, or sometimes seed. Sudangrass following barley has been tried with irrigation, but the practice is not considered feasible. Greater returns are expected with a single crop of grain, corn, alfalfa, soybeans, potatoes, dry beans, or sugar beets.

Western Great Plains Range and Irrigated Region

The climate of this region is milder than the Northern Great Plains, but because of unfavorable soils, steep slopes, and undependable moisture, dry farming is uncertain.

The summer fallow system with small grains is practiced extensively throughout the semiarid wheat producing areas. One of the prime interests at present in Montana is the search for alternatives to this system because of "saline seep". It is believed that the practice of summer fallowing for two or three decades has caused saline seep in the glacial till soils which contain high concentrations of salts (Kurt C. Fellner, Montana State University, personal correspondence).

In Wyoming on irrigated farms, intercropping with a cereal grain and alfalfa as companion crops is a common practice. The season is too short for double cropping; per se, except that a cereal grain crop may be harvested early. The stubble is then used as a seedbed in which a legume or grass is seeded. The late season precipitation is too low for this to be a good practice under dryland conditions.

With sprinkler irrigation, some farmers have broadcast alfalfa seed at the last cultivation of corn. This allows the alfalfa to become established before winter but must be done on clean land.

In north central Nebraska, rye (*Secale cereale* L.) is seeded in some of the irrigated sandy corn fields by airplane in the standing corn to provide fall pasture, but this seeding is primarily to control wind erosion. Research has shown that alfalfa can be seeded in irrigated corn and avoid a season's delay, but farmers have not adopted the practice (D. G. Hanway, University of Nebraska, Lincoln, personal correspondence).

Central Great Plains Winter Wheat and Range Region

Although precipitation is generally low, temperatures are warm enough to permit some double cropping. In south central Nebraska, wheat is sometimes followed by sorghum, or corn is followed by fallow in nonirrigated areas.

Where irrigation of soybeans following wheat is possible in central Kansas, double cropping can be successful. Some producers and researchers propose to aerially seed soybeans into the wheat crops about 1 May and then keep the soil moist with irrigation until the soybeans are well established. Others prefer to plant soybeans in May or June and then follow with wheat because the soil is mellow and seedbed preparation is minimal following soybeans. Sometimes, however, wet conditions in the fall prevent planting of wheat. Grain sorghum (short season variety) is grown only on a limited scale following wheat.

Multiple cropping is also widely used in Oklahoma but is primarily limited to cropping in bermudagrass sod. The lack of rainfall at critical periods is the most limiting factor.

In the Texas highlands, cotton and sorghum have been grown in alternating four row blocks across a field perpendicular to the prevailing wind. This system was to have provided protection to the younger crop, but the practice was never widely accepted. In the peanut (*Arachis hypogaea* L.) producing area of Cross Timbers and Rio Grande Plain, this practice is used.

Southwestern Plateaus and Plains Range and Cotton Region

The climate of this southern extension of the Great Plains is generally warm with mild winters.

The semitropical lower Rio Grande Valley has the greatest potential for multiple cropping in the region because of the 330+ days of growing season. Vegetables and field crops are grown in a multiple of relay, double, and intercropping combinations, depending on market prices.

Central Feed Grains and Livestock Region

The part of this general region which falls within the western states includes the eastern portions of South Dakota, Nebraska, and Kansas and a small part of Oklahoma. Temperatures are conducive to permit some double cropping.

In South Dakota, intercropping by growing corn and soybeans together in the same row is commonly done to increase protein content when the crop is cut for silage. A modified alternate strip form of intercropping with corn and legumes has been investigated, but results indicated that it was not a feasible method. The system omitted every third row of corn, leaving a 2-m (7-foot) spacing to which alfalfa was planted. The next year, two normally spaced rows of corn were planted in the legume sod, again leaving the 2-m space previously in corn to be planted to legumes (Fred E. Shubeck, South Dakota State University, personal correspondence). In northeastern Nebraska, oat is grown as a companion crop when establishing alfalfa, but this practice has declined in recent years.

For double cropping to be feasible in South Dakota and Nebraska, it would be necessary to develop short season crops with low moisture requirements.

Double cropping is a widely accepted practice in southeastern Kansas where soybeans are frequently planted as a double crop following wheat. To do so, however, soil moisture must be adequate and seeding of soybeans must be done by early July. If conditions are favorable, yields of 680 to 777 kg (25-30 bu) are possible. To prepare the seedbed, some producers burn the straw and disk; others prefer to plow the soil, but no-tillage is gaining interest. Moisture loss becomes a problem when the soil is cultivated.

East and Central General Farming and Forest Region

Although the climate is generally mild enough for double cropping, summers are relatively dry. The terrain is not favorable for cultivated crops and farms are small. Where the land can be cultivated, interplanting of legumes with small grains or with corn has potential for forage and feed production, but little multiple cropping is practiced.

Southwestern Prairie Cotton and Forage Region

Except for the hot dry winds which blow during the summer, the region has a mild climate, and the potential for double cropping is good where irrigation water can be applied. Cotton is the main cash crop which could be followed with small grains.

Interplanting of legumes with small grains has been successfully used in Oklahoma and Texas for winter, spring, and summer grazing. The cropping sequence of multiple cropping and rotation has been shown to be important from the standpoint of fertilizers required. Oat does not do well following sweetclover (*Melilotus indica*) or cotton.

Gulf Slope Cash Crop, Forest, and Livestock Region

This area has mild winters and a long growing season but because of the high evapotranspiration rate and low water holding capacity of the soil, crops are often limited by moisture. Where soils are deep, cotton is the main cash crop which is occasionally followed by double cropping with grain sorghum.

Gulf Coast Lowland Forest and Truck Crop Region

The climate is subtropical with up to 330 days growing season. The potential for multiple cropping in this region is good where cultivation is practiced.

Where rice (*Oryza sativa* L.) is grown, it is followed by planting cereal grains, flax (*Linum usitatissimum* L.), or pasture species directly into the rice stubble. Rotation of rice and pasture has increased both beef and rice production and has controlled undesirable grasses and weeds.

Where cotton is the principle crop, it is generally followed by corn or grain sorghum. Winter legumes are also grown in double cropping patterns in rotation with row crops.

GENERAL OBSERVATIONS

In the final analysis, in the western U. S., little double or relay cropping is done north of latitude 37°N., or above 600 m elevation. The short growing season restricts the planting and maturing of soybeans or sorghum after harvesting small grains, and rainfall is usually inadequate to permit germination and establishment of a second crop. Even with irrigation, the season is normally too short to permit effective double cropping as a common practice. Good managers, however, may recognize seasonal weather patterns in an occasional year when they can take advantage of a double cropping system.

Fallowing to increase soil moisture and intercropping with companion crops during the establishment of a permanent pasture or legume crop can be used effectively in many of the western states, but again, inadequate rainfall late in the growing season is often the limiting factor.

The only areas normally suited for double cropping with present agronomic crops and varieties are those having growing seasons longer than 200 days (Fig. 3) and which have adequate irrigation water. Because of the variability in soils, climate, and evapotranspiration requirements (Fig. 4) it is not possible to relate multiple cropping success to precipitation pattern except as it occurs locally from year to year. It would appear, however, that areas where double cropping is practiced without irrigation must receive more than 75 cm of annual precipitation (Fig. 5). Intercropping, especially in the northern latitude, is successful where precipitation is greater than 50 cm.

RANGE AS A MULTIPLE CROPPING SYSTEM

By its nature, physical characteristics, and resultant multiple species forage crop, the western rangelands provide food for man only when harvested by grazing animals, and because these lands cannot profitably produce cul-

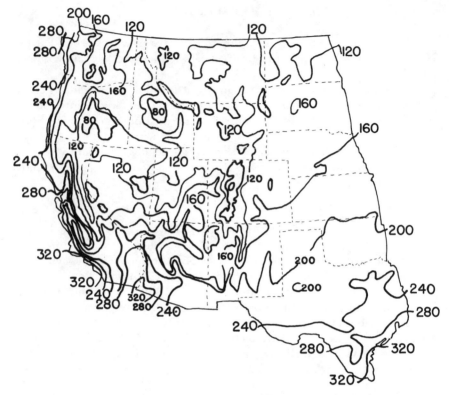

Figure 3. Average length of frost-free period (days), adapted from *Climate and Man Yearbook of Agriculture* (USDA, 1941).

tivated crops, they will continue to produce rough forages. Nevertheless, much is being done to improve, harvest, and manage this natural intercropping system.

The type of animal used to harvest the forage, whether cattle, sheep or big game, is determined by the physical environment and species growing there. The availability of forage also may determine the class of animal that will be managed. Some ranges are suitable only for wildlife habitat, but generally they would be most productive if managed in a dual-use system with livestock so as to balance the species of grazing animals to their most efficient use of the available forage.

Because of the destructive use of range around the turn of the century, about 238 million hectares were seriously depleted (USDA, 1936). Improvement and renovation practices can restore much of the rangeland to a highly productive level by changing the species composition and by proper management (Vallentine, 1971, p. 301–317).

With proper management, crested wheatgrass (*Agropyron cristatum*) ranges can be used for spring and fall grazing in the same season, and essentially produce two crops of high quality forage (Hyder & Sneva, 1963).

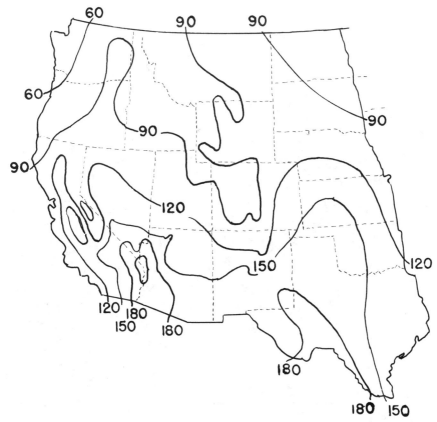

Figure 4. Mean annual evaporation (centimeters), adapted from *Water Encyclopedia* (Todd, 1970).

The removal of nonedible plants with herbicides or by mechanical means has permitted good forage species to recover and increase in production. Water wastage and the decline in forage production has been well documented in brush infested areas in the southwest and Texas. After brush control, the feed supply from these ranges is more than doubled (Herbel et al., 1973, Schultz et al., 1959). Similar results have been obtained by removing dense stands of piñon (*Pinus edulis*)-juniper (*Juniperus* sp.) and sagebrush (*Artemisia* sp.) in the intermountain areas (Clary, 1974). Improving these ranges not only increases forage production there but also allows more efficient use of the summer mountain ranges and the winter desert ranges (Cook, 1966).

Fertilization of native grasslands has also been used to change species composition and to increase production of desirable forage plants (Rogler & Lorenz, 1957).

Interseeding and pitting have been widely used on the western range with varying degrees of success. Interseeding (row intercropping) with yellow sweetclover was used successfully in South Dakota to increase forage

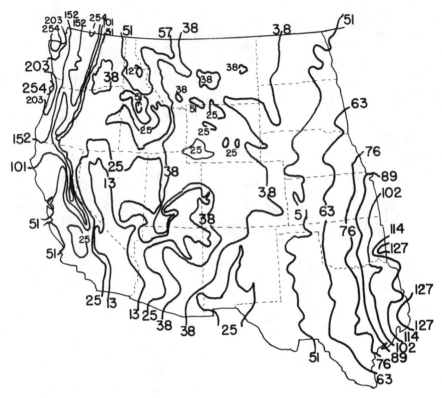

Figure 5. Average annual precipitation (centimeters), adapted from *Soil Yearbook of Agriculture* (USDA, 1957).

production (Nichols, 1969). In Wyoming, pitting increased forage production for two and one-half decades (Rauzi, 1974), and in Montana, both pitting and interseeding with cool season grasses increased production on shortgrass ranges when precipitation was normal or above normal (Ryerson et al., 1970; Wight & White, 1974; J. E. Taylor, 1967. Range pitting and nitrogen fertilization on mixed prairie rangelands in northern Montana. M.S. Thesis, Montana State University). Interseeding with browse and forbs into perennial grass stands is also recommended on intermountain game ranges (Plummer, 1968).

Nature's preferred way is to have a mixed species multiple crop. Ecologically, it is the most productive in terms of total biomass because the resultant community is closed. It is using all of the resources available for plant growth. The only opportunity an invading species has to enter the community is if the factors to which it is tolerant are not fully occupied by another species.

Mixtures provide two additional major advantages to consider when planting: (i) they are better suited for the diverse conditions of soil, topography, and microclimate that might occur within the planned seeding; and

(ii) mixtures provide variety in the animal's diet and might be used more effectively in meeting the animal's needs on a year-long basis.

Since animal species have differing preferences for plant types, care must be used in managing so as not to eliminate the desired species. A well-managed range in the intermountain area might rotate periodically between cattle and sheep to keep the grasses and forbs in better balance. The presence of big game animals adds other dimensions to forage management problems.

LITERATURE CITED

Austin, M. E. 1965. Land resource regions and major land resource areas of the United States. Agric. Handbook 296. (Rev. 1972). USDA Soil Conservation Service, Washington, D. C.

Clary, W. P. 1974. Response of herbaceous vegetation to felling of alligator juniper. J. Range Manage. 27:387-389.

Cook, C. W. 1966. Development and use of foothill ranges in Utah. Utah Agric. Exp. Stn. Bull. 461.

Frey, H. Thomas. 1973. Major uses of land in the United States. Summary for 1969. Agric. Economic Rpt. No. 247. USDA Econ. Res. Serv., Washington, D. C.

Herbel, C. H., G. H. Abernathy, C. C. Yarbrough, and D. K. Gardner. 1973. Root plowing and seeding arid rangelands in the southwest. J. Range Manage. 26:193-197.

Hyder, D. N., and F. A. Sneva. 1963. Morophological and physiological factors affecting the grazing management of crested wheatgrass. Crop Sci. 3:267-271.

Nichols, James T. 1969. Range improvement practices on deteriorated dense clay wheatgrass range in western South Dakota. South Dakota Agric. Exp. Stn. Bull. 552.

Plummer, A. Perry. 1968. Restoring big-game ranges in Utah. Utah Div. of Fish and Game. Publ. No. 68-3.

Rauzi, Frank. 1974. Mechanical and chemical range renovation in southeastern Wyoming. J. Range Manage. 27:48-52.

Rogler, G. A., and R. J. Lorenz. 1957. Nitrogen fertilization of northern Great Plains rangelands. J. Range Manage. 10:156-160.

Ryerson, D. E., J. E. Taylor, L. O. Baker, H. A. R. Houlton, and D. W. Stroud. 1970. Club moss on Montana rangelands. Montana Agric. Exp. Stn. Bull. 645.

Schultz, E. M., D. R. Cable, and J. J. Warwick. 1959. Effects of a semidesert grass shrub range. J. Range Manage. 12:34-37.

Stith, L. S., and R. L. Voigt. 1962. Here's a two-for-one deal with sorghum. Progressive Agriculture in Arizona, Univ. of Arizona. 14(2):7.

Todd, David K. (ed.). 1970. The Water Encyclopedia. Water Information Center, Inc., Port Washington, N. Y.

U. S. Department of Agriculture. 1936. The Western Range. Senate Document No. 199. USDA, Washington, D. C.

U. S. Department of Agriculture. 1941. Climate and man. Yearbook of Agriculture. U. S. Government Printing Office, Washington, D. C. 1248 p.

U. S. Department of Agriculture. 1957. Soil. Yearbook of Agriculture. U. S. Government Printing Office, Washington, D. C.

Vallentine, John F. 1961. Range development and improvements. Brigham Young Univ. Press, Provo, Utah.

Wight, J. R., and L. M. White. 1974. Interseeding and pitting on a sandy range site in eastern Montana. J. Range Manage. 27:206-210.

Multiple Cropping in Some Countries of the Middle East[1]

Hikmat George Nasr[2]

Multiple cropping is a third dimension (the other two dimensions being increasing yield per crop and increasing area of arable land) that many underdeveloped countries of the tropical and subtropical climates have utilized to increase food production in response to high increases in population. This especially was the case of Egypt and the eastern Mediterranean coast of the Middle East. In other parts of the Middle East and where the climate is temperate, arid, or semiarid multiple cropping has been practiced only to a small extent. The countries that will be covered in this report are Egypt, Iran, Iraq, Jordan, Lebanon, Saudi Arabia, and Syria.

MULTIPLE CROPPING—AN ANCIENT PRACTICE

Double cropping has a long history in the Middle East. In Egypt and Babylon, as reported by Dalrymple (1971), the development of double cropping closely paralleled the growth of irrigation systems. It is not certain when double cropping began in Babylon, but one estimate places the beginning of irrigation at 4,000 to 6,000 years ago (Dalrymple, 1971). Around 77 AD, Pliny observed that in Babylon, "They cut the blade twice, then let the cattle pasture on it a third time." During the Islamic conquest of Iran from the 7th to the 11th century, the arable plains of Dasht Run produced four crops a year under irrigation.

In Egypt it is also not clear when double cropping began. Irrigation is thought to have originated as early as 3000 to 5000 BC. However, there is no evidence of double cropping beginning that early. Compertz (cited by Dalrymple, 1971) reported that about 300 BC a letter was written by Appolponius to a farm manager in Memphis stating, "The king has ordered us to sow the land twice. As soon as you gather the crops, irrigate the soil im-

[1]Contribution from the Faculty of Agricultural Sciences, American University of Beirut, Journal Number 460. Financed partially by Lebanese National Council for Scientific Research.
[2]Assistant professor in plant breeding and genetics, American University of Beirut, Lebanon. Now on leave of absence as wheat training officer in CIMMYT, Mexico.

mediately. . .after irrigation, sow three months wheat." Multiple cropping has also existed early in history in the Fayum region southeast of Cairo. A large dam was built in this region about 2000 BC, and the lake created, Lake Moeris, was used for irrigation. During the reign of Ptolemy II, one historian credited the king with imposing double cropping in Egypt.

In the recent history (19th century) multiple cropping on a commercial scale was introduced to Egypt by Mohammad Ali (Dalrymple, 1971). Construction of larger and deeper canals on the Delta was started in 1821, which increased irrigation water and thus, the cropping index. In the Delta a cropping index of 230 was reported on 400 ha of land. During the latter part of the 19th century and after the construction of dams and barrages was completed, the cropping index of all arable land of Egypt increased from 100.4 in 1879 to 138.2 in 1899. The cropping index as indicated in Table 1 kept constantly increasing and reached 159.1 in the year 1946–47 with about 1.4 million hectares under multiple cropping.

CURRENT STATUS

Before multiple cropping can be practiced commercially, factors of potential must be available. Some of these factors are climate, water, early maturing varieties, machinery, proper cropping patterns and rotations, and farmer motivation.

Climate

The climate of the middle eastern countries is mostly arid at low latitude in the temperate region. Exceptions are the subtropical coastal lands of Syria, Lebanon, and Iran near the Caspian Sea, where more precipitation occurs, and the mountainous region of Lebanon, Syria, Iraq, Iran, and Jordan, where the summers are cooler and drier. These types of climate provide for feasibility of multiple cropping if water and other factors are available.

Table 1. Multiple cropped area and indexes in Egypt (Dalrymple, 1971)

Year or season	Multiple cropped	
	Area	Index
	1,000 ha	
1879	8	100.4
1899	808	138.2
1906–1907	938	141.8
1916–1917	1,000	145.7
1926–1927	1,294	156.2
1936–1937	1,278	158.3
1946–1947	1,414	159.1

Water

Due to the shortage of rain and because rainfall is limited to the period October to April, irrigation becomes a "must factor" for multiple cropping. In the region only one-third of the present arable land can be irrigated (Table 2). Only in Egypt is the arable land entirely under irrigation since there is no rainfed agriculture. This is also true in other desertic parts of the region. On the other hand, in Jordan, where only 5% of the arable land is under irrigation, irrigation projects will increase the area of the irrigated land but not necessarily that of the arable land. New irrigation projects (Euphrates of Syria and Iraq, Aswan of Egypt, Litani of Lebanon, El-Zarka of Jordan, and excavations for underground water sources in most of the middle eastern countries) are underway and when completed will provide for higher potential of multiple cropping.

Early Maturing Varieties

The availability of adapted early maturing varieties is an important factor in multiple cropping. The shorter the growing season required by individual crops, the greater is the possibility of growing other crops. This factor is especially important where the winter temperatures reach below freezing (Beqa'a plain of Lebanon, northeastern Jordan and north central Iran, central and south central Syria). Also, it is important to grow varieties that are not photoperiod sensitive and which mature within a given period unless temperature is a limiting factor. Through efforts of plant breeders throughout the world, varieties with the above-mentioned characteristics can be made available to the middle eastern farmer, and thus multiple cropping could be practiced more efficiently.

Table 2. Arable land and area under irrigation of eight Middle Eastern countries (FAO, 1972)*

Country	Arable land	Irrigated land	Proportion of irrigated/arable
	———————— 1,000 ha ————————		
Egypt	2,400	2,400	1.00
Iran	16,154	5,251	0.32
Iraq	10,000	3,675	0.37
Jordan	1,132	60	0.05
Lebanon	240	68	0.28
Saudi Arabia	765	131	0.17
Syria	5,641	450	0.08
Total	36,332	12,035	0.33

* El-Tobgy, 1974. Contemporary Egyptian agriculture.

Machinery

Farm mechanization and the availability and proper use of farm machinery represent an important factor in sequential cropping. To insure a successful second or third crop per year on the same land, optimal efficiency becomes necessary. This requires that proper harvesting and seedbed preparation and planting machinery be on hand and that knowledgeable operators be available. The availability of modern farm machinery is not a major problem in the Middle East. However, skillful operators are not always available. Therefore, training programs in farm mechanization are essential for practicing multiple cropping.

Cropping Patterns and Rotations

Cropping patterns and rotations must be well designed for the different climates, soils, crop adaptations, and markets of the region. This will reduce the hazards of commercially practicing a cropping pattern that is not climatically possible or economically feasible. Knowledge is limited due to insufficient national and regional research. Also, information concerning the proper management (fertilizer needs, dates of planting, and irrigation needs) of specific cropping patterns is deficient in many parts of the region and high yields are not normally attained.

Farmer Motivation

Another important factor in multiple cropping is the willingness of the middle eastern farmer to adopt the practice. Normally, multiple cropping will result in an increase in the farmer's work load. However, it should result in increased net profit and food production. Like other farmers of the world, the middle eastern farmer must see before believing. Therefore, effective extension methods must be developed to improve the attitude of the farmer towards practicing multiple cropping.

CURRENT STATUS OF MULTIPLE CROPPING

Egypt

Multiple or at least double cropping is the general practice in the irrigated arable land of Egypt. This is due to the need for increased food production, the small area of arable irrigated land, and the proper climate for multiple cropping. With an area of 2.4 million hectares of arable and irrigated land, the total cropped area was 3.95, 4.23, 4.32, 4.42, and 4.52 million ha for the periods 1950-54, 1955-59, 1960-64, 1965-69, and 1970-

Table 3. Cropping pattern of a 3-year cotton rotation in Egypt*

Season	Year		
	I	II	III
Winter	winter berseem (1 or 2 cuttings)	berseem or other winter legume	wheat or barley
Summer	cotton	corn, sorghum, rice or other summer vegetable	corn, sorghum, rice, or other summer vegetable

* El-Tobgy, 1974. Contemporary Egyptian agriculture.

72.[3] The cropping indexes during these periods were 165, 176, 180, 184, and 188, respectively. According to El-Tobgy, when the areas cropped to sugarcane (*Saccharum officinarium* L.) and permanent orchards (186,000 ha) were subtracted from both the arable and the cropped areas, the cropping index of 1972 became 200. Also, he reported that the cropping index of the vegetable crop areas was 300 for the same period. It is clear from these data that the cropping index is steadily increasing. With more research on crop evaluation, triple cropping among field crops or combinations of field and vegetable crops could become possible and thus the cropping index could be further increased.

The important crops in Egypt are divided into three groups according to the cropping season. With an agriculture year that starts 1 Nov. and ends the following 31 Oct., the cropping seasons are winter, summer, and Nili (named after the Nile summer floods). In the winter season, winter cereals [wheat (*Triticum aestivum* L.) and barley (*Hordeum vulgare* L.)], winter legumes [berseem (*Trifolium alexandrinum*), broad beans (*Vicia faba*), lentil (*Lens culinaris*), fenugreek (*Trigonella foenum-graecum*), chickpea (*Cicer* sp.), and lupine (*Lupinus* sp.)], winter onions (*Allium* sp.), flax (*Linum* sp.), and winter vegetables are usually planted from October to December and harvested from April to June. In the summer season, cotton (*Gossypium* sp.), summer cereals [rice (*Oryza sativa* L.), corn (*Zea mays* L.), and sorghum (*Sorghum bicolor*)], summer onions, peanut (*Arachis hypogaea* L.), sesame (*Sesamum indicum*), kenaf (*Hibiscus cannabinus*), and summer vegetables are planted from March to June and harvested from August to November. In the Nili season corn, sorghum, rice, and summer vegetables are planted in July or August and harvested in October and November.

The cropping patterns or crop rotations within a year and between years are many and differ with different parts of the country. One of the most common is a 3-year cotton rotation which includes cotton once every 3 years and a double cropping pattern in every year (Table 3). Other rotations and cropping patterns are also practiced. In the northern half of the Delta, rice is

[3]H. A. El-Tobgy, 1974. Contemporary Egyptian agriculture. Unpublished data.

usually the summer crop and follows winter cereals or winter legumes. In the southern half of the Delta, corn is the main summer crop following winter cereals or winter legumes and further south, sorghum replaces corn as the main summer crop. Still further south, sugarcane replaces cotton and a special 3- to 6-year sugarcane rotation is practiced.

Relay cropping was also reported where berseem is planted in rice or corn fields. Also companion or intercropping such as cotton and summer onions is practiced in the fertile lands of the southern half of the Delta.[4] The onion crop, although planted with cotton, is usually harvested a few months earlier than cotton. Another example of intercropping is broad beans with sugarcane. In regions specializing in vegetable crops, particularly near urban areas, three or four crops per year are common.

Iran

Multiple cropping is practiced in two regions, the Caspian region in the north where the climate is subtropical with substantial precipitation (1,000 to 1,300 mm) and in the south (Khuzistan) where the low latitude climate is arid (B. Sadr, Seed and Plant Improvement Institute, Karaj, Iran, personal communication, 8 May 1975). Some of the cropping patterns involve winter grains followed with summer legumes [beans (*Phaseolus* sp.)], summer vegetables [tomatoes (*Lycopersicon esculentum*) or watermelon (*Citrullus vulgaris*)] or rice, and winter legumes followed by summer grain, corn, or cotton.

Iraq

In Iraq, one of the homes of ancient multiple cropping, the current status is that double cropping of barley-rice and barley-cotton is practiced on the irrigated lands of Tigris-Euphrates area. Other cropping patterns are also used. These include winter and summer crops, as well as winter cereals or legumes, followed by summer vegetables or field crops. In a committee report on land and water resources development for agricultural utilization in Iraq, a recommendation is given for more intensive cropping in areas with good drainage.[5] In another committee report, emphasis was made to increase grain production in Iraq by increasing double cropping hectarages of barley-rice and rice-rice (Ministry of Agriculture of Iraq, 1975b. Committee report. Modern agricultural practices and their effects on yield improvement. Paper presented at "The use of science and technology for the development of agri-

---

[4] El-Toby, 1974. Contemporary Egyptian agriculture.

[5] Ministry of Agriculture of Iraq, 1975a. Committee report. Land and water resources development for agricultural utilization. Paper presented at "The use of science and technology for the development of agriculture in Iraq." Baghdad, 3–9 May 1975. In Arabic.

culture in Iraq." Baghdad, 3–9 May 1975. In Arabic). Maroof, based on a 1-year study on varietal evaluation of two crops of rice per year (March to October), recommended double cropping of rice-rice to be practiced in the Misan district at 6,250, 12,500, and 20,000 ha/year for the years 1976, 1977, and 1978, respectively.[6] The potential for more multiple cropping in Iraq is increasing with the greater availability of water for irrigation with improved drainage systems and with increasing interest in multiple cropping system of agriculture.

Saudi Arabia

In Saudi Arabia irrigated arable land is small (131,000 ha) relative to the total area of the country and the area of arable land (765,000 ha). Double cropping is only practiced to a small extent in the Taef and near El-Riad area with winter cereals or winter vegetables followed by sorghum, corn, or summer vegetables [eggplant (*Solanum melongena*), pepper (*Capsicum* sp.), watermelon].

Syria

Syria and Jordan have the smallest proportions of irrigated-to-arable land in the region (Table 2). Multiple cropping in Syria is in practice but to a small extent and limited to irrigated areas (Z. Arfeh and M. N. Nschokati, agronomists, Syrian Research Institute, Douma, personal communication, 28 May 1975). These were specified as Ghottah (near Damascus), El-Gab, El-Dolb, and Hama and Homs areas. Some of the double cropping patterns involve winter cereals or legumes followed by summer vegetables [tomatoes, beans, pepper, eggplant, squash (*Cucurbita* sp.) or summer grain crops (corn or sorghum). With the availability of more irrigation, as with Syria's Euphrates dam, which upon completion will provide water for an additional 640,000 ha (Pitcher, 1975), the potential for multiple cropping will increase.

Jordan

Only about 20% of the area of irrigated land (85,000 ha) is under double cropping (Z. Ghosheh, Head of Field crop Section, Research and Extension Division, Ministry of Agriculture, The Hashimite Kingdom of Jordan, personal communication, 2 July 1975). This is located mostly in Ghor Valley where the climate is semiarid low latitude, and some in Wadi Dalleil in the

---

[6]R. S. Maroof, 1975. Adoption of doubling rice cultivation increases total yield per unit area in the season. Paper presented at "The use of science and technology for the development of agriculture in Iraq." Baghdad, 3–9 May 1975. In Arabic.

northeastern part of the country with an arid desert climate. Some of the cropping patterns practiced are winter cereals followed by summer grain or vegetables and winter vegetables followed by summer grain. Ghosheh, in a study of agriculture irrigation development of Ghor Valley of Jordan, proposed a cropping pattern of 62,000 ha of irrigated land with a cropping index of 175 (Z. Ghosheh, 1975. Agriculture irrigation development of Jordan Valley. Unpublished data in Arabic). This pattern includes 11,954 ha of winter field crops [sugar beet (*Beta vulgaris* L.), oil crops, and berseem], 20,644 ha of winter vegetables [tomatoes, potatoes (*Solanum tuberosum* L.), pepper, cabbage (*Brassica oleracea* var. *capitata*), cauliflower (*B. oleracea* var. *botrytis*)], 10,500 ha of summer vegetables [watermelon, cucumber (*Cucumis sativus* L.), squash, potatoes], and 18,900 ha of summer field crops [corn, sorghum, sunflower (*Helianthus annuus* L.), and soybean (*Glycine max* L. Merr.)]. In another report on the development of vegetable production in Jordan (Ministry of Agriculture of Jordan, 1974), an agriculture pattern was proposed for vegetable production in 26,400 ha of irrigated land which is currently cropped at a cropping index of 110 to be cropped at an index of 120, 130, 140, 150, and 160 for the years 1980, 1985, 1990, 1995, and 2000, respectively. This is to involve sugar beet and corn, in addition to the several winter and summer vegetable crops.

Lebanon

Multiple cropping in Lebanon is extensively practiced in the coastal plains where vegetables (winter and summer), such as squash, cucumber, potatoes, tomatoes, radish (*Raphanus sativus*), onions, and green beans, constitute most of the crops grown. It is not uncommon to find three or four crops grown per year.[7] In the Akkar plains of the North, several double cropping patterns are practiced. Some of these involve peanuts as a summer crop following winter cereals (wheat and barley), potatoes, other winter vegetables, and broad beans. Also, double cropping of vegetable-vegetable is practiced.[8] In the Beqa a plain where the winter temperatures are low and frost is likely to occur about 6 months of the year (early November to mid-April), double cropping is practiced by many farmers with irrigated land. Some of the cropping patterns used are turnip (*Brassica rapa*), potatoes, cucumber, squash, field beans, cabbage, lettuce (*Lactuca sativa* L.), and cauliflower after lentils, wheat, barley, potatoes, and garlic (*Allium sativum* L.)—in all combinations. Also, broad beans-potatoes and potatoes-corn are being practiced.

More irrigation projects are being developed, and the potential for double and triple cropping will increase with the increase in irrigation.

---

[7]H. G. Nasr and L. Tannir, 1975. Survey of cropping patterns in Lebanon. Unpublished data.

[8]Nasr and Tannir, 1975. Survey of cropping patterns.

RESEARCH ACTIVITIES

Research on different aspects of double, multiple, or any form of intensive cropping are absent in Syria (Z. Arfeh and M. N. Nschokati, agronomists, Syrian Research Institute, Douma, personal communication, 28 May 1975). Also, there is no record available of any multiple cropping research carried out in Iran and Saudi Arabia. In Jordan, one study was conducted by Ghosheh (1962) where three double cropping patterns were evaluated for net return and yield. The cropping patterns were cauliflower-watermelon, wheat-sesame, and peas (*Pisum sativum* L.)-sorghum. No additional research was conducted on multiple cropping in Jordan, and in a 5-year plan of research, activities on field and vegetable crops multiple cropping was not mentioned (Ministry of Agriculture of Jordan, 1975).

In Iraq, Maroof worked on a varietal yield evaluation of a double cropping pattern, rice-rice.[9] His results revealed that double cropping yielded 155 to 200% more than a single crop of rice. He recommended that double cropping hectarages be increased in the Misan district. A call for more research on multiple cropping was made by the land and water resources committee.[10]

In Egypt, where double cropping is the general practice, there is only limited published research on multiple cropping. The literature is extensive on management of different crops (vegetables or field) but not on the management of double or triple cropping patterns. Hussein et al. (1974) reported variation in yield and other agronomic characteristics of corn grown after flax, wheat, barley, field beans, and berseem. Yield of corn was higher after legumes than after nonlegumes. Also, such plants silked earlier, were taller, and had more leaves. Other research revealed that corn after field beans yielded more than corn after wheat, barley, or flax (Shalaby et al., 1958).

In Lebanon at the Agricultural Research and Education Center of the American University of Beirut, located in the Central Beqa'a plain of Lebanon, research on multiple cropping has been conducted by the author since 1970. The research was centered on two main objectives:

1. To identify and establish economically feasible cropping patterns for the region through economic-agronomic evaluation of a large number of double and triple cropping patterns involving a number of crops, including barley, wheat, lentils, barley plus vetch (*Vicia* sp.) for forage as winter crops; and corn, soybean, sunflower, safflower (*Carthamus tinctorius*), potatoes, chick peas, broad beans, field beans, onions, and sorghum plus sudangrass (*Sorghum vulgare sudanense*) as summer crops. This study was expanded in 1973 to include another location at Abdeh, representing the coastal plains.
2. To increase yields of certain economically feasible cropping patterns (based on results of Objective 1 above) and to further improve net returns through management practices. This work started in 1974

---

[9]Maroof, 1975. Adoption of doubling rice cultivation increases total yield.
[10]Ministry of Agriculture of Iraq, 1975a. Land and water resources development for agricultural utilization.

in one location (Beqa'a) and included different fertility levels (nitrogen and phosphorus). The cropping patterns used were barley plus vetch-corn and barley plus vetch-sunflower. Another project, the effect of minimum tillage on a double cropping pattern, corn-corn for silage, was started in 1975. The advantage of minimum tillage is to save time between the harvesting of the first corn crop and the establishment of the second. This work is conducted by the Farm Mechanization Department at the American University of Beirut at the Beqa'a.

Results of the above experiments revealed that several cropping patterns proved economically feasible for the Beqa'a and Akkar regions. In the former, cropping patterns, such as barley silage-corn silage-corn silage, barley grain-field beans, corn silage-corn silage, barley silage-corn grain, sunflower-corn silage, potatoes-corn silage, sunflower-proso millet (*Panicum mileaceum* L.), barley grain-corn grain, soybean grain-corn silage, wheat-cucumber, chick peas-cucumber, lentils-corn grain, lentils-potatoes, barley plus vetch-sudan, were successful. In Akkar, barley grain-corn grain, barley grain-soybean grain, barley silage-sunflower, chick peas-sunflower, and corn grain-corn silage were among the successful cropping patterns (Nasr & Ghosheh, 1973; Nasr & Alameddin, 1975; H. G. Nasr and L. Tannir, 1975. Multiple cropping evaluation study in Beqa'a, Lebanon. Unpublished data).

Current research on multiple cropping in the Middle East is limited and insufficient to satisfy the needs for development of multiple cropping in this region. With inadequate knowledge of multiple cropping, the farmers' risks of practicing certain cropping patterns are great in view of its geographical, as well as agronomic and economic, feasibility. The author on one occasion witnessed a large double cropping failure in the Beqa'a in 1972, when one farmer with over 50 ha of potatoes double cropped to corn for forage waited too long (beyond early November) to harvest his corn. As a result, the corn froze and the crop was lost. Proper knowledge of management of double cropping would have saved his crop.

The author strongly recommends that all countries of the region include multiple cropping in research planning. More specifically:

1. Multiple cropping research should be conducted in the national programs of every country of the region with the same two objectives being followed at the American University of Beirut and with additional objectives to include relay cropping, intercropping, and irrigation management practices. Vegetable crops and combinations of field and vegetable crops should also be included.
2. A regional multiple cropping research program should be developed with the objectives above.

CONCLUSIONS

Multiple cropping has been and still is practiced to some extent in the Middle East, but most extensively in Egypt. The potential for more multiple cropping is increasing as more irrigation projects are being developed. However, more research is needed in the entire region which will aide in developing improved cropping patterns and in managing such patterns. Also, a good extension program is needed to help educate the farmers to practice multiple cropping properly.

ACKNOWLEDGMENT

The author wishes to acknowledge the help of all who contributed through personal communication and to the Lebanese National Council for Scientific Research for sponsoring the study and the trip to present the paper at the Symposium. Special thanks to Dr. James Karr of the Animal Production and Protection Department of the American University of Beirut for editing the manuscript.

LITERATURE CITED

Dalrymple, Dama G. 1971. Survey of multiple cropping in less developed nations. Foreign Economic Development Service, USDA.

Food and Agricultural Organization. 1972. Production yearbook. FAO, United Nations. Rome, Italy.

Ghosheh, Z. 1962. Study of rotation in Jordan Valley. Agricultural Research Department, Ministry of Agriculture. Deir Alla, Jordan. In Arabic.

Hussein, M. A., M. S. Kamel, S. E. Shafshak, and M. S. Salem. 1974. The effect of preceding winter crops and nitrogen fertilizer on the growth and yield of maize. J. Trop. Agric. Vet. Sci. 3:263-273.

Ministry of Agriculture of Jordan. 1974. Development of vegetable production. Research and Extension Division, Ministry of Agriculture, The Hashimite Kingdom of Jordan. Amman, Jordan. In Arabic.

Ministry of Agriculture of Jordan. 1975. Research projects of the field crops section during 5-year plan (1976-1980). Agriculture Research and Extension Division, Ministry of Agriculture. The Hashimite Kingdom of Jordan. Amman, Jordan.

Nasr, H. G., and M. Alameddin. 1975. Multiple cropping project 1973-74. Annual report, Department of Crop Production and Protection. Faculty of Agric. Sci., Am. Univ. Beirut, Lebanon.

Nasr, H. G., and Z. Ghosheh. 1973. Maize and sorghum in a multiple cropping study in Beqa'a Lebanon. EUCARPIA Proc. Maize and Sorghum VIIIth meeting.

Pitcher, S. 1975. Syria's Euphrates dam promises rapid agricultural development. Report, U. S. Embassy. Beirut, Lebanon.

Shalaby, Y. Y., S. Saker, and M. A. Moursi. 1958. The effect of preceding winter crops and nitrogen on the yield of maize. Annual Agriculture Science, Faculty of Agriculture, Ain Shams University 3:91-95.

Plant Interactions in Mixed Crop Communities

B. R. Trenbath[1]

In the search for methods of increasing agricultural productivity, crop-ping systems are being proposed (Andrews & Kassam, 1976) in some of which, through either the whole or part of the year, farmers' fields contain not sole crops but mixed crop communities (intercrops). The components of these mixtures are usually different crop species (occasionally varieties) but are sometimes different age-classes of the same genotype. In this chapter, the principles governing the common forms of interaction between plant genotypes and how they affect the yields of intercrops will be outlined. The ways in which less common forms of interaction can increase intercrop yields will be explained with reference to instances where this has been achieved.

Although the various types of interaction between neighboring plants are often described as forms of "competition", to allow a more detailed analysis this term will be used only where there is competition *for* something, i.e. for growth factors such as light, water or nutrients. Competition will be defined in this way because interactions between plant neighbors may also involve the action of toxic plant exudates (allelopathy), the transfer of mi-crobially fixed nitrogen, and processes concerning other types of organisms such as rhizosphere saprophytes, parasitic (disease-causing) microorganisms, and herbivorous (pest) insects.

The intensity of the interaction observed between components in a mix-ture must depend on the proportion of interplant contacts that are between individuals of different components. The three main types of intercropping— mixed, row and strip—differ greatly (for say, a 1:1 proportion of the com-ponents) in the frequency of intercomponent contacts. Some patterns which might be used experimentally or in a hand-planted crop are shown in Figure 1. Although the pattern used is likely to be influenced by convenience for sowing, weeding, and harvesting, the farmer should be aware that the yields of the components (including weeds) may depend on the planting pattern

[1] Research Fellow, Department of Environmental Biology, Research School of Biologi-cal Sciences, Australian National University, Canberra City, Australia.

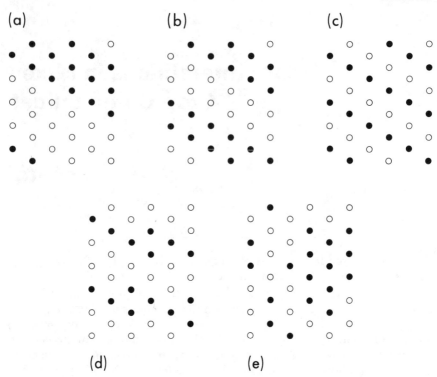

Figure 1. Planting arrangements differing in the frequency of contacts between the two components of 1:1 intercrops. The average number of such contacts (out of 6) in the patterns is: (a), 1; (b), 2; (c), 4; (d) and (e), 3. The type of intercropping is: (a) and (b), strip; (c), row; (e), mixed.

(Pendleton & Dungan, 1958; Santhirasegaram & Black, 1968a; Harper, 1961; Donald, 1963; Austenson & Larter, 1969; IRRI, 1975; R. R. Harwood and G. R. Banta, 1974. Intercropping and its place in Southeast Asia. Paper presented at the 1974 meeting of the American Society of Agronomy, Chicago, Ill. 10–15 Nov.). By his choice of planting arrangement, the farmer can maximize the types of between-component interaction which will be described in the following sections.

SHARING OF GROWTH FACTORS—COMPETITION

Plants require the growth factors light, water, nutrients, oxygen, and carbon dioxide for growth. Light and CO_2 are absorbed by the leaves, and water, nutrients, and oxygen mainly by the roots. In healthy young plants, growth is responsive to the rate of absorption of any one of them when it is in relatively short supply.

In a young, simultaneously-established, dense sole crop, the leaf area index (LAI) and root density are low enough for the per-plant supply, interception, and absorption of growth factors to equal that in isolated plants growing under the same conditions. As growth proceeds, the proximity of shoots and root systems leads to mutual interference in the interception and absorption (or uptake) of growth factors. Growth rates fall below those found in isolated plants to an extent depending on the degree of interference (and thus on the plant density).

In a situation where the proximity of neighbors is causing most plants to have a suboptimal absorption rate of growth factors, variation in the size and/or activity of individual plants' shoot and root systems leads to variation between plants in the share of the limited supply of growth factors that each obtains. The process of competition is a complex of all the processes which produce this inequitable distribution of growth factors between plants. The varying growth responses to this uneven distribution of growth factors lead to variation in plant size. Although some of the final differences in size may have been established before mutual interference began, after this time, competition for growth factors usually tends to amplify earlier differences in size and the final differences will be predominantly the result of competition.

In a field sown to strip intercrops, most of the early interference and competition will be between plants of the same component. The plants in the strips will differ little from those of a sole crop. Gradually, however, starting at the interfaces between strips, competition will develop between plants of different components and hence to within-component competition will be added between-component competition. In a field sown to a regular pattern designed to maximize contact between components (e.g. using the pattern of Fig. 1c or a checkerboard planted on a square grid), between-component competition will predominate from the start. The two sorts of competition process are in principle the same but differences in the plant distribution and the shoot and root geometry of the components will make the spatial relationships and intensities of effect different. Thus, at the between-component level, competition will lead to a distribution of growth factors which is inequitable relative to the numbers of plants (or areas) of the components sown. This uneven sharing of resources between components (as between plants within a component) tends to become accentuated with time and can, unless checked by management or a differential effect of, say, a pest, lead to the suppression and death of a less-vigorous component.

In the next section, the mechanisms of between-component competition for various factors and allelopathy are discussed together with ways of regulating the intensity of the competition effects. A later section contains a description of the effects of competition on the yields of intercrop components and of the types of interaction which allow intercrops to sometimes outyield (or be outyielded by) sole crops.

MECHANISMS OF INTERACTIONS BETWEEN GENOTYPES

Competition between plants for resources is usually occurring in crops planted at agricultural densities. Its occurrence between components is the inevitable accompaniment of a high level of interception of growth factors in

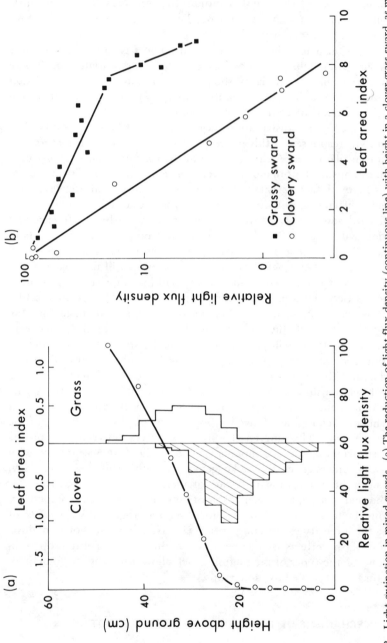

Figure 2. Light extinction in mixed swards. (a) The leaf area profiles of clover (hatched) and grass (unhatched) are given in LAI units. (b) The reduction of light flux density on a horizontal sensor with height in two swards. In the grassy sward, the break in the line marks the top of the clover canopy. (Stern & Donald, 1962a.)

a mixed or row intercrop, but it may develop only rather late in growth in a strip intercrop. The processes involved depend on which growth factor is the subject of competition.

Competition for Light and CO_2

When the photosynthetic canopy (leaves and/or green stems) of one component is set higher than those of another, otherwise similar component, the taller canopy intercepts the greater share of light. If the soil conditions are nonlimiting and the crops are still vegetative, the photosynthesis and growth rates of their canopies are near to proportional to the radiation which they intercept. This has been shown to be true both for sole crops (Baker & Meyer, 1966; Puckridge & Donald, 1967) and for components of mixed intercrops (Stern & Donald, 1962b; Santhirasegaram & Black, 1968b).

The reduction of light flux density (intensity) due to interception within a leaf canopy (Fig. 2a) is usually exponential. This is indicated by the straight-line graphs obtained when the logarithms of relative values are plotted against the LAI through which the light has passed as illustrated in Figure 2b (Monsi & Saeki, 1953; Allen et al., 1976). Consequently, in mixed intercrops where soil conditions are so good that competition is only for light, slight differences in height, even early in growth, can lead to strong competition effects. A planted mixture of small and large seeds of subterranean clover (*Trifolium subterraneum*) 'Bacchus Marsh' gave a sward where plants from the small seeds were so suppressed that they obtained only 2% of the incident light after 82 days (Black, 1958). Even during grain-filling in cereals, a difference of height can profoundly affect the yield of grain of a shorter component, mostly through an effect on grain-size as shown in Figure 3 (Trenbath & Harper, 1973).

Measurements of light fluxes in leaf canopies (Monsi & Saeki, 1953) show that the inclination of the leaves greatly influences the amount of light which is intercepted by the canopies of taller intercrop components or shade trees and hence the amount which is available to shorter components. For example, one unit of LAI of prostrate-leaved white clover (*T. repens*) absorbed 50% of the incoming light whereas the same LAI of erect-leaved perennial rye grass (*Lolium perenne*) absorbed only 26% (Brougham, 1958). The growth response of crops to leaf inclination seems to have been sufficiently studied (Monsi et al., 1973; Trenbath & Angus, 1975) for mathematical models of the processes involved to give reasonably reliable predictions. Using such a model (Trenbath, 1974b), growth of a two-component mixed intercrop was simulated with three combinations of leaf inclinations of the taller and shorter components. The combinations of leaf inclinations (short, tall) were 75°, 15°; 45°, 45°; and 15°, 75°, the leaf light responses were those typical of a species with a C_3 photosynthetic pathway, e.g. rice (*Oryza sativa*), and the conditions simulated were those of the equator with planting date 20 Jan. After 60 days of growth, the ratios of predicted shoot weight (short/tall) of the two components in 1:1 mixed

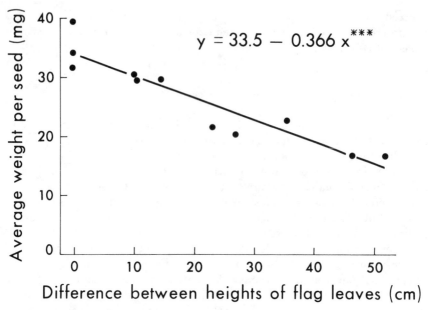

Figure 3. Effect on weight per seed of varying degrees of submergence of plants of *Avena sativa* in canopies of three intercropped species of *Avena*. The three points corresponding to zero difference of height are those of the *A. sativa* sole crop. (Redrawn from Trenbath & Harper, 1973.)

intercrops were 0.070, 0.127, and 0.286. Although taller components always compete more effectively for light, large variations of leaf inclination are likely to affect the magnitude of competition effects.

Although there is little relevant experimental evidence, the shading effect of a taller component seems likely to be enhanced by direct as opposed to diffused light, by low solar elevations, and by low incident light intensities. Using a model[2] of daily photosynthesis, the magnitudes of these effects can be predicted (Fig. 4). Although the contrast of "all light diffuse" versus "sunny" at constant total light flux density is not found in the field, the contrasts of Figure 4b and c are realistic and suggest strong effects, especially at high LAI's, on relative photosynthesis rates. If these simulations correctly estimate differences of growth rate, relative biomass yields may be significantly affected by time of year and latitude under either sunny or overcast conditions.

While the balance between the yields of the components of an intercrop can be regulated by planting proportion, fertilizer applications or, very effectively by relative time of planting (Harper, 1961),[3] the farmer may wish to select a crop variety with high ability in competition for light. Characters

[2]B. R. Trenbath, 1972. The productivity of varietal mixtures of wheat. Ph.D. Thesis, University of Adelaide.

[3]W. A. T. Herrera, 1975. Corn-legume combinations: recent IRRI multiple cropping results. Paper presented at the 6th Annual Conference of the UPLB-NFAC Intensified Corn Production Program, University of the Philippines, Los Baños, 14–16 Jan. 1975.

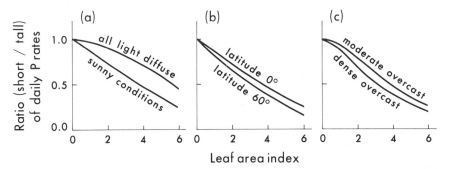

Figure 4. Predicted effect of varied light conditions on the daily photosynthesis (P) rates of two components of a mixed intercrop. The leaf canopy of the tall component is completely above that of the equal-sized canopy of the short component. The predictions refer to 21 March at latitude $0°$ unless otherwise stated. The photosynthesis light responses assumed are those of rice. (a) Varied proportion of light which is diffuse; (b) sunny conditions but with varied latitude and hence varied solar elevation; (c) overcast but with varied light level (the level in "dense overcast" is one-quarter of that in "moderate overcast").

conferring this are: rapid expansion of a tall canopy (Donald, 1963), large leaves to minimize penumbra effects (Norman et al., 1971), leaves horizontal under overcast conditions (Monsi & Saeki, 1953) and plagiotropic under sunny conditions (Brougham, 1958), leaves with the C_4 photosynthesis pathway (Black et al., 1969) and low transmissivity (Saeki, 1960), leaves forming a mosaic leaf arrangement (Acock et al., 1970), a climbing habit (Monsi & Murata, 1970),[4] a high allocation of dry matter to building a tall stem (Iwaki, 1959), and rapid stem extension in response to shading (Williams, 1964).

Although shading by a taller mixture component generally reduces photosynthesis rates in the lower canopy, providing that the shading is not too intense the plants of the shaded canopy will continue to grow and will adapt to the low light levels. These adaptations will be competition effects. Adaptations to low light intensity include reduced rates of dark respiration (Thomas & Hill, 1949; Kumura, 1968), lowered root/shoot ratio (Brouwer, 1966), and greater leaf area/leaf weight ratio (Blackman, 1956; Iwaki, 1959). These changes increase the chances of survival by increasing the interception of light and reducing the respiratory load. Increased stem extension usually occurs in shaded plants and can sometimes prevent a shorter component being overtopped (Williams, 1964; Grime, 1966); if the shading is too intense, however, extension is reduced (Lockhart, 1961; Trenbath & Harper, 1973). Nonadaptive changes include a reduction of maximum photosynthesis rate (Iwaki, 1959; Bowes et al., 1972), earlier senescence of leaves (Puckridge & Donald, 1967) and overextension of stems leading to lodging (Grime, 1966). Of less certain adaptive significance are the increases of nutrient content commonly found in shaded components where there is no competition for nutrients (Donald, 1958).

---

[4]Herrera, 1975. Corn-legume combinations.

Although competition between components for CO_2 is theoretically possible, the turbulence within canopies is usually so great (Kanemasu et al., 1969) that it seems unlikely to occur (de Wit, 1965; Inoue, 1974). So far it has been demonstrated only within sealed enclosures (Menz et al., 1969).

Competition for Soil Factors

Roots take up water, nutrients, and oxygen (soil factors) from the soil. When a crop is at the seedling stage, the roots will be far enough apart for uptake by one radicle not to interfere with supplies of soil factors to its nearest neighbor. However, since the surface area of the root system may be over 100 times that of the shoot (Dittmer, 1937), the soil soon becomes crowded and competition for supplies may begin.

The uptake of dissolved nutrient or oxygen by a root surface tends to establish a concentration gradient down which further supplies of the substance diffuse towards the root (Nye, 1966; Dunham & Nye, 1974). Similarly, water uptake produces a gradient of water content down which water flows in the same direction (Dunham & Nye, 1973; Newman, 1974). The movement of substances by diffusion (nutrients in the aqueous phase, and oxygen in both liquid and gaseous phases) and by mass flow in water through the soil to the root depletes the soil of these substances in the vicinity of the root. Because water and nitrate ions are more mobile in soil than potassium and phosphate (Bray, 1954; Barley, 1970) and are usually taken up at faster rates (Brewster & Tinker, 1970; Hanway & Weber, 1971), the zones of their depletion around active roots are expected to increase in size fastest and to overlap the soonest (Bray, 1954; Andrews & Newman, 1970). Until there is an overlapping of depletion zones of roots of the different components of an intercrop, competition for soil factors between different components cannot begin (although competition between individual roots and root systems of the same type may begin much earlier).

To give an idea of the distances involved, some figures concerning depletion zones can be quoted. Depending on a series of factors such as the hydraulic conductivity of the soil, the soil water content maintained at the root surface compared with that in the bulk soil, and the time over which this difference of contents has existed, the depletion zone for water can be calculated to extend up to 25 cm from a single root (Klute & Peters, 1969); water has been observed to start flowing in a wet soil towards a root system 12 cm away in less than 6 days (Dunham & Nye, 1973). Observations in the field suggest still greater mobility (Stone et al., 1973).

Since mobile ions like nitrate are carried passively in moving soil water, their depletion zones will be as large as those for water, providing the ions are taken up as fast as they arrive at the root (Barber, 1962; Barley, 1970). If there is little transpiration from the shoots, there will be little flow of water to the roots and movement of nutrients will be mostly by diffusion. Nutrients like phosphorus (and cations like ammonium, calcium, and potassium), being adsorbed strongly onto the surfaces of soil particles, are at low concentrations in the soil water and therefore move almost exclusively by diffusion (Olsen & Kemper, 1968; Brewster & Tinker, 1970). Since diffusion is a relatively slow process, a phosphate depletion zone may extend only 0.7 cm from the root surface after a week (Bhat & Nye, 1973).

The effects of interference between individual roots has been recently studied using an electrical analog (Baldwin et al., 1973). Large reductions in uptake (e.g. by 60%) are expected where the roots are clumped rather than distributed at random. For the uptake of mobile nutrients, roots may easily become redundant if they are close together. For the uptake of nonmobile nutrients, however, proximity has much less effect because the depletion zones are so much narrower. Both predictions are supported by experimental comparisons of the uptake of nitrate and phosphate by wheat plants (*Triticum aestivum* L.) with varied root densities (Cornforth, 1968; Andrews & Newman, 1970).

If the narrowness of the depletion zones for nonmobile nutrients tends to prevent interference between individual roots at anything but high root densities, it will tend also to prevent competition for these nutrients between root systems of different components of an intercrop (Bray, 1954; Baldwin et al., 1972). This has been confirmed experimentally using wheat plants with overlapping root systems where the root density was about 1.2 to 8 cm/cm^3 (Andrews & Newman, 1970). Competition for phosphorus does, however, sometimes occur (Donald, 1963; Snaydon, 1971). Since the same principles apply to competition between individual roots as apply to competition between whole plants, the spatial distribution of individual roots in regions of root-system overlap could influence the intensity of competition effects. In homogeneous soil, the distributions of individual roots are usually random, although significant deviations have been found (Litav & Harper, 1967; Baldwin & Tinker, 1972).

Although their spatial distribution may make some roots redundant for the uptake of mobile nutrients in sole crops, this is not true in intercrops. If the components have similar root properties, the mobile nutrient in the volume of the root-system overlap is shared in proportion to the root lengths of the components present in that volume (Andrews & Newman, 1970; Baldwin et al., 1972). Since degree of overlap between components' root-systems determines the intensity of competition effects (Cable, 1969; Trenbath, 1975b), a knowledge of the distribution and density patterns of the roots of intercrop components becomes important. The variation of form of root system, between species (Cannon, 1949) and between varieties of the same species (Raper & Barber, 1970a; McClure & Harvey, 1962), has been studied by a range of methods (Baldwin et al., 1971; Ellis & Barnes, 1973); a good correlation is often observed between root abundance and uptake activity (Nye & Foster, 1961; Barley, 1970).

As with competition for light, it is possible to recognize some characteristics likely (at least in certain circumstances) to contribute to success in competition for water and nutrients. These include: early, fast penetration of the soil (Pavlychenko & Harrington, 1934; Harris, 1967; McCown & Williams, 1968); high root density (Andrews & Newman, 1970); high root/shoot ratio (Idris & Milthorpe, 1966); high root length/root weight (Harris, 1967; Olsen & Kemper, 1968); a high proportion of the root system actively growing (Slatyer, 1967; Barley, 1970; Andrews & Newman, 1970); long root hairs (Dittmer, 1949; Drew & Nye, 1969; Barley, 1970); and a high uptake potential for the nutrient (Idris & Milthorpe, 1966; Barrow et al., 1967; Nye & Tinker, 1969; Raper & Barber, 1970b; Bowen, 1973). Earlier uptake, whatever the mechanism, seems to be the key to success in competition for mobile nutrients (Ponnamperuma, 1965; Kawano et al., 1974) and water (Cohen, 1970; Troughton, 1974). Luxury consumption, i.e. uptake with minimal or inefficient utilization, may also confer a competitive advantage (Blaser & Brady, 1950; Walker & Adams, 1958; Cohen, 1970).

Since specialization of a genotype for success in competition for soil factors, for instance by increased root/shoot ratio, may imply a loss of prospects in competition for light, a change from conditions of low soil fertility (with intense root competition) to conditions of high soil fertility (with intense shoot competition) seems likely to produce reversals of dominance in intercrops. Thus, in mixtures of components adapted to soils of different nutrient status, the species or genotypes adapted to low nutrient soils have been found to be the more aggressive on such soils, both where competition for light may have affected the result (van den Bergh & Elberse, 1962; Ramakrishnan, 1970) and also where it was ruled out (Snaydon, 1971). Where competition for light occurs as well as for nutrients, nutrient additions will give especially strong reversals of dominance because the shoot growth of species adapted to high nutrient conditions usually responds more to increased nutrient supplies than does that of species adapted to low nutrient conditions (Snaydon & Bradshaw, 1961; Bradshaw et al., 1964; Asher & Loneragan, 1967). It is therefore hardly surprising that the relative aggressiveness of a genotype in a given mixture varies greatly from crop to crop in responses to environmental conditions (Trenbath, 1974c).

Competition for water and nutrients will have two main types of effect on the less successful component of an intercrop. First, within the soil, the roots of the inferior component may develop less on the side(s) towards plants of the more aggressive component (Baldwin & Tinker, 1972); within-component competition for soil factors has a similar effect (Haynes & Sayre, 1956). Because roots grow more slowly in soil depleted of water (Klute & Peters, 1969) or of nutrients (Duncan & Ohlrogge, 1958), root systems of plants at low density or in row intercrops may tend to avoid each other (Rogers & Head, 1969; T. B. Paltridge, 1971, personal communication; Baldwin & Tinker, 1972). Adaptive effects in an unsuccessful competitor for soil factors may include increased capacity for uptake by roots (increased nutrient demand, Nye & Tinker, 1969; and increased root suction, Gardner, 1960), greater exudation of substances able to mobilize deficient nutrients (Brown & Ambler, 1973), or increased root elongation in the case of nitrogen deficiency (Bosemark, 1954). If one part of the root system is in depleted soil, the remaining part shows compensatory activity and vigor (Litav & Wolovitch, 1971; Crossett et al., 1975). Second, on the whole-plant scale, plants affected by competition for soil factors are likely to show an increased root/shoot ratio (Crist & Stout, 1929; Weaver & Clements, 1938). Competition for water may lead to wilting and growth depression due to water-stress (Salter & Goode, 1967; Slatyer, 1967), and competition for nutrients may lead to visible symptoms of mineral deficiency, reduced content of the competed-for element (Donald, 1958; Snaydon, 1971), and physiological impairment (Murata, 1969; Natr, 1972). This physiological handicap usually leads to the worse-affected component being yet further handicapped by the positive feedback process described below in the section on interaction of processes.

If it is only the deficiency of some soil factor in a suppressed mixture component that is responsible for its yield depression, it should be possible, providing this component is not shorter than the other, to so augment the supply of the factor that this component's yield is restored to the level of a sole crop. This has been achieved experimentally in several crops where the depression was due to weeds (Blackman & Templeman, 1938; Myers & Lipsett, 1958; Nieto & Staniforth, 1961) or to added plants of a second crop (Kurtz et al., 1952). The effect can be shown diagrammatically (but non-rigorously) using the approach of Myers and Lipsett (1958) and Welbank (1961b) to explain the effect of added weeds. We take the curve of Figure 5

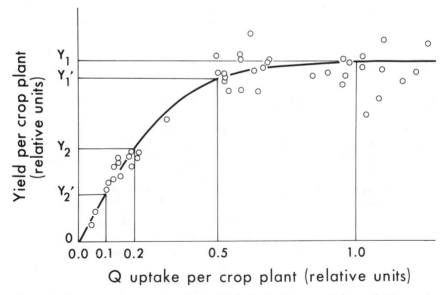

Figure 5. Crop response to uptake (absorption) of a limiting growth factor Q. The uptake of Q needed to give maximum yield is taken as 1 unit. The curve is based on the plotted data of Stanford et al. (1973) concerning wheat biomass and nitrogen uptake. For yields below half the maximum, the relationship is close to linear through the origin.

as the per-plant yield response of a crop to uptake of Q, a factor subject to competition, where uptake has been varied by application of Q at a constant crop density. For illustrative purposes, we make two simplifying assumptions: (i) that the same curve is obtained by varying the density at a constant level of Q application and (ii) that all the Q present in the soil of a plot is taken up by the plants growing on it at all levels of application used. Consider a weed-free crop at density $D1$; Q has been added to the soil to bring the 0.2 units of Q per crop plant present in the unfertilized soil up to 1.0 unit, and the (per-plant) crop yield is Y_1 (Fig. 5). If now weeds (or another component) of growth habit and competitive ability identical to those of the crop are also present at $D1$, the Q present will be evenly shared between crop and weed. The crop's Q uptake will be 0.5 units and its yield will be Y_1'. Application to the soil of 1.0 unit of Q will compensate for the loss to the weed and restore the crop yield to Y_1. On the original unfertilized soil, weeds (again at $D1$) will reduce the crop's uptake from 0.2 to 0.1 units with a corresponding depression of yield from Y_2 to Y_2'. Here, only an extra 0.2 units of Q need be applied to the weedy crop to restore the yield to the weed-free level.

Besides this yield restoration, two further principles can be illustrated with this system. First, judging by Figure 5, an application of 0.8 units of Q will give a larger yield increase $(Y_2' - Y_1')$ in the weedy crop than in the weed-free crop $(Y_2 - Y_1)$. Weedy crops indeed have been found to be more responsive than clean crops to applications of a competed-for nutrient (Blackman & Templeman, 1938; Nieto & Staniforth, 1961). Of course, this greater response is at a lower yield level. The second principle, which is difficult to verify experimentally, may help to identify the factor most subject to competition. Yield reductions due to a given density of weeds (or added second crop) are often greater when soil fertility is low than when it is high (Russell et al., 1942; Stahler, 1948; Nieto & Staniforth, 1961; Kurtz et al., 1952). With this in mind, arguing from a typical response curve (Fig. 5), Welbank (1961b) suggested that if a single soil factor can be found which at an increased level of supply can relieve a competition effect, then competition for that factor is implicated in the production of the effect. In Figure 5, $(Y_1 - Y_1')$ is clearly less than $(Y_2 - Y_2')$ and so the depression of Y_2' below Y_2 would be presumed to be due to competition for Q. Although this principle is often invoked in the interpretation of mixture experiments, no rigorous demonstration of its wide applicability has been made. In fact, its general validity is doubtful because increasing the supply of a limited soil factor is likely to lead to competition for light which, depending on the forms of the shoot systems (unless they are separated by partitions), could produce either a greater or lesser depression of the component suppressed at the low nutrient level. The application of the principle to competition for light (Edwards & Allard, 1963) seems however supported by the predicted reduction of competition effect by the higher light level in Figure 4c.

The success of a component in competition for one soil factor usually leads to its enhanced absorption of other soil factors (Litav & Seligman,

1970; Hall, 1974); if the availability of these factors is not high, competition may then occur for them also. This is often found in mixed pastures and mixtures of legume and nonlegume species. On low-nitrogen soils the non-legume is often either suppressed (Stern & Donald, 1962a) or has little ad-vantage (MacLeod & Bradfield, 1963), but on high nitrogen soils the strong growth response of the nonlegume usually causes it to dominate the legume by shading it (Trumble & Shapter, 1937; Stern & Donald, 1962a). The vigor-ously growing nonlegume (usually a grass) takes up large amounts of nutri-ents such as phosphorus, potassium and sulfur [the last two sometimes with luxury consumption (Blaser & Brady, 1950; Walker & Adams, 1958)], and the legume may suffer deficiency on soils low in these. The effects of this combined competition for light and P, K, or S can sometimes be mitigated by appropriate fertilizer applications (Trumble & Shapter, 1937; Blaser & Brady, 1950; MacLeod & Bradfield, 1963; Walker & Adams, 1958; MacLeod, 1965).

No investigation has yet clearly implicated competition for oxygen al-though the possibility exists. Except in very wet soils, diffusion of molecular oxygen seems to be sufficient to supply the respiratory needs of roots (Grable, 1966; Greenwood, 1969) although the topic is controversial (Mc-Intyre, 1970).

Allelopathy

Allelopathy is "any direct or indirect harmful effect that one plant has on another through the production of chemical compounds that escape into the environment" (Rice, 1974; Grümmer, 1955). The wide range of phyto-toxins present in plants (del Moral & Cates, 1971; Whittaker & Feeny, 1971) shows that toxins could possibly be released from many species. Indeed, root leachates from eight commonly associated pasture species chosen with-out regard to prior evidence of allelopathic activity all caused significant in-hibition of growth when applied to plants of the same eight species (Newman & Rovira, 1975). It seems possible therefore that some species or crop vari-eties may be unsuitable as intercrop components or shade trees because they produce toxins.

According to the above definition, allelopathic substances (allelochemi-cals) have inhibitory effects, but negative allelopathy could occur, e.g. through the release of growth-stimulating hormones (Tukey, 1970). Appar-ent stimulation due to a water-borne substance was reported in a series of field experiments using row-intercropped rice varieties (Roy, 1960). By com-mon consent, the release of nitrogenous compounds from species harboring symbiotic N-fixing microorgansims is not considered to be a form of allelo-pathy. As regards specificity of action, allelochemicals may either inhibit more the growth of plants of species other than the producer species (allo-inhibition, Newman & Rovira, 1975) or inhibit more strongly plants of the producer species itself (auto-inhibition). The active substance may be released as such from some plant organ (true allelopathy) or be released as a precursor which is transformed into an active substance by more-or-less closely associated microorganisms (functional allelopathy, Trenbath, 1977).

Research into allelopathy has aroused some controversy because experiments have often given conflicting results (Trenbath, 1974c). Some of the disagreements between authors may be related to genetic or environmentally-induced variation in rates of production of allelochemicals (Grümmer in de Wit, 1960; Groner, 1974; Hale et al., 1971; Rice, 1974), but even if this is so, it is difficult or impossible within a nonsterile system to prove conclusively that true allelopathy is operating (McPherson & Muller, 1969; Trenbath, 1977). Three types of allelopathic interaction will be described.

A first source of allelochemicals is the living leaves of the producer plant. The substances may be simply leached from the leaves by rain (McPherson & Muller, 1969; Bode, 1958; Groner, 1974), they may collect in fog-drip (del Moral & Muller, 1969), may volatilize (del Moral & Muller, 1970), or may fall to the ground in the frass of leaf-eating insects (B. R. Trenbath, unpublished). In this latter case, frass from Chrysomelid insects feeding on *Eucalyptus globulus* leaves reduced the germination rate of mustard seeds (*Brassica* sp.) to less than one-tenth of that in water controls and was, weight-for-weight, three times more powerful as an inhibitor of germination than the most powerful of eight preparations involving the original leaves.

A second source of allelochemicals is the living roots. A considerable quantity of organic substances, more than 2 to 12% of the total gross photosynthate (Grodzinsky, 1974b), is lost as exudates from the roots of plants. The exudates comprise a wide range of substances, many of which are biologically active (Rovira, 1969). Organic molecules can move between neighboring herbaceous plants (Ivanov, 1962) and can move more than 9 m between trees of different species (Woods, 1970). Species of which living roots have been shown to exert allelopathic inhibitions through exudates include walnut (*Juglans nigra*) and cucumber (*Cucumis sativus*) (allotoxic, Massey, 1925; Putnam & Duke, 1974); *Grevillea robusta* (autotoxic, Webb et al., 1967); and peach (*Prunus persica*) (both auto- and allo-toxic, Hirano & Morioka, 1964). The last case (peach) requires microorganisms to convert a nontoxic precursor into an active toxin (Patrick, 1955), and is thus an example of functional allelopathy. It also provides an example of a species which suffers replant problems (soil fatigue, Grodzinsky, 1974a; Rice, 1974). Another type of functional allelopathy is illustrated by a low shrub, heather (*Calluna vulgaris*), the roots of which produce a substance which inhibits the symbiotic mycorrhizae of spruce (*Picea abies*) thereby preventing growth (Robinson, 1972). The effect of inhibition of a symbiotic microorganism is therefore hardly distinguishable from an effect due to direct action between higher plants.

A third source of allelochemicals is the dead and decaying parts of plants. Substances from this source could affect young plants of crops planted between mature plants (relay cropping) or into the stubble (sequential cropping) of the preceding crop. The accumulation of leaf litter of some species changes the microflora of the surface soil under mature trees in such a way that seedlings of the same species will not grow in it, e.g. *Eucalyptus pilularis* (Florence & Crocker, 1962) and *Sequoia sempervirens* (Florence, 1965). If the apparent autotoxicity in *E. pilularis* is due, as suggested by Evans et al. (1967), to a commonly associated microorganism, then this relationship between the mature trees and seedlings is one of functional allelopathy. Further examples of this type of allelopathy concern decaying stubble (wheat, Kimber, 1973), rhizomes (*Agropyron repens,* Welbank, 1961a), and roots (peach, Patrick, 1955). Observed plant reactions to functional allelopathy are likely to be the result of the action of a spectrum of substances, some stimulatory and some inhibitory, which are produced by the various microorganism populations involved (Yurchak & Seredyuk, 1974).

Interaction of Processes

In young agricultural crops, per-plant absorption rates of not one but several growth factors may be suboptimal. After interference between plants further lowers absorption rates (relative to those in isolated plants), competition for these factors and possibly others will begin. In addition, allelopathy may occur at any stage. A statement made earlier for soil factors can now be generalized: if a plant individual or a component of an intercrop absorbs less than its share of one competed-for growth factor, it is likely to acquire a correspondingly small share of *all* growth factors (Donald, 1958; Milthorpe, 1961). A plant with an unusually short shoot in a dense sole crop will experience an especially unfavorable light regime; the resulting especially scarce supply of photosynthate will lead to a low root/shoot ratio (see the earlier section on competition for light and CO_2). The relatively small root, in its turn, will compete even less effectively for soil factors than its shoot is competing for light, and so the shoot will become still less efficient through lack of water and nutrients. This system of positive feedback will cause slow-growing individuals, or indeed whole components of intercrops, to be suppressed especially fast if competition is for a series of growth factors (Donald, 1958, 1963; Milthorpe, 1961). An illustration of this important effect appears to be provided by an experiment where plants of cultivated oats (*Avena sativa*) were grown in plots with four species added at two densities (Trenbath & Harper, 1973). In the replicate with the shallowest soil, the competition effects (Fig. 6c) were about four times greater than they were in the replicate on the deepest soil (Fig. 6a); the replicate with intermediate soil depth showed effects of intermediate intensity (Fig. 6b). Although competition must have been principally for light (LAIs were up to 14), relatively slight shortages of water and/or nutrients towards the end of growth greatly amplified the dominance relationships established earlier by competition for light.

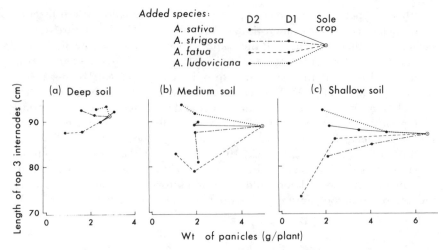

Figure 6. Amplification of competition effects due to the addition of competition for soil
   factors to a situation where there is already competition for light. The points show
   the performance of *Avena sativa* in sole crop (open circles) and with three added
   species (and itself) at increasing densities $D1$ and $D2$ (filled circles). The points refer
   to performance in individual plots in replicates sited on soil of varying depth: (a)
   deep; (b) medium depth; (c) shallow. (Redrawn from Trenbath & Harper, 1973.)

To test whether competition develops first for light or for soil factors in
a mixed intercrop, ingenious attempts have been made to separate the effects
of competition between shoots and competition between roots by experiments in specially prepared containers with partitions (references in Trenbath, 1974c). Although continuous swards can be used (Eagles, 1972) to
imitate closely the light relationships found in the field, the aggregation of
roots on the surface of the container (23% of the total length in a pot experiment of Brewster & Tinker, 1970) introduces some unreality and must bias
the results in favor of the generally observed earlier root competition. While
it is usually difficult to discover in the field which sort of competition begins
first, a safe generalization is that a relatively scarce supply of a growth factor
promotes the earlier onset of competition for that factor. Hence, competition for light will start first if soil conditions are near optimal, but competition for soil factors will start first if light levels are high and soil factors so
deficient that the LAI develops slowly.

EFFECTS OF PLANT INTERACTIONS ON YIELDS OF COMPONENTS
OF INTERCROPS

Land Equivalent Ratio

To help judge whether a series of m crops should be grown as an m-
component intercrop rather than as sole crops, the concept of Land Equiva-

lent Ratio (LER) has been used (IRRI, 1974, 1975). If the overall yield, y_i, of the i-th component from a unit area of intercrop is expressed as a fraction of the yield, y_{ii}, of that component grown as a sole crop over the same area, the LER of the intercrop is given as a sum of the fractions:

$$\text{LER} = \sum_{i=1}^{m} \frac{y_i}{y_{ii}}$$

If this LER is unity, the various yields harvested from the intercrop could have been obtained from the unit area planted to sole crops, each occupying an appropriate fraction of the total area. When LER = 1, the overall yield per unit area of intercrop is never greater than that of the most productive sole crop.

If however the LER exceeds unity and the sole crop yields are identical, an LER of $1 + x$ implies that the intercrop outyields the sole crops by $100x\%$. If x is large enough, such a yield advantage can provide a clear justification for intercropping. On the other hand, for a given x, if the sole crop yields are sufficiently different, the LER will not be large enough to imply an overall yield advantage for the intercrop. In such a case, intercropping may still be advantageous for, with LER = $1 + x$, an extra x units of area of sole cropping would be necessary to produce the array of yields, $y_1, y_2, ..., y_m$, obtained from the unit area of intercrop. If the proportions of the different types of yield in this array are acceptable, as also are any increased costs of managing an intercrop, then intercropping may have an advantage.

If observed LER values are to be used in formulating cropping policies, it seems important to explore how various values can arise. This is attempted in the following sections.

Intercrops where LER = 1

To avoid an effect on LER due simply to plant density the intercrop and the sole crops with which it is to be compared may be grown at a uniform overall density.[5] The LER value calculated will then be the Relative Yield Total (RYT) of de Wit and van den Bergh (1965). This measure of mixture productivity has been extensively used by pasture agronomists in two-component mixed intercrops (Trenbath, 1974c).

Where competition is for a single growth factor Q, the value of RYT (or constant-density LER) has a simple interpretation, especially in the case of a 1:1 two-component intercrop. If the deficient supply of Q is limiting yields, the biomass yield response of an individual plant to the quantity of Q absorbed will be nearly linear at low levels of absorption. This can be demon-

---

[5]Density is still effectively uniform if n_1 plants of one component, n_2 plants of another component, . . .(etc.) are everywhere taken to be equivalent to 1 plant of some component chosen as the standard.

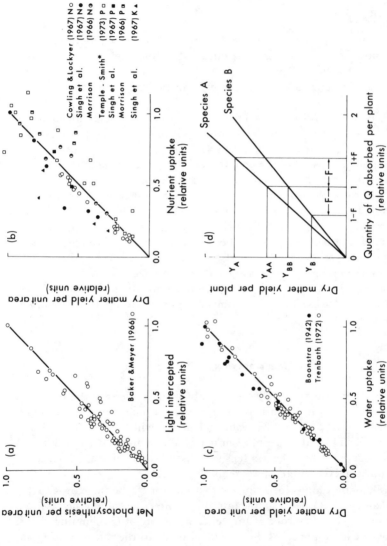

Figure 7. Responses (a–c) of crops to quantities of limiting growth factors absorbed, and a model (d), based on these responses, of the biomass yields of the two components in a 1:1 intercrop. In each of the graphs showing experimental data, the quantity of factor absorbed and the crop response are scaled so that the observation with the highest response lay well off the linear regression line, the observation with the highest absorption was taken instead.) In (b), observations suggesting nutrient toxicity effects have been excluded. For explanation of (d), see text. Figure 7d is redrawn from Trenbath, 1974c (*M. G. Temple-Smith, 1973. Some factors responsible for differences between plant species in absorption and utilization of phosphate. Ph.D. Thesis, University of Tasmania).

strated for sole crops in cases of limiting light, nitrogen, and water (Fig. 7a–c), and may sometimes be true for other nutrients. It has been shown to be true also in intercrops under conditions of limiting light (Santhirasegaram & Black, 1968b), nitrogen (Kawano & Tanaka, 1967), and water.[6] If we consider a case where Q is a deficient mobile soil factor like nitrogen or water, the uptake (absorption) in a 1:1 intercrop and comparable sole-crops of the two components will be near to complete (nitrogen, Donald, 1951; water, Black, 1968) and therefore approximately the same in all three types of stand. Let this quantity taken up represent unit uptake of Q. If supplies are limiting growth, the biomasses of two crop species A and B will respond to Q uptake with the strict proportionality shown in Figure 7d; in the Figure, A uses Q more efficiently than does B in the production of biomass and so the sole-crop (per-plant) yield of A, Y_{AA}, is greater than that of B, Y_{BB}. In the intercrop, if plants of A are more effective in competition for Q, per-plant uptake by A increases by a proportion F over the unit uptake in its sole crop. The per-plant uptake by B will correspondingly decrease by a proportion F below that in its sole crop (Fig. 7d). Given strict proportionality in the responses to Q (Fig. 7a–c), the per-plant yields, Y_A and Y_B, of A and B in the intercrop will both differ from the corresponding sole crop yields by the same proportion, namely F. If the per-plant yields in the intercrop are given by

$$Y_A = Y_{AA}(1 + F)$$

$$Y_B = Y_{BB}(1 - F)$$

and the RYT in this two-component 1:1 intercrop is given (de Wit & van den Bergh, 1965; Trenbath, 1974c) by

$$\text{RYT} = \sum_{i=1}^{2} \frac{y_i}{y_{ii}} = \frac{y_A}{y_{AA}} + \frac{y_B}{y_{BB}} = \frac{1}{2}\left(\frac{Y_A}{Y_{AA}} + \frac{Y_B}{Y_{BB}}\right)$$

then

$$\text{RYT} = \frac{1}{2}(1 + F + 1 - F) = 1.$$

Given the simple competitive situation described by Figure 7d, the expected RYT (i.e. LER at constant density) is therefore unity. Since the observed RYT's in two component intercrops (excluding those which are legume-nonlegume mixtures) are usually close to unity in Figure 8 (van den Bergh, 1968; Trenbath, 1974c), the situation evidently often conforms to Figure 7d. Given an intercorrelation among the quantities of different factors absorbed, Q could be a complex of factors. When competition between similar components is only for light, the theoretical expectation of RYT is also close to unity (Trenbath, 1974b).

---

[6]Trenbath, 1972. The productivity of varietal mixtures.

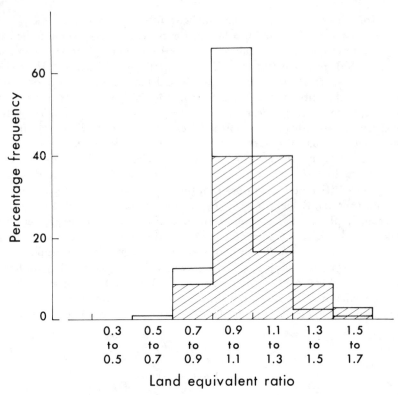

Figure 8. Comparison of the distributions of values of land equivalent ratio of mixtures with and without legume-nonlegume combinations: hatched, legume + nonlegume (35 values, data of Roberts & Olson, 1942; Aberg et al., 1943; Donald, 1946; Williams, 1962); unhatched, components either both legume or nonlegume (572 values, data in Trenbath, 1974c). The LER's are calculated using only data from experiments where intercrop and sole crops were grown at the same density; the LER values are therefore relative yield totals.

When LER is measured without total plant density being constant in intercrop and sole crops, the value obtained may well vary with the general density level of the experiment. Consider two sole crops of the similar species A and B, each at $D1$, and a 1:1 intercrop made by interplanting the two species, each at $D1$, to make the overall density ($D2$) equal to twice $D1$. If $D1$ is a rather low density, the amount of space available per plant (analogous to per-plant absorption of Q) in the sole crop of either species will be large; it will not be used efficiently in the production of the per-plant yields, Y_{AA} and Y_{BB}. Assume that the species' yields respond to available space in exactly the same way (Fig. 9), and so $Y_{AA} = Y_{BB} = Y_1$. In the mixture at D_2, the halved quantity of space per plant will almost certainly be used more efficiently. Given equal competitive ability for space (de Wit, 1960), the yields of both A and B will be Y_2, i.e. $Y_A = Y_B = Y_2$. The area which produced Y_1 in the sole crops will produce what Figure 9 shows to be much more, namely $2Y_2$, in the mixture. If now the competitive ability of A is

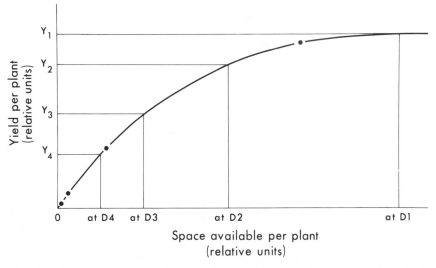

Figure 9. Typical response of per-plant biomass yield to spacing (data of wheat, Puckridge & Donald, 1967). Each density in the sequence $D1$ to $D4$ is twice the previous density.

greater than that of B, then $Y_A > Y_2$ and $Y_B < Y_2$. In either case, however, providing A does not use all of B's space, the LER value is greater than unity. In contrast, if the density of the sole crops is higher, say $D3$ which is four times $D1$, and the density of the intercrop is double this, $D4$ which is eight times $D1$, Figure 9 shows that over this density range per-plant yields are close to being strictly proportional to available space. In the case where competitive abilities are equal, $Y_A = Y_B = Y_4$, but, because $2Y_4$ is hardly greater than Y_3, yield per area is hardly greater in the mixture than in the $D3$ sole crops. Where one species competes more effectively for space, the situation is close to that represented by Figure 7d. In either case, however, at this higher density level the LER is approximately equal to unity.

The above example suggests that density is important in measurements of LER. The definition (IRRI, 1974; B. T. Samson and R. R. Harwood, 1975. The effect of plant population density and row arrangement on productivity of corn-rice intercrop. Presented at 6th Annual Convention of the Crop Science Society of Philippines, Bacolod City, 8–10 May 1975) of LER requires that the sole crops used in the calculation be at their optimum densities but few LER measurements have so far made use of sole crop data from the necessary range of densities. Since there is an obvious danger of confounding the effects of beneficial interactions between components with a simple response to changed density, a critical measurement of LER involves a demonstration that the sole crop density used is the optimum. It could however be argued that if the performance of an intercrop at some arbitrary density is to be compared with that of sole crops at their optima, it would be more correct to use intercrop performance measured at the intercrop's own optimum density. Since such requirements would make LER measurements laborious, it may be easier to use the constant density LER (RYT) where the objective is simply to identify beneficial crop combinations (Trenbath, 1976b). Without the certainty that the sole crop density is optimal, LER's involving varying densities could be misleading (see footnote 5).

When the LER value (measured with either varying or constant density) is unity in one set of proportions of intercrop components, it is likely to be unity also for a wide range of proportions. This has been exhaustively demonstrated by van den Bergh (1968) for many mixed intercrops of pasture species. With constant LER = 1, as with RYT = 1 (van den Bergh, 1968; Trenbath, 1974c), the overall yield of the intercrop at any proportion lies between the yields of the most and least productive sole crops of the components. Thus, if the ranked yields y_{ii} of the m sole crops corresponding to an m-component intercrop are in descending order $S_1, S_2, ..., S_m$, then LER = 1 implies that the overall intercrop yield $I = \Sigma y_i$ lies between S_1 and S_m (more strictly, $S_1 \geqslant I \geqslant S_m$). In a two-component intercrop ($m = 2$), if the component with the higher-yielding sole crop is the more aggressive, then I is greater than the average, $\bar{S}$, of the yields of the sole crops, i.e. $S_1 \geqslant I > \bar{S} = (S_1 + S_2)/2$. Similarly, in a multicomponent intercrop ($m \geqslant 3$), if the components with the higher-yielding sole crops are the more aggressive, the I value will lie between $\bar{S} = (\Sigma S_i)/m$ and S_1 (strictly, $S_1 \geqslant I > \bar{S}$). Where the component(s) with the higher-yielding sole crops are the less aggressive, the I value will be below $\bar{S}$, i.e. $\bar{S} > I \geqslant S_m$. If the components are all equally aggressive or are at too low a density to interact, the contributions of the components to I will depend only on their proportions p_i in the intercrop and their yields y_{ii} in sole crops. Thus, their contributions here are their *expected* yields, $p_1 y_{11}, p_2 y_{22}, ..., p_m y_{mm}$ so that the expected intercrop yield I_E is $\Sigma p_i y_{ii}$. However, at the densities used in agriculture, interaction normally occurs and, through competition and possibly also occasionally allelopathy, the I value usually deviates from I_E.

To indicate the effects on intercrop yields of interaction between components, Figure 10f–j diagrammatically shows five main ways in which the yields y_i of the two components of a binary intercrop may change when the proportions of the components vary. The types are illustrated (Fig. 11a–e) by experimental data. Except in the anomalous type 3, the lines through the points were calculated using the model of de Wit (1960) and Thomas (1970). We will consider here types 1 to 3 which have LER = 1. In type 1 there is no apparent interaction ($I = I_E = \Sigma p_i y_{ii}$). In type 2, component A is the more aggressive; using the model of de Wit (1960), the intercrop yield is predicted as

$$I = \sum_{i=1}^{m} \frac{b_i p_i y_{ii}}{\sum_{j=1}^{m} b_j p_j}$$

where each term in the summation is the yield y_i of the i-th component, and b_i is the "activity coefficient", a measure of aggressiveness, of the i-th com-

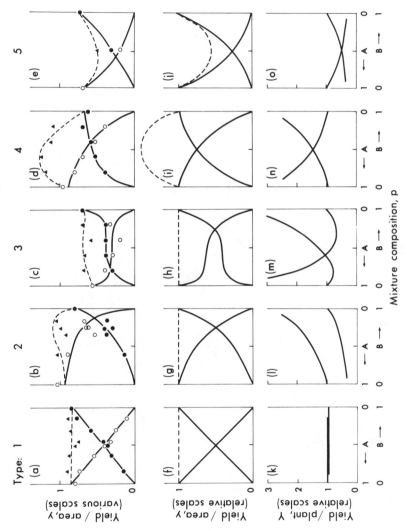

Figure 10. Typical patterns of interaction in two-component intercrops of varied proportion at constant density. Examples using experimental data are due to: (a, b) van den Bergh (1968), the components were grasses; (c, d) Ennik (1969), the components were in each case a grass and a legume; (e) Ahlgren & Aamodt (1939), two grasses. Graphs (f–j) give idealized per-area yields, and (k–o) give corresponding per-plant yields. Solid lines, components' yields; broken lines, mixture yields.

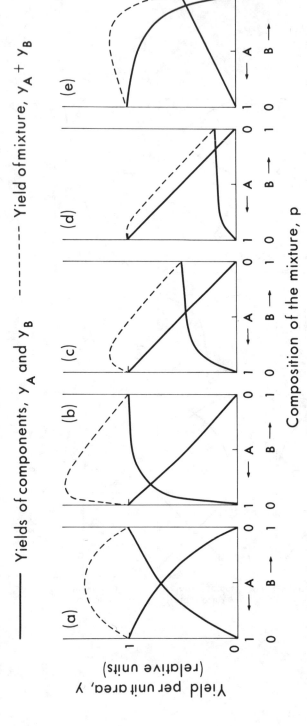

Figure 11. Effect of differences in the relative aggressiveness and sole crop yields of the components on intercrop yield. All yield curves were generated using the de Wit (1960) model. In all the 1:1 mixtures the LER = 1.3, but overyielding by the intercrop is only found at this proportion in (a, b, and e).

ponent species relative to that of the first (hence, $b_1 = 1$). This type 2 is by far the commonest, and much experimental and theoretical work has confirmed the applicability of de Wit's model to it (van den Bergh, 1968; Trenbath, 1974b, c, 1976b). In type 3, the activity coefficients vary with proportion; each species is the more aggressive when it is at low proportion in the mixture. Few examples of this type have been observed (Ennik, 1969; Putwain & Harper, 1972), no model is available to predict the component's yields and explanations can only be tentative (Trenbath, 1976b). Below the examples using per-area yield (y_i) are shown the corresponding responses of per-plant yield Y_i to mixture composition (Fig. 10k-o). Presented in relative units, the values were obtained as $Y_i = y_i/p_i$.

Intercrops where LER $>$ 1

It is assumed here that the LER has either been measured at constant density or that, if not, a density response has been ruled out.

Figure 10d and i represents the type 4 case where LER $>$ 1 and where there is overyielding $(I > S_1)$; in the figure, the components are of equal aggressiveness and sole crop yield. Figure 11 shows how differences of relative aggressiveness and sole crop yield in the components affect the degree of overyielding achieved by varying the proportions of the components in intercrops; all have identical LER's (= 1.30) when measured in 1:1 mixtures. As already explained, even where there is no overyielding, LER $>$ 1 may nevertheless indicate an advantage for an intercrop. It seems misleading however to describe an intercrop with LER $>$ 1 as having a higher "productivity" than any component's sole crop (IRRI, 1974, 1975) for in the usually accepted terms of overall weight of yield per unit area (Richards & Bevege, 1967), this is not necessarily true (e.g. the 1:1 mixtures in Fig. 11c, d).

Values of LER exceeding unity may be produced in many ways but the most common is that where the intercrop components exploit the environmental supplies of growth factors in differing ways. Such complementary use of resources is "annidation" (Ludwig, 1950). The various forms of annidation so far recognized will be described (see also Trenbath, 1974c).

ANNIDATION IN SPACE

The leaf canopies of intercrop components may occupy different vertical layers with the tallest component having foliage tolerant of strong light and high evaporative demand, and the shorter component(s) having foliage requiring shade and/or relatively high humidity. This advantageous combination is used in north African desert oases where three layers are often planted, e.g. date palm (*Phoenix dactylifera*), citrus, and vegetables (Baldy, 1963). The use of shade trees for tropical crops such as cocoa (*Theobroma cacao*) and tea (*Camellia sinensis*) has the same effect (Aiyer, 1949; Hadfield, 1974).

In intercrops where the taller component has steeply inclined leaves and the shorter component has prostrate leaves, there is a possibility of LER > 1 (Rhodes, 1970; Trenbath, 1974b, c).

On patchy soils, mixed intercrops of cereals are sometimes able to give more uniform yields than sole crops because in each sort of patch the failure of one crop is compensated by the greater aggressiveness, and therefore yield, of the other (de Wit, 1960).

Exploitation by intercrop components of different layers of the soil may lead to increased LER's (Whittington & O'Brien, 1968; Trenbath, 1975b). In the north African Oases mentioned earlier, the root systems of vegetables occupy the cultivated surface soil while the roots of trees occupy the deeper horizons (Baldy, 1963). Some degree of root stratification must be common in intercrops of dissimilar components on deep soil.

ANNIDATION WITH RESPECT TO NUTRIENTS

In intercrops of leguminous with nonleguminous species, the legume obtains much of its N by the fixation of molecular nitrogen in its nodules whereas the other component(s) exploit the NO_3^- and NH_4^+ in the soil solution. On soils deficient in available N, legume-nonlegume intercrops may achieve high LER's (e.g. up to 6.7, Ennik, 1969) and it is on such soils that legume components are most useful. Usually, however, the effect of an added legume on LER is less dramatic (Fig. 8) (de Wit et al., 1966; IRRI, 1975). The main advantage from the use of legume components is in the saving of N-fertilizer; if young rubber trees (*Hevea brasiliensis*) are intercropped with groundnuts rather than with a nonlegume, less fertilizer needs to be applied to the trees to achieve satisfactory growth rates (Pushparajah & Tan, 1970). While leguminous plants will not usually compete with other species for nitrogen, they will of course compete for other growth factors and some loss of yield in the main crop is normal (Donald & Neal-Smith, 1938; Richards & Bevege, 1967; Enyi, 1973). Other species which harbor N-fixing microorganisms are also likely to be useful in intercrops, e.g. alder (*Alnus* spp.) (Pogrebniak, 1962).

Plant species making differing demands on the nutrient pool of a site is another example of annidation. Foresters know well the advantages of growing certain tree species in "self-correcting" mixtures (Boulton & Jay, 1944). The intercropping of crop types with strongly contrasting nutrient requirements (Aiyer, 1949; Challinor, 1968) or uptake abilities (Aiyer, 1949; Vergris et al., 1973) seems likely to lead to high LER's but this has not been demonstrated. Although the ability of some species apparently to cure nutrient deficiencies in neighboring plants of other species (Bevege & Richards, 1970; Kashirad & Marschner, 1974) may not result from annidation, it deserves further investigation.

ANNIDATION IN TIME

Differences in length of growing season can lead to LER > 1 in mixed intercrops of flax and linseed (*Linum usitatissimum*) (Harper, 1968), or barley (*Hordeum vulgare*) and oats (*Avena sativa*) (Trenbath, 1974c) and of early and late potatoes (*Solanum tuberosum*) (Schepers & Sibma, 1976). When the earlier component has matured, conditions become especially favorable for the other component. A similar annidation in time is achieved in row intercrops when a new crop is relay planted among the maturing plants of the preceding one. The lack of response often found in cereals (Jensen & Federer, 1965; Green et al., 1971) to thinning during grain ripening implies that cereal plants at this stage make relatively small demands on nutrients and light. Thus, sweet potatoes (*Ipomoea batatas*) planted into rice as much as 7 weeks before the rice was mature only caused a 6 to 12% depression of yield (Chao, 1975); the data suggest that the advantage to the sweet potatoes of the extra 7 weeks growth must have been well over 60%. It would be interesting to know to what extent the relay planted crop (here sweet potato) was depressed by the maturing plants of the preceding crop. To measure this, results from a sole crop of the relay planted crop would be needed; with these data, an LER could also be calculated.

Besides annidation, there are several other ways in which interactions between intercrop components could lead to LER > 1. A series of possible physiological mechanisms will be considered first, then two physical mechanisms, and finally the response of intercrops to pests and pathogens.

VARIATION IN ALLOCATION RATIOS

The proportion of a component's dry matter that is allocated to harvestable yield may vary with the degree to which its plants are suppressed through competition with neighbors (Williams, 1964; Trenbath, 1974a). The same effect can be simulated by shading sole crops (Willey & Holliday, 1971). Two contrasting responses to suppression are shown by wheat (B. R. Trenbath, unpublished) and *Chenopodium album* (Williams, 1964) (Fig. 12a, b). The possible effect of this on intercrop productivity is shown by the following example. Suppose that, in a range of intercrops of varying proportion, biomass yields of two components are calculated using the well validated model of de Wit (1960). If the curve of Figure 12a is applied to all biomass yields, the resulting grain yield graph (Fig. 12c) deviates only slightly from the frequently found pattern of Figure 10b. If the curve of Figure 12b is used instead, the result is similar (Fig. 12d). If now the curve of Figure 12a is applied to the biomass of the more aggressive component *A* and the curve of Figure 12b to the less aggressive component *B*, mixtures can overyield significantly in grain weight (Fig. 12e, maximum LER = 1.39). In contrast, if

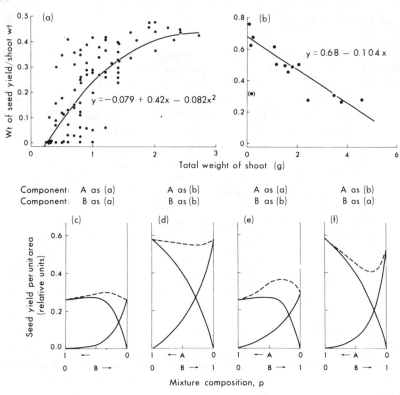

Figure 12. Two types of response of reproductive efficiency (seed yield/shoot weight) to suppression through competition, and the theoretical consequences of these responses for yield of seed from intercrops. (1) Wheat (B. R. Trenbath, unpublished); (b) *Chenopodium album* (Williams, 1964). In (c–f) the relationships of (a) and (b) are applied to biomass values of the common type 2 case, Figure 10g, 1 (LER = 1). Rescaling of the yields of B, in (e) ($\times$ 0.5) and in (f) ($\times$ 2), has led to significant over- and under-yielding by the mixtures in these two examples.

the curves are applied the other way around, mixtures can underyield (Fig. 12f, minimum LER = 0.71). To identify this sort of effect, data of both biomass and marketable yield are needed. It is not known whether any observed LER deviations have been due to variation in allocation ratios but such variation could possibly be exploited.

NONPROPORTIONALITY IN THE RESPONSE TO LIMITING GROWTH FACTOR(S)

If the response curve of the suppressed component to Q uptake is convex (as in Fig. 5) over the range of absorptions found in sole crop and intercrop, it will use the factor more efficiently in the intercrop. If the response of the aggressor remains roughly linear with the line passing through the origin, there will be an overall increase in efficiency of factor utilization in the intercrops, leading to LER > 1. This type of effect may make mixtures of tall "sun" species and short "shade" species advantageous.

In cases where the supply of some factor is supra-optimal to a species as a sole crop, in an intercrop the over-supply of this factor can sometimes be corrected by a suitable companion crop. Thus, some extreme shade species actually benefit from being the "loser" in competition for light (Paner, 1975) and stands of some leguminous trees benefit from having the soil N level reduced by interplanted nitrophilous species (Pogrebniak, 1962). Although it is here excess of a factor which is limiting growth, the result of intercropping can still be interpreted using response curves.

ALLELOPATHY

If species liberate specific autotoxins, they may grow better as intercrops (Webb et al., 1967). Similarly, if genotypes liberate substances which stimulate others, mixture LER's are likely to exceed unity; the only known example concerns the rice varieties of Roy (1960). Some species used as shade trees have marked effects on the vegetation beneath. Although usually the trees and the underplanted crop seem to simply compete for the same resources (Walker et al., 1972), other types of interaction may occasionally occur. Thus, in Australia, the presence of one species of *Eucalyptus* has been said to double pasture production (Story, 1967) while other species are used in parks to suppress grass growth. Allelopathy has been invoked in both cases (Story, 1967, del Moral & Muller, 1969; Rice, 1974).

RHIZOSPHERE EFFECTS

The activity of rhizosphere and root-surface microorganisms can affect nutrient uptake and plant growth (Bowen & Rovira, 1969) and so the observation that the presence of plants of other species can change the rhizosphere flora (Christie et al., 1974) is of great importance. In the only investigation of this effect (Christie et al., 1974), biomass LER exceed unity in two independent experiments.

PHYSICAL SUPPORT

Erect-growing species may provide support for intercropped climbing species (Aiyer, 1949); the greater vertical separation of the leaves probably improves the photosynthetic effectiveness of the leaf area of the climbers (Trenbath & Angus, 1975). Nonlodging cereals usually hold up lodging-susceptible types if they are grown together in mixed intercrop but, depending on the components' proportions, lodging types may sometimes cause nonlodging ones to fall over (Trenbath, 1974c). LER deviations from unity may thus be either positive or negative.

PHYSICAL PROTECTION

Taller, robust components may provide a windbreak for more delicate components (Marshall, 1967; Brown & Rosenberg, 1970). In south Australia, citrus is intercropped with apricots (*Prunus armeniaca*) as a protection from wind; similarly, in Taiwan, young relay planted vegetables are protected by the mature rice (T. Wang, personal communication). In mixed intercrops of cereals frost-tolerant varieties may in some way protect susceptible types (Borojević & Mišić, 1962) and varieties of barley with ears at different heights may show less shattering when knocked together by wind (Clay & Allard, 1969; R. E. Clay, personal communication).

EFFECT OF PESTS AND DISEASES

In certain intercrops, the presence of pathogens (*sensu lato* = pests and disease organisms) can lead to LER > 1 and thus, possibly to overyielding. The main processes responsible for this are (i) the loss of dispersing individuals from the populations of specialized pathogens through their settling on nonhost components of the intercrop (the "fly-paper effect", Trenbath, 1975a), and (ii) compensating growth by unattacked components which strengthens the fly-paper effect. The compensation effect is more obvious and will be treated first.

If one component (*A*) of a two-component intercrop is attacked, its plants compete less effectively for resources. The increased uptake of growth factors by plants of the unattacked component (*B*) may produce enhanced growth compensating for the yield lost by *A* plants (Fig. 13a) (Reestman, 1946; Chester, 1950; Bardner & Lofty, 1971; IRRI, 1975). Considering the possible outcomes in more detail, if the attack on component *A* reduces the competitive ability of *A* plants but not their yield in sole crop, then LER ≈ 1 (Fig. 13b, c) (Sibma et al., 1964). Alternatively, if both are reduced and the *B* plants are vigorous enough to absorb all the *Q* not taken up by the *A* plants, then LER > 1 (only simulated examples can be given, see the following and Fig. 14b–e). If the *B* plants are too old when *A* plants are attacked, they will not be able to benefit from the increased availability of resources (Fig. 13d) (Klages, 1936; Sandfaer, 1970); in this case, LER ≈ 1. Similarly, compensatory growth seems less likely if growing conditions are unfavorable; this is exemplified by the corn (*Zea mays*)-rice (*Oryza sativa*) intercrop (IRRI, 1975) where, after the rice had been killed, compensation did not occur on the unfertilized plots (but did on the fertilized plots). If, prior to the attack, *B* plants are being heavily suppressed, a sudden destruction of *A* may be only partially compensated for by enhanced growth of the enfeebled *B* plants. In a pot experiment using two tomato (*Lycopersicon esculentum*) varieties and a root-knot nematode, the unattacked plants in mixed stand were still smaller than those in pure stand at the final harvest (Fig. 13c, f) (B. R. Trenbath, unpublished). The LER exceeded unity however because the vigor of the *B* plants allowed them to begin to utilize some of the *Q* left unabsorbed by the virtually destroyed *A* plants. Planting patterns with a low frequency of *A–B* interfaces (Fig. 1a, b, d, e) or a low absolute density of *B* are likely to result in incomplete compensation.

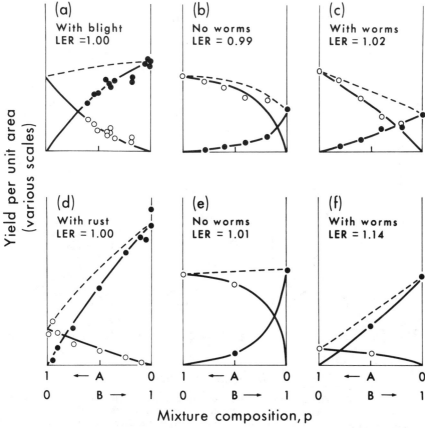

Figure 13. Effect of selective attack by disease and pests. Component A is always the attacked genotype. Data are due to: (a) Reestman (1946), attacked and unattacked
potatoes + *Phytophthora infestans* blight; (b, c) Sibma et al. (1964) oats and a resistant
barley + *Heterodera avenae* eelworm; (d) Klages (1936), susceptible and partially resistant wheat varieties + *Puccinia graminis* rust; and (e, f) B. R. Trenbath (unpublished),
biomass of susceptible and resistant tomato varieties + *Meloidogyne javanica* rootknot
nematode. Graphs a, d redrawn from de Wit (1960); graphs b, c from the author's
original paper.

The fly-paper effect is likely to operate where the dispersal phase of a
pathogen's life cycle involves passive transportation or random, undirected
movement. Here, the number of individuals contacting susceptible hosts relative to that contacting nonhosts depends on the relative abundance of exposed tissue, e.g. LAI for leaf rusts (*Puccinia* spp.), of the two kinds.
Assuming that the proportion of susceptible LAI was proportional to
the proportion of susceptible plants, Leonard (1969) successfully predicted
the growth of rust epidemics in two-component mixed intercrops (multilines) of oat varieties. This assumption however neglected any effect due
to compensatory growth. Indeed, in the treatments where two rust races
were attacking a single host, the observed rust growth rate was considerably

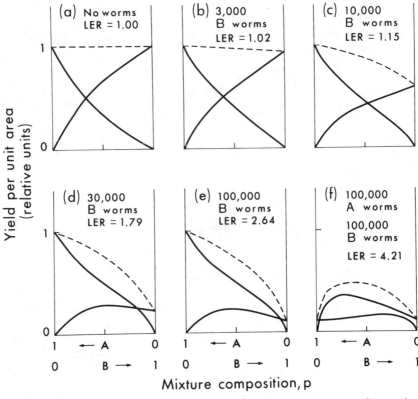

Figure 14. Predicted response of intercrops to increasing populations of a rootknot
nematode which attacks only one component. Component B is here the only attacked
component except in (f) where both A and B are attacked each by a selective nematode.

below that predicted. Since the attacked oat variety is likely to have suffered
some growth check, enhanced growth of the unattacked variety could have
strengthened the fly-paper effect.[7] Apart from the work of Leonard (1969)
and Burdon and Chilvers (1975), there have been few quantitative estimates
of the influence of the fly-paper effect and certainly no investigation of the
extent to which it is strengthened by compensatory growth. This shortage
of data makes it difficult to predict the effect of pathogens on the LER's of
intercrops.

---

[7]With this possibility in view it seems premature to explain the apparently low rust
growth rate as due to a "competitive inhibition" (Leonard, 1969) among disease races
growing on a common host. Although the genetic effects of multilines on pathogen
populations are outside the scope of this chapter, it must be emphasized that the useful-
ness of multilines is still uncertain (Trenbath, 1975a). Preliminary results of a simple
model (B. R. Trenbath, unpublished) suggest that the competitive disadvantage of a
universally-virulent "super-race", when growing with races of more limited virulence on
host mixtures, must be much greater than usually observed in order to prevent its explosive growth. Furthermore, while "induced resistance" (Johnson & Allen, 1975) has
only recently been referred to in discussions on multilines, the possibility of induced susceptibility (Brown & Sharp, 1970) needs to be considered. Instead of stabilizing varietal
boom-and-bust cycles, multilines could breed new, more virulent races of pathogens.

Where a two-component intercrop is attacked simultaneously by two selective pathogens, one on each component, LER will almost certainly exceed unity. Results obtained using a model (B. R. Trenbath, unpublished) of the tomato-nematode system referred to earlier, gave an LER of 4.21 in a 1:1 intercrop in which each variety is attacked by just one of two theoretical species of nematodes (Fig. 14f). When only one nematode species is taken to be present, even assuming full compensation in the intercrop, the model only predicts LER > 1 when the pest population is high enough to depress sole crop yield in the susceptible variety (Fig. 14a-e).

Individual pathogen species often attack preferentially those individuals in pure stands which are either unshaded and dominant, e.g. spruce budworm (*Choristoneura fumiferana*) (Wellington et al., 1950) and rust (Agrios, 1969), or shaded and suppressed, e.g. many species of insects (Graham & Knight, 1965) and of fungi (Grime, 1965). When grown in an intercrop rather than as a sole crop, all the plants of a component may reach a size equivalent to that of either dominants or suppressed plants in a corresponding sole crop (Fig. 10k-o). Although relevant data are scanty, it seems likely that, as with the behavior of plants competing for growth factors, the changes of disease susceptibility in response to the changed conditions in intercrops will ultimately be predictable from measured responses of pure cultures to modified environments.

LITERATURE CITED

Aberg, E., I. J. Johnson, and C. D. Wilsie. 1943. Associations between species of grasses and legumes. J. Am. Soc. Agron. 35:357-369.

Acock, B., J. H. M. Thornley, and J. Warren Wilson. 1970. Spatial variation of light in the canopy. p. 91-101. In I. Setlík (ed.) Prediction and measurement of photosynthetic productivity. Proceedings of the IBP/PP Technical Meeting, 1969. Wageningen, Pudoc.

Agrios, G. N. 1969. Plant pathology. Academic Press, New York.

Ahlgren, H. L., and O. S. Aamodt. 1939. Harmful root interactions as a possible explanation for effects noted between various species of grasses and legumes. J. Am. Soc. Agron. 31:982-985.

Aiyer, A. K. Y. N. 1949. Mixed cropping in India. Indian J. Agric. Sci. 19:439-543.

Allen, L. H., T. R. Sinclair, and E. R. Lemon. 1976. Radiation and microclimate relationships in multiple cropping systems. p. 171-200. In R. I. Papendick, R. A. Sanchez, and G. B. Triplett (ed.) Multiple cropping. Spec. Pub. No. 27. Am. Soc. of Agron., Madison, Wis.

Andrews, D. J., and A. H. Kassam. 1976. The importance of multiple cropping in increasing world food supplies. p. 1-10. In R. I. Papendick, P. A. Sanchez, and G. B. Triplett (ed.) Multiple cropping. Spec. Pub. No. 27. Am. Soc. of Agron., Madison, Wis.

Andrews, R. E., and E. I. Newman. 1970. Root density and competition for nutrients. Oecol. Plant. Gauthier-Villars 5:319-334.

Asher, C. J., and J. F. Loneragan. 1967. Response of plants to phosphate concentration in solution culture. I. Growth and phosphorus content. Soil Sci. 103:225-233.

Austenson, H. M., and E. N. Larter. 1969. Effect of direction of seeding on yields of barley and oats. Can. J. Plant Sci. 49:417-420.

Baker, D. N., and R. E. Meyer. 1966. Influence of stand geometry on light interception and net photosynthesis in cotton. Crop Sci. 6:15-18.

Baldwin, J. P., P. H. Nye, and P. B. Tinker. 1973. Uptake of solutes by multiple root systems from soil. III. A model for calculating the solute uptake by a randomly dispersed root system developing in a finite volume of soil. Plant Soil 38:621-635.

Baldwin, J. P., and P. B. Tinker. 1972. A method of estimating the lengths and spatial patterns of two interpenetrating root systems. Plant Soil 37:209–213.

Baldwin, J. P., P. B. Tinker, and F. H. C. Marriott. 1971. The measurement of length and distribution of onion roots in the field and the laboratory. J. Appl. Ecol. 8: 543–554.

Baldwin, J. P., P. B. Tinker, and P. H. Nye. 1972. Uptake of solutes by multiple root systems from soil. II. The theoretical effects of root density and pattern on uptake of nutrients from soil. Plant Soil 36:693–708.

Baldy, C. 1963. Cultures associées et productivité de l'eau. Ann. Agron. 14:489–534.

Barber, S. A. 1962. A diffusion and mass-flow concept of soil nutrient availability. Soil Sci. 93:39–49.

Bardner, R., and J. R. Lofty. 1971. The distribution of eggs, larvae and plants within crops attacked by wheat bulb fly *Leptohylemyia coarctata* (Fall.). J. Appl. Ecol. 8: 683–686.

Barley, K. P. 1970. The configuration of the root system in relation to nutrient uptake. Adv. Agron. 22:159–201.

Barrow, N. J., C. J. Asher, and P. G. Ozanne. 1967. Nutrient potential and capacity. III. Minimum value of potassium potential for availability to *Trifolium subterraneum* in soil and in solution culture. Aust. J. Agric. Res. 18:55–62.

Bergh, J. P. van den. 1968. An analysis of yields of grasses in mixed and pure stands. Versl. Landbouwkd. Onderz. 714:1–71.

Bergh, J. P. van den, and W. T. Elberse. 1962. Competition between *Lolium perenne* L. and *Anthoxanthum odoratum* L. at two levels of phosphate and potash. J. Ecol. 50:87–95.

Bevege, D. I., and B. N. Richards. 1970. Nitrogen in the growth of *Araucaria cunninghamii* Ait. underplanted in *Pinus* stands. Ecology 51:134–142.

Bhat, K. K. S., and P. H. Nye. 1973. Diffusion of phosphate to plant roots in soil. I. Quantitative autoradiography of the depletion zone. Plant Soil 38:161–175.

Black, C. A. 1968. Soil-plant relationships, 2nd ed. Wiley, New York.

Black, C. C., T. M. Chen, and R. H. Brown. 1969. Biochemical basis for plant competition. Weed Sci. 17:338–344.

Black, J. N. 1958. Competition between plants of different initial seed sizes in swards of subterranean clover (*Trifolium subterraneum* L.). Aust. J. Agric. Res. 9:299–318.

Blackman, G. E. 1956. Influence of light and temperature on leaf growth. p. 151–169. *In* F. L. Milthorpe (ed.) The growth of leaves. Butterworth, London.

Blackman, G. E., and W. G. Templeman. 1938. The nature of the competition between cereal crops and annual weeds. J. Agric. Sci. 28:247–271.

Blaser, R. E., and N. C. Brady. 1950. Nutrient competition in plant associations. Agron. J. 42:128–135.

Bode, H. R. 1958. Beiträge zur kenntnis allelopathischer Erscheinungen bei einigen Juglandaceen. Planta 51:440–480.

Boonstra, A. E. H. R. 1942. Rasverschillen bij bieten. VI. Med. Inst. voor suikerbietenteelt 12:13–96 (Quoted from de Wit, 1958).

Borojević, S., and T. Mišić. 1962. Ispitivanje vrednosti sortnih mašavina pšenice. Poljoprivreda 10:3–15.

Bosemark, N. O. 1954. The influence of nitrogen on root development. Physiologia Plantarum 7:497–502.

Boulton, E. H. B., and B. A. Jay. 1944. British timbers. Adam & Charles Black, London.

Bowen, G. D., and A. D. Rovira. 1969. The influence of micro-organisms on growth and metabolism of plant roots, p. 170–201. *In* W. J. Whittington (ed.) Root growth. Butterworth, London.

Bowen, J. E. 1973. Kinetics of zinc absorption by excised roots of two sugar cane clones. Plant Soil 39:125–129.

Bowes, G., W. L. Ogren, and R. H. Hageman. 1972. Light saturation, photosynthesis rate, RuDP carboxylase activity, and specific leaf weight in soybeans grown under different light intensities. Crop Sci. 12:77–79.

Bradshaw, A. D., M. J. Chadwick, D. Jowett, and R. W. Snaydon. 1964. Experimental investigations into the mineral nutrition of several grass species. IV. Nitrogen level. J. Ecol. 52:665–676.

Bray, R. H. 1954. A nutrient mobility concept of soil-plant relationships. Soil Sci. 78: 9–22.

Brewster, J. L., and P. B. Tinker. 1970. Nutrient cation flows in soil around plant roots. Soil Sci. Soc. Am. Proc. 34:421-426.

Brougham, R. W. 1958. Interception of light by the foliage of pure and mixed stands of pasture plants. Aust. J. Agric. Res. 9:39-52.

Brouwer, R. 1966. Root growth of grasses and cereals. p. 153-166. In F. L. Milthorpe and J. D. Ivins (ed.) The growth of cereals. Butterworth, London.

Brown, J. C., and J. E. Ambler. 1973. "Reductants" released by roots of Fe-deficient soybeans. Agron. J. 65:311-314.

Brown, J. F., and E. L. Sharp. 1970. The relative survival ability of pathogenic types of Puccinia striiformis in mixtures. Phytopathology 60:529-533.

Brown, K. W., and N. J. Rosenberg. 1970. Effect of wind breaks and soil water potential on stomatal diffusion resistance and photosynthetic rate of sugar beets (Beta vulgaris). Agron. J. 62:4-8.

Burdon, J. J., and G. A. Chilvers. 1976. Epidemiology of Pythium-induced damping-off in mixed species seedling stands. Ann. Appl. Biol. 82:233-240.

Cable, D. R. 1969. Competition in the semidesert grass-shrub type as influenced by root systems, growth habits, and soil moisture extraction. Ecology 50:27-38.

Cannon, W. A. 1949. Tentative classification of root systems. Ecology 30:542-548.

Challinor, D. 1968. Alteration of surface soil characteristics by four tree species. Ecology 49:286-290.

Chao, C. 1975. Improvements for increasing the cropping intensity of paddy fields in Taiwan in the past 5 years. p. 219-230. In Proceedings Cropping Systems Workshop, 18-20 March 1975. IRRI, Los Banos, Philippines.

Chester, K. S. 1950. Plant disease losses: their appraisal and interpretation. Plant Dis. Rep. Suppl. 193:189-364.

Christie, P., E. I. Newman, and R. Campbell. 1974. Grassland species can influence the abundance of microbes on each other's roots. Nature (London) 250:570-571.

Clay, R. E., and R. W. Allard. 1969. A comparison of the performance of homogeneous and heterogeneous barley populations. Crop Sci. 9:407-412.

Cohen, D. 1970. The expected efficiency of water utilization in plants under different competition and selection regimes. Isr. J. Bot. 19:50-54.

Cornforth, I. S. 1968. Relationships between soil volume used by roots and nutrient accessibilities. J. Soil Sci. 19:291-301.

Cowling, D. W., and D. R. Lockyer. 1967. A comparison of the reaction of different grass species to fertilizer nitrogen and to growth in association with white clover. II. Yield of nitrogen. J. Br. Grassl. Soc. 22:53-61.

Crist, J. W., and G. J. Stout. 1929. Relation between top and root size in herbaceous plants. Plant Physiol. 4:63-85.

Crossett, R. N., D. J. Campbell, and H. E. Stewart. 1975. Compensatory growth in cereal root systems. Plant Soil 42:673-683.

Dittmer, H. J. 1937. A quantitative study of the roots and root hairs of a winter rye plant (Secale cereale). Am. J. Bot. 24:417-420.

Dittmer, H. J. 1949. Root hair variations in plant species. Am. J. Bot. 36:152-155.

Donald, C. M. 1946. Competition between pasture species with reference to the hypothesis of harmful root interactions. J. Counc. Sci. Indust. Res. 19:32-37.

Donald, C. M. 1951. Competition among pasture plants. I. Intra-specific competition among annual pasture plants. Aust. J. Agric. Res. 2:355-376.

Donald, C. M. 1958. The interaction of competition for light and for nutrients. Aust. J. Agric. Res. 9:421-435.

Donald, C. M. 1963. Competition among crop and pasture plants. Adv. Agron. 15:1-118.

Donald, C. M., and C. A. Neal-Smith. 1938. The establishment of pastures on deep sands in the Upper South-East of South Australia. II. The influence of cover crops and fertilizer treatment on the establishment of selected herbage species. Bull. Counc. Sci. Indust. Res. 122:12-23.

Drew, M. C., and P. H. Nye. 1969. The supply of nutrient ions by diffusion to plant roots in soil. II. The effect of root hairs on the uptake of potassium by roots of rye grass. Plant Soil 31:407-424.

Duncan, W. G., and A. J. Ohlrogge. 1958. Principles of nutrient uptake from fertilizer bands. II. Root development in the band. Agron. J. 50:605-608.

Dunham, R. J., and P. H. Nye. 1973. The influence of soil water content on the uptake of ions by roots. II. Soil water content gradients near a plane of onion roots. J. Appl. Ecol. 10:585-598.

Dunham, R. J., and P. H. Nye. 1974. The influence of soil water content on the uptake of ions by roots. II. Chloride uptake and concentration gradients in soil. J. Appl. Ecol. 11:581-595.

Eagles, C. F. 1972. Competition for light and nutrients between natural populations of Dactylis glomerata. J. Appl. Ecol. 9:141-152.

Edwards, K. J. R., and R. W. Allard. 1963. The influence of light intensity on competitive ability. Am. Nat. 97:234-248.

Ellis, F. B., and B. T. Barnes. 1973. Estimation of the distribution of living roots of plants under field conditions. Plant Soil 39:81-91.

Ennik, G. C. 1969. White clover/grass relationships: competition effects in laboratory and field. p. 165-174. In Proceeding White Clover Research Symposium. Belfast, Sept. 1969.

Enyi, B. A. C. 1973. Effects of intercropping maize or sorghum with cowpeas, pigeon peas, or beans. Expl. Agric. 9:83-90.

Evans, G., J. B. Cartwright, and N. H. White. 1967. The production of a phytotoxin, nectrolide, by some root-surface isolates of Cylindrocarpon radicicola. Plant Soil 26:253-260.

Florence, R. G. 1965. Decline of old-growth redwood forests in relation to some soil microbiological processes. Ecology 46:52-64.

Florence, R. G., and R. L. Crocker. 1962. Analysis of Blackbutt seedling growth in a blackbutt forest soil. Ecology 43:670-679.

Gardner, W. R. 1960. Dynamic aspects of water availability to plants. Soil Sci. 89:63-73.

Grable, A. R. 1966. Soil aeration and plant growth. Adv. Agron. 18:57-106.

Graham, S. A., and F. B. Knight. 1965. Principles of forest entomology, 4th ed. McGraw-Hill, New York.

Green, J. T., V. C. Finkner, and W. G. Duncan. 1971. Effects of seasonal timing of competition on grain yield components of winter barley. Agron. J. 63:469-472.

Greenwood, D. J. 1969. Effect of oxygen distribution in the soil on plant growth, p. 202-223. In W. J. Whittington (ed.) Root growth. Butterworth, London.

Grime, J. P. 1965. Shade tolerance in flowering plants. Nature (London) 208:161-163.

Grime, J. P. 1966. Shade avoidance and shade tolerance in flowering plants. p. 187-207. In R. Bainbridge, G. C. Evans, and O. Rackham (ed.) Light as an ecological factor. Blackwell, Oxford.

Grodzinsky, A. M. 1974a. Problems of soil fatigue and allelopathy, Issue 5, p. 3-9. In physiological and biochemical foundations of plant interaction in phytocenoses. Naukova Dumka, Kiev.

Grodzinsky, A. M. 1974b. Role of root systems in chemical interaction of plants, Issue 5, p. 10-14. In Physiological and biochemical foundations of plant interaction in phytocenoses. Naukova Dumka, Kiev.

Groner, M. G. 1974. Intraspecific allelopathy in Kalanchoe daigremontiana. Bot. Gaz. 135:73-79.

Grümmer, G. 1955. Die gegenseitige Beeinflussung höheren Pflanzen—Allelopathie. G. Fischer, Jena.

Hadfield, W. 1974. Shade in north-east Indian tea plantations. I. The shade pattern. J. Appl. Ecol. 11:151-178.

Hale, M. G., C. L. Foy, and F. J. Shay. 1971. Factors affecting root exudation. Adv. Agron. 23:89-109.

Hall, R. L. 1974. Analysis of the nature of interference between plants of different species. II. Nutrient relations in a Nandi Setaria and greenleaf Desmodium association with particular reference to potassium. Aust. J. Agric. Res. 25:749-756.

Hanway, J. J., and C. R. Weber. 1971. Accumulation of N, P, and K by soybean (Glycine max (L.) Merrill) plants. Agron. J. 63:406-408.

Harper, J. L. 1961. Approaches to the study of plant competition. Symp. Soc. Exp. Biol. 15:1-39.

Harper, J. L. 1968. The regulation of numbers and mass in plant populations. p. 139-158. In E. C. Lewontin (ed.) Population biology and evolution. Proc. Symp. on Population Biology, Syracuse Univ. Press.

Harris, G. A. 1967. Some competitive relationships between Agropyron spicatum and Bromus tectorum. Ecol. Monog. 37:89-111.

Haynes, J. L., and J. D. Sayre. 1956. Response of corn to within-row competition. Agron. J. 48:362–364.

Hirano, S., and S. Morioka. 1964. On the inter-relation of the growth retarding activity of the root-excretion among various kinds of fruit trees. J. Jap. Soc. Hort. Sci. 33: 13–22.

Idris, H., and F. L. Milthorpe. 1966. Light and nutrient supplies in the competition between barley and charlock. Oecol. Plant. 1:143–164.

International Rice Research Institute. 1974. Annual Report 1973. IRRI, Los Baños, Philippines.

International Rice Research Institute. 1975. Annual Report 1974. IRRI, Los Baños, Philippines.

Inoue, K. 1974. Numerical experiments of effects of advection on CO_2 environment and photosynthesis of crop fields. Bull. Nat. Inst. Agric. Sci., Ser. A, 21:1–25.

Ivanov, V. P. 1962. Mutual effect through the root system of a mixed crop of corn and broad beans. Fiziol. Rast. 11:630–637.

Iwaki, H. 1959. Ecological studies on interspecific competition in a plant community. I. An analysis of growth of competing plants in mixed stands of buckwheat and green grams. Jap. J. Bot. 17:120–138.

Jensen, N. F., and W. T. Federer. 1965. Competing ability in wheat. Crop Sci. 5:449–452.

Johnson, R., and D. J. Allen. 1975. Induced resistance to rust diseases and its possible role in the resistance of multiline varieties. Ann. Appl. Biol. 80:359–363.

Kanemasu, E. T., G. W. Thurtell, and C. B. Tanner. 1969. Design, calibration and field use of a stomatal diffusion porometer. Plant Physiol. 44:881–885.

Kashirad, A., and H. Marschner. 1974. Iron nutrition of sunflower and corn plants in mono and mixed culture. Plant Soil 41:91–101.

Kawano, K., H. Gonzalez, and M. Lucena. 1974. Intraspecific competition, competition with weeds and spacing response in rice. Crop Sci. 14:841–845.

Kawano, K., and A. Tanaka. 1967. Studies on the competitive ability of rice plant in population. J. Fac. Agric. Hokkaido Univ., Sapporo 55:339–362.

Kimber, R. W. L. 1973. Phytotoxicity from plant residues. III. The relative effect of toxins and nitrogen immobilization on the germination and growth of wheat. Plant Soil 38:543–555.

Klages, K. H. W. 1936. Changes in the proportions of the components of seeded and harvested cereal mixtures in abnormal seasons. J. Am. Soc. Agron. 28:935–940.

Klute, A., and D. B. Peters. 1969. Water uptake and root growth. p. 105–134. In W. J. Whittington (ed.) Root growth. Butterworth, London.

Kumura, A. 1968. Studies on dry matter production of soybean plant. IV. Photosynthetic properties of leaf as subsequently affected by light condition. Proc. Crop Sci. Soc. Japan 37:583–588.

Kurtz, T., S. W. Milsted, and R. H. Bray. 1952. The importance of nitrogen and water in reducing competition between intercrops and corn. Agron. J. 44:13–17.

Leonard, K. J. 1969. Factors affecting rates of stem rust increase in mixed plantings of susceptible and resistant oat varieties. Phytopathology 58:1845–1850.

Litav, M., and J. L. Harper. 1967. A method for studying spatial relationships between the root systems of two neighbouring plants. Plant Soil 26:389–392.

Litav, M., and N. Seligman. 1970. Competition between Oryzopsis holciformis (M. B.) Hack and annual plants. II. Performance of O. holciformis and two annuals when grown in mixtures of differing ratios. Isr. J. Bot. 19:517–528.

Litav, M., and S. Wolovitch. 1971. Partial separation of roots as a means of reducing the effect of competition between two grass species. Ann. Bot. 35:1163–1178.

Lockhart, J. A. 1961. Photoinhibition of stem elongation by full solar radiation. Am. J. Bot. 48:387–392.

Ludwig, W. 1950. Zur Theorie der Konkurrenz: die Annidation (Einnischung) als fünfter Evolutionsfaktor. Zool. Anz. Ergänzungsband zu Band 145:516–537.

MacLeod, L. B. 1965. Effect of nitrogen and potassium on the yield, botanical composition, and competition for nutrients in three alfalfa-grass associations. Agron. J. 57: 129–134.

MacLeod, L. B., and R. Bradfield. 1963. Effect of liming and potassium fertilization on the yield and composition of an alfalfa-orchardgrass association. Agron. J. 55: 435–439.

McClure, J. W., and C. Harvey. 1962. Use of radiophosphorus in measuring root growth in sorghums. Agron. J. 54:457–459.

McCown, R. L., and W. A. Williams. 1968. Competition for nutrients and light between the annual grassland species *Bromus mollis* and *Erodium botrys.* Ecology 49:981–990.

McIntyre, D. S. 1970. The platinum microelectrode method for soil aeration measurement. Adv. Agron. 22:235–283.

McPherson, J. K., and C. H. Muller. 1969. Allelopathic effects of *Adenostoma fasciculatum*, "chamise", in the California chaparral. Ecol. Monogr. 39:177–198.

Marshall, J. K. 1967. The effect of shelter on the productivity of grasslands and field crops. Field Crop Abstr. 20:1–16.

Massey, A. B. 1925. Antagonism of the walnuts (*Juglans nigra* and *J. cinerea*) in certain plant associations. Phytopathology 15:773–784.

Menz, K. M., D. N. Moss, R. Q. Cannell, and W. A. Brun. 1969. Screening for photosynthetic efficiency. Crop Sci. 9:692–694.

Miller, E. E., and J. M. Norman. 1971. A sunfleck theory for plant canopies. II. Penumbra effect: intensity distributions along sunfleck segments. Agron. J. 63:739–743.

Milthorpe, F. L. 1961. The nature and analysis of competition between plants of different species. Symp. Soc. Exp. Biol. 15:330–355.

Monsi, M., and Y. Murata. 1970. Development of photosynthetic systems as influenced by distribution of matter. p. 115–129. *In* I. Šetlík (ed.) Prediction and measurement of photosynthetic productivity. Proceedings of the IBP/PP Technical meeting, 1969. Wageningen, Pudoc.

Monsi, M., and T. Saeki. 1953. Über den Lichtfaktor in den Pflanzengesellschaften und seine Bedeutung für die Stoffproduktion. Jpn. J. Bot. 14:22–52.

Monsi, M., Z. Uchijima, and T. Oikawa. 1973. Structure of foliage canopies and photosynthesis. Ann. Rev. Ecol. Syst. 4:301–327.

Moral, R., del, and R. G. Cates. 1971. Allelopathic potential of the dominant vegetation of western Washington. Ecology 52:1030–1037.

Moral, R. del, and C. H. Muller. 1969. Fog drip: a mechanism of toxin transport from *Eucalyptus globulus*. Bull. Torrey Botanical Club 96:467–475.

Moral, R., del, and C. H. Muller. 1970. Allelopathic effects of *Eucalyptus camaldulensis*. Am. Midl. Nat. 83:254–282.

Morrison, J. 1966. The nitrogen and phosphorus fertilization of perennial ryegrass grown at high altitudes in Kenya. J. Br. Grassl. Soc. 21:218–223.

Murata, Y. 1969. Physiological responses to nitrogen in plants. p. 235–259. *In* J. D. Eastin, F. A. Haskins, C. Y. Sullivan, and C. H. M. van Bavel (ed.) Physiological aspects of crop yield. Am. Soc. of Agron., Crop Sci. Soc. of Am., Madison, Wis.

Myers, L. F., and J. Lipsett. 1958. Competition between skeleton weed (*Chondrilla juncea* L.) and cereals in relation to nitrogen supply. Aust. J. Agric. Res. 9:1–12.

Natr, L. 1972. Influence of mineral nutrients on photosynthesis of higher plants. Photosynthetica 6:80–99.

Newman, E. I. 1974. Root and soil water relations. p. 363–440. *In* E. W. Carson (ed.) The plant root and its environment. University Press of Virginia, Charlottesville, Va.

Newman, E. I., and A. D. Rovira. 1975. Allelopathy among some British grassland species. J. Ecol. 63:727–737.

Nieto, J. H., and D. W. Staniforth. 1961. Corn-foxtail competition under various production conditions. Agron. J. 53:1–5.

Norman, J. M., E. E. Miller, and C. B. Tanner. 1971. Light intensity and sunfleck-size distribution in plant canopies. Agron. J. 63:743–748.

Nye, P. H. 1966. The effect of nutrient intensity and buffering power of a soil, and the absorbing power, size and root hairs of a root, on nutrient absorption by diffusion. Plant Soil 25:81–105.

Nye, P. H., and W. N. M. Foster. 1961. The relative uptake of phosphorus by crops and natural fallow from different parts of their root zone. J. Agric. Sci. 56:299–306.

Nye, P. H., and P. B. Tinker. 1969. The concept of a root demand coefficient. J. Appl. Ecol. 6:293–300.

Olsen, S. R., and W. D. Kemper. 1968. Movement of nutrients to plant roots. Adv. Agron. 20:91–151.

Paner, V. E. 1975. Multiple cropping research in the Philippines. p. 188–202. *In* Proceedings of the cropping systems workshop. IRRI, Los Baños, Philippines.

Patrick, Z. A. 1955. The peach replant problem in Ontario. II. Toxic substances from microbial decomposition products of peach root residues. Can. J. Bot. 33:461–486.

Pavlychenko, T. K., and J. B. Harrington. 1934. Competitive efficiency of weeds and cereal crops. Can. J. Res. 10:77–94.

Pendleton, J. W., and G. H. Dungan. 1958. Effect of row direction on spring oat yields. Agron. J. 50:341–343.

Pogrebniak, P. S. 1962. Creation of mixed stands as a method for raising the productivity of forests. p. 483–484. In Proceedings of 5th World Forestry Congress, Vol. 1.

Ponnamperuma, F. N. 1965. Review of the symposium on the mineral nutrition of the rice plant. p. 461–482. In The mineral nutrition of the rice plant. IRRI. John Hopkins Press, Baltimore.

Puckridge, D. W., and C. M. Donald. 1967. Competition among wheat plants sown at a wide range of densities. Aust. J. Agric. Res. 18:193–211.

Pushparajah, E., and S. Y. Tan. 1970. Tapioca as an intercrop in rubber. p. 128–138. In E. K. Blencowe and J. W. Blencowe (ed.) Crop diversification in Malaysia. Incorporated Society of Planters, Kuala Lumpur.

Putnam, A. R., and W. B. Duke. 1974. Biological suppression of weeds: evidence for allelopathy in accessions of cucumber. Science 185:370–371.

Putwain, P. D., and J. L. Harper. 1972. Studies in the dynamics of plant populations. V. Mechanisms governing the sex ratio in Rumex acetosa and R. acetosella. J. Ecol. 60:113–130.

Ramakrishnan, P. S. 1970. Nutritional requirements of the edaphic ecotypes in Melilotus alba Medic. III. Interference between the calcareous and acidic populations in the two soil types. New Phytol. 69:81–86.

Raper, C. D., and S. A. Barber. 1970a. Rooting systems of soybeans. I. Differences in root morphology among varieties. Agron. J. 62:581–584.

Raper, C. D., and S. A. Barber. 1970b. Rooting systems of soybeans. II. Physiological effectiveness as nutrient absorption surfaces. Agron. J. 62:585–588.

Reestman, A. J. 1946. De betekenis van de virusziekten van de aardappel naar aanleiding van proeven met gekeurd en ongekeurd pootgoed. Tijdschr. Plantenziekten 52:97–118 (Quoted from de Wit, 1960).

Rhodes, I. 1970. The production of contrasting genotypes of perennial ryegrass (Lolium perenne L.) in monocultures and mixed cultures of varying complexity. J. Br. Grassl. Soc. 25:285–288.

Rice, E. L. 1974. Allelopathy. Academic Press, New York.

Richards, B. N., and D. I. Bevege. 1967. The productivity and nitrogen economy of artificial ecosystems comprising various combinations of perennial legumes and coniferous tree species. Aust. J. Bot. 15:467–480.

Roberts, J. L., and F. R. Olson. 1942. Interrelationships of legumes and grasses grown in association. J. Am. Soc. Agron. 34:695–701.

Robinson, R. K. 1972. The production by roots of Calluna vulgaris of a factor inhibitory to growth of some mycorrhizal fungi. J. Ecol. 60:219–224.

Rogers, W. S., and G. C. Head. 1969. Factors affecting the distribution and growth of roots of perennial woody species. p. 280–295. In W. J. Whittington (ed.) Root growth. Butterworth, London.

Rovira, A. D. 1969. Plant root exudates. Bot. Rev. 35:35–57.

Roy, S. K. 1960. Interaction between rice varieties. J. Genet. 57:137–152.

Russell, E. W., B. A. Keen, and H. H. Mann. 1942. Studies in soil cultivation. XI. The effect of inter-tillage on the sugar beet crop. J. Agric. Sci. 32:330–337.

Saeki, T. 1960. Interrelationships between leaf amount, light distribution and total photosynthesis in a plant community. Bot. Mag. Tokyo 73:55–63.

Salter, P. J., and J. E. Goode. 1967. Crop responses to water at different stages of growth. Res. Rev. No. 2, Commonwealth Agricultural Bureaux, Farnham Royal.

Sandfaer, J. 1970. An analysis of the competition between some barley varieties. Danish Atomic Energy Commission. Risö Rept. No. 230.

Santhirasegaram, K., and J. N. Black. 1968a. The distribution of leaf area and light intensity within wheat crops differing in row direction, row spacing and rate of sowing; a contribution to the study of undersowing pasture with cereals. J. Br. Grassl. Soc. 23:1–12.

Santhirasegaram, K., and J. N. Black. 1968b. The relationship between light beneath wheat crops and growth of undersown clover. J. Br. Grassl. Soc. 23:234–239.

Schepers, A., and L. Sibma. 1976. Yield and dry matter content of early and late potatoes, as affected by mono and mixed cultures. Potato Res. 19:73–90.

Sibma, L., J. Kort, and C. T. de Wit. 1964. Experiments on competition as a means of detecting possible damage by nematodes. p. 119–124. Jaarb. I. B. S. 1964.

Singh, R. N., D. C. Martens, S. S. Obenshain, and G. D. Jones. 1967. Yield and nutrient uptake by orchard grass as affected by 14 annual applications of N, P and K. Agron. J. 59:51–53.

Slatyer, R. O. 1967. Plant-water relationships. Academic Press, New York.

Snaydon, R. W. 1971. An analysis of competition between plants of *Trifolium repens* L. populations collected from contrasted soils. J. Appl. Ecol. 8:687–697.

Snaydon, R. W., and A. D. Bradshaw. 1961. Differential response to calcium within the species *Festuca ovina* L. New Phytol. 60:219–231.

Stahler, L. M. 1948. Shade and soil moisture as factors in competition between selected crops and field bindweed, *Convolvulus arvensis*. J. Am. Soc. Agron. 40:490–502.

Stanford, G., J. O. Legg, and S. J. Smith. 1973. Soil nitrogen availability evaluations based on nitrogen mineralization potentials of soils and uptake of labeled and unlabeled nitrogen by plants. Plant Soil 39:113–124.

Stern, W. R., and C. M. Donald. 1962a. Light relationships in grass-clover swards. Aust. J. Agric. Res. 13:599–614.

Stern, W. R., and C. M. Donald. 1962b. The influence of leaf area and radiation on the growth of clover in swards. Aust. J. Agric. Res. 13:615–623.

Stone, L. R., M. L. Horton, and T. C. Olson. 1973. Water loss from an irrigated sorghum field: I. Water flux within and below the root zone. Agron. J. 65:492–497.

Story, R. 1967. Pasture patterns and associated soil water in partially cleared woodland. Aust. J. Bot. 15:175–187.

Thomas, M. D., and G. R. Hill. 1949. Photosynthesis under field conditions. p. 19–52. *In* J. Franck and W. E. Loomis (ed.) Photosynthesis in plants. Univ. Press, Ames, Iowa.

Thomas, V. J. 1970. A mathematical approach to fitting parameters in a competition model. J. Appl. Ecol. 7:487–496.

Trenbath, B. R. 1974a. Neighbour effects in the genus *Avena*. II. Comparison of weed species. J. Appl. Ecol. 11:111–125.

Trenbath, B. R. 1974b. Application of a growth model to problems of the productivity and stability of mixed stands. Int. Grassland Congr. Proc. 12th, Moscow. 1:546–558.

Trenbath, B. R. 1974c. Biomass productivity of mixtures. Adv. Agron. 26:177–210.

Trenbath, B. R. 1975a. Diversify or be damned? Ecologist 5:76–83.

Trenbath, B. R. 1975b. Neighbour effects in the genus *Avena*. III. A diallel approach. J. Appl. Ecol. 12:189–200.

Trenbath, B. R. 1976. Models and the interpretation of mixture experiments. *In* J. R. Wilson (ed.) Plant relations in pastures. CSIRO Division of Tropical Agronomy, Brisbane. (in press).

Trenbath, B. R. 1977. Some aspects of methodology in Australian research into allelopathy. *In* Allelopatiya. Naukova Dumka, Kiev. (in press).

Trenbath, B. R., and J. F. Angus. 1975. Leaf inclination and crop production. Field Crop Abstr. 28:231–244.

Trenbath, B. R., and J. L. Harper. 1973. Neighbour effects in the genus *Avena*. I. Comparison of crop species. J. Appl. Ecol. 10:379–400.

Troughton, A. 1974. The development of leaf water deficits in plants of *Lolium perenne* in relation to the sizes of the root and shoot systems. Plant Soil 40:153–160.

Trumble, H. C., and R. E. Shapter. 1937. The influence of nitrogen and phosphorus treatment on the yield and chemical composition of Wimmera rye-grass and subterranean clover, grown separately and in association. Bull. Counc. Sci. Ind. Res. 105:25–36.

Tukey, H. B., Jr. 1970. The leaching of substances from plants. Ann. Rev. Plant Physiol. 21:305–324.

Vergris, J., M. Drake, W. G. Colby, and J. Bart. 1953. Chemical composition of weeds and accompanying crop plants. Agron. J. 45:213–218.

Walker, J., R. M. Moore, and J. A. Robertson. 1972. Herbage response to tree and shrub thinning in *Eucalyptus populnea* shrub woodlands. Aust. J. Agric. Res. 23:405–410.

Walker, T. W., and A. F. R. Adams. 1958. Competition for sulphur in a grass-clover association. Plant Soil 9:353-366.

Weaver, J. E., and F. E. Clements. 1938. Plant ecology. McGraw-Hill.

Webb, L. J., J. G. Tracey, and K. P. Haydock. 1967. A factor toxic to seedlings of the same species associated with living roots of the non-gregarious subtropical rain forest tree *Grevillea robusta*. J. Appl. Ecol. 4:13-25.

Welbank, P. J. 1961a. Competitive effects of *Agropyron repens*. p. 105-106. Rothamsted Experimental Station Annual Report for 1960.

Welbank, P. J. 1961b. A study of the nitrogen and water factors in competition with *Agropyron repens* (L.) Beauv. Ann. Bot. (London) N. S. 25:116-137.

Wellington, W. G., J. J. Fettes, K. B. Turner, and R. M. Belyea. 1950. Physical and biological indicators of the development of outbreaks of the spruce budworm, *Choristoneura fumiferana* (Clem.) (Lepidoptera: Tortricidae). Can. J. Res. Sect. D. 28:308-331.

Whittaker, R. H., and P. P. Feeny. 1971. Allelochemics: chemical interactions between species. Science 171:757-770.

Whittington, W. J., and T. A. O'Brien. 1968. A comparison of yields from plots sown with a single species or a mixture of grass species. J. Appl. Ecol. 5:209-213.

Willey, R. W., and R. Holliday. 1971. Plant population and shading studies in barley. J. Agric. Sci. Camb. 77:445-452.

Williams, E. J. 1962. The analysis of competition experiments. Aust. J. Biol. Sci. 15: 509-525.

Williams, J. T. 1964. A study of the competitive ability of *Chenopodium album* L. I. Interference between kale and *C. album* grown in pure stands and in mixtures. Weed Res. 4:283-295.

Wit, C. T. de. 1958. Transpiration and crop yields. Versl. Landbouwkd. Onderz. 64:1-88.

Wit, C. T. de. 1960. On competition. Versl. Landbouwkd. Onderz. 66.8:1-82.

Wit, C. T. de. 1965. Photosynthesis of leaf canopies. Versl. Landbouwkd. Onderz. 663: 1-57.

Wit, C. T. de, and J. P. van den Bergh. 1965. Competition between herbage plants. Neth. J. Agric. Sci. 13:212-221.

Wit, C. T. de, P. G. Tow, and G. C. Ennik. 1966. Competition between legumes and grasses. Versl. Landbouwkd. Onderz. 687:1-30.

Woods, F. W. 1970. Interspecific transfer of inorganic materials by root systems of woody plants. J. Appl. Ecol. 7:481-486.

Yurchak, L. D., and L. S. Seredyuk. 1974. Active metabolites of microorganisms decomposing *Lupinus*. p. 100-103. *In* Physiological and biochemical foundations of plant interaction in phytocenoses. Issue 5, Naukova Dumka, Kiev.

Radiation and Microclimate Relationships in Multiple Cropping Systems

L. H. Allen, Jr., T. R. Sinclair, and E. R. Lemon[1]

Radiation interception and exchange should be a primary focal point in considering theoretical and practical aspects of multiple cropping systems. First, solar radiation provides the energy for the green-plant photosynthetic apparatus. Obviously, shading in intercropping systems would reduce the energy available to one or more of the crops. Second, solar radiation provides the primary energy source to drive evapotranspiration and sensible heat exchange. Partially shaded plants may be under less water stress than fully-exposed plants. Third, the spectral qualities of radiation will change with depth into plant canopies because leaves absorb solar radiation differently. Changes in radiation quality may affect plant photomorphogenic processes.

Since most detailed radiation and microclimate data are available for monocultures rather than for multiple cropping systems, we will first discuss general radiation and microclimate relationships in plant communities. Then, we will apply these fundamental relationships to two types of multiple cropping systems, sequential cropping and intercropping.

The following format will be used:

a. Radiation source and source distribution
b. Radiation quantity, photosynthesis, and the energy balance in crops
c. Radiation quality in crops
d. Radiation fluctuations in crops
e. Application of relationships to sequential cropping systems
f. Application of relationships to intercropping systems

[1] Soil scientist, USDA, Agricultural Research Service, University of Florida, Gainesville, and plant physiologist and soil scientist, USDA, Agricultural Research Service, Cornell University, Ithaca, respectively.

RADIATION SOURCE AND SOURCE DISTRIBUTION

   Solar elevation angle determines the solar irradiance at the top of the atmosphere. Solar elevation angle is determined primarily by the longitude, latitude, time of day, and time of year.

   The irradiance arriving at the earth's surface is decreased by Rayleigh scattering, by atmospheric gases, by turbidity (aerosol), and by clouds. Particulates and water vapor may increase atmospheric turbidity. Direct-beam solar irradiance, I, may be approximated by

$$I = I_O (\sin \alpha) \tau^{-\sin \alpha} \qquad [1]$$

where I_O = solar irradiance constant, α = solar elevation angle, and τ = transmissivity of the atmosphere.

   About half of the energy in the solar spectrum falls in wavelengths below 700 nm (Fig. 1), and is referred to as photosynthetically active radiation (PAR). The other half lies at wavelengths greater than 700 nm, and is referred to as near infrared radiation (NIR).

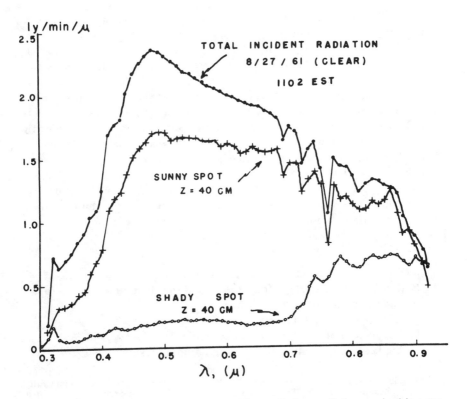

Figure 1. Solar radiation spectra of total incident radiation, radiation received in a sun-fleck in a corn crop at 40 cm, and radiation received in a shady spot in a corn crop at 40 cm. (Yocum et al., 1964; Lemon, 1963).

The spectral ratios of scattered (or diffuse skylight) radiation to total (or global) shortwave (SW, 300 to 3,000 nm) radiation depend on sky conditions; e.g., clear, scattered cumulus clouds, or hazy (Fig. 2). Under clear sky conditions, a larger fraction of radiation is scattered at the blue end of the spectrum than at the red end of the spectrum than under cloudy or hazy conditions. The ratios of the values in Figure 2 at 400 nm to those at 700 nm were 3:1, 2.4:1, and 1.8:1, for clear, scattered cloud, and hazy conditions, respectively. The ratio of the difference between the scattered cloud and the clear sky conditions was also about 1.8:1, so the clouds were spectrally scattering radiation much the same way as haze.

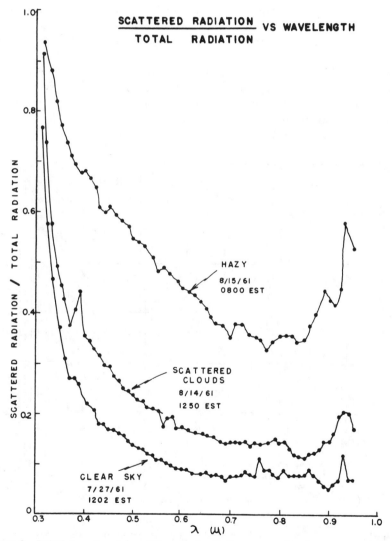

Figure 2. Relative scattered (or diffuse sky) radiation spectra for clear, scattered clouds, and hazy conditions, near Ithaca, New York. (Data computed from Yocum et al., 1964).

RADIATION QUANTITY, PHOTOSYNTHESIS, AND THE ENERGY BALANCE

Radiation penetration into plant canopies decreases exponentially (Fig. 3) if the horizontal distribution of leaf elements is approximately random (Allen & Brown, 1965). This exponential decrease of radiation penetration, assuming a horizontally random leaf element distribution (de Wit, 1965; Duncan et al., 1967), can be expressed as

$$P_z = \exp\left(-K \cdot L_z / \sin \theta\right) \qquad [2]$$

where P_z is the proportion of radiation penetrating to the depth z in the canopy, K is the extinction coefficient which is explicitly dependent upon the leaf angle distribution and on θ, the source angle, L_z is the cumulative leaf area index from the top of the canopy to depth z, and θ is the altitude angle of the radiation source. Equation [2] can be used to calculate both the penetration of direct-beam solar radiation and the penetration of diffuse sky-source radiation of any sky-source elevation section. With refinements, this basic radiation penetration model has been used as the first stage in computing PAR on leaf elements of plant canopies in photosynthesis simulation models (Allen et al., 1974; Stewart & Lemon, 1969).

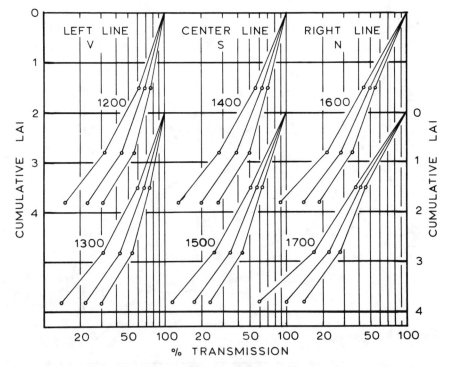

Figure 3. Percent transmission profiles of PAR (labeled V), total shortwave (S) and near infrared (N) radiation at hourly intervals in the afternoon of 13 Sept. 1963, in corn near Ithaca, New York. (Allen & Brown, 1965).

Equation [2] gives the average penetration of radiation to any depth within a canopy. However, solar and skylight radiation are not uniformly attenuated with depth into canopy. Allen and Lemon (1972) showed a bimodal distribution of net radiation prevailed in mid-canopy of maize (*Zea mays* L.) on clear days. The largest component of the net radiation was the direct-beam solar irradiance. Sinclair and Lemon (1974) reported distributions of irradiance ratios (ratios of transmitted irradiance to above-crop irradiance) for maize which showed the bimodal distribution of PAR even more clearly (Fig. 4). Most of the leaf area either was clearly irradiated by

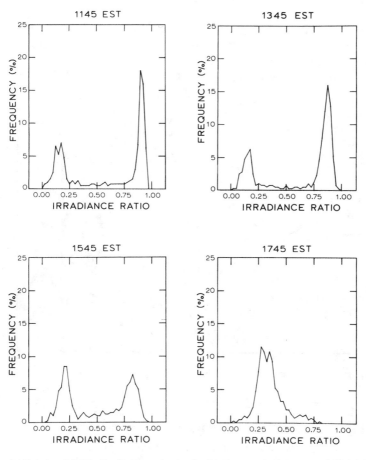

Figure 4. Graphs of PAR distribution obtained with a traversing sensor at 160-cm level in Cornell M-3 corn for successive periods on 28 Aug. 1969. The irradiance ratio interval width was 0.025. (Sinclair & Lemon, 1974).

the sun, or was clearly shaded. At the top of the crop, most of the leaf area was exposed to direct-beam solar radiation, whereas deep in the canopy most of the leaf area was shaded, and hence exposed to low levels of radiation. Furthermore, under cloudy conditions (Allen & Lemon, 1972), the bimodal distribution tends to merge into one peak as the diffuse skylight component became more important and the direct-beam became less important.

Most crop photosynthesis models compute photosynthesis based on the theoretical distribution of leaf area elements into many PAR load classes (based on bimodal PAR distributions and leaf angle distributions) and sum the contributions based on photosynthetic responses of leaves to a given PAR load (e.g., Stewart & Lemon, 1969; Allen et al., 1974). This procedure is more realistic than predicting photosynthesis based on the spatial average penetration of Eq. [2].

Many experiments have been conducted on photosynthetic light response curves of leaves. In general, the C_4-type plants have higher levels of photosynthesis at high PAR flux densities (Hesketh, 1963) but many of the C_3 crop plants also have high levels of photosynthesis, e.g., soybean (*Glycine max* L. Merr.) (Beuerlein & Pendleton, 1971). If PAR flux densities are increased enough, leaves will "light saturate", i.e., a point will be reached where leaves will fix no additional CO_2 even though PAR is increased.

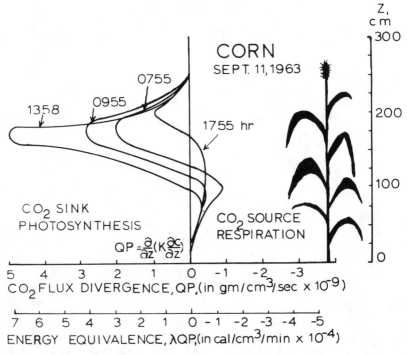

Figure 5. Source-sink intensity distribution of CO_2 (QP) and photochemical energy (λQP) for indicated time in a corn crop near Ithaca, New York. Positive values indicate net photosynthesis whereas negative values indicate net respiration. (Lemon & Wright, 1969).

Leaves of maize (Hesketh & Musgrave, 1962), sugarcane (*Saccharum officinarum* L.) (Moss, 1962), and other tropical grasses generally do not become light saturated in full sunlight. Leaves of C_3 crops like sugar beet (*Beta vulgaris* L.) or soybean may saturate at about half of full sunlight. Leaves of many forest and natural species saturate at much lower levels of solar radiation (Hesketh, 1963; Stephens & Waggoner, 1970; Bazzaz, 1974), and understory leaves may even perish if exposed to full solar radiation (Tio, 1962; Stephens & Waggoner, 1970). Leaf light saturation is also influenced by the ecological conditions where they are grown; sun or shade (Björkman & Holmgren, 1966; Beuerlein & Pendleton, 1971).

The most obvious shift in radiation loads in monocultures is with depth into the plant canopy (Fig. 1 and 3). Photosynthesis as a function of depth has been computed using both micrometeorological techniques (Lemon & Wright, 1969; Lemon, 1965; 1967) and by modeling techniques (Allen & Lemon, 1975; Allen et al., 1974; Waggoner, 1969; Uchijima & Inoue, 1970; Stewart, 1970; Stewart & Lemon, 1969). The vertical source and sink density distribution of CO_2 in a maize crop (Fig. 5) computed from a momentum balance technique (Lemon & Wright, 1969) shows a region of intense photosynthetic activity near the top of the vegetation where PAR is plentiful, and shows a region near the base of the canopy, at low PAR levels, where respiration apparently exceeds photosynthesis, i.e., more CO_2 is evolved than is taken up by the crop. Energy balance techniques in a short crop of red clover (*Trifolium pratense*) showed similar patterns (Lemon, 1965).

Table 1 shows the source-sink intensity distribution of CO_2 uptake in maize with a Leaf Area Index (LAI) of 3.63 computed by a Soil-Plant-

Table 1. Source-sink intensity distribution of CO_2, water vapor (latent heat), and sensible heat as a function of height and leaf area density computed by the SPAM model for maize (LAI = 3.63) based on 1200 EST, 18 Aug. 1968 data. Each of the layers contained the same LAI (0.242)

Layer	Height	Leaf area density	CO_2 sink intensity	Water vapor source intensity	Sensible heat source intensity
	cm	cm^2 leaf area/cm^3	g/cm^3 per sec $\times 10^{-9}$	cal/cm^3 per min $\times 10^{-3}$	cal/cm^3 per min $\times 10^{-3}$
1	188.7	0.0046	0.60	1.25	0.53
2	154.7	0.0158	1.80	4.08	1.75
3	142.0	0.0242	2.40	5.90	2.47
4	132.5	0.0269	2.34	6.18	2.47
5	123.8	0.0285	2.06	6.22	2.44
6	115.5	0.0302	1.85	6.18	2.19
7	107.3	0.0285	1.47	5.14	1.92
8	98.8	0.0285	1.28	4.67	1.64
9	89.9	0.0278	1.04	4.28	1.25
10	81.2	0.0275	0.78	4.00	0.92
11	72.4	0.0263	0.41	3.55	0.67
12	63.2	0.0263	0.20	3.28	0.50
13	53.1	0.0218	0.05	2.69	0.29
14	39.8	0.0157	−0.02	1.51	0.26
15	16.1	0.0075	−0.03	0.66	0.13

Atmosphere Model (SPAM) (Stewart & Lemon, 1969; Stewart, 1970; Lemon et al., 1971). The maximum sink intensity in this simulation was 2.4×10^{-9} g/cm^2 per sec, whereas the maximum sink intensity reported by Lemon and Wright (1969) was about 5×10^{-9} g/cm^3 per sec. Both the simulation (Table 1) and the experimental calculations (Fig. 6) showed a source of CO_2 in the bottom of the maize canopies. The maximum source intensity was -0.038

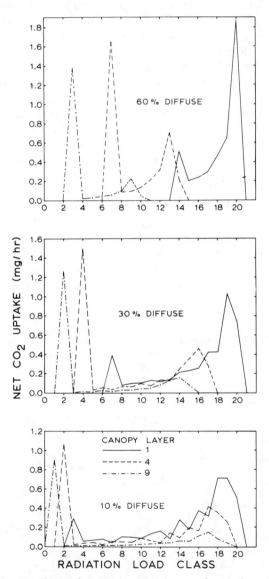

Figure 6. Net photosynthesis of *Cecropia* per decimeter of ground area predicted by the SPAM model as a function of radiation load class for three canopy layers under three diffuse radiation conditions.   1212 apparent solar time, 14 Nov. 1967, Turrialba, Costa Rica. LAI = 3.3. (Allen et al., 1974).

$\times 10^{-9}$ g/cm^3 per sec of CO_2 in the simulation and about -0.9×10^{-9} g/cm^3 per sec in the experimental calculations. Both procedures suggest that PAR may be limiting photosynthesis in the base of the plant canopies, especially if leaf respiration rates are high.

Allen, Stewart, and Lemon (1974) simulated the effects of leaf PAR response curves and percent diffuse radiation for two Costa Rican forest canopies with different maximum photosynthesis rates. Leaves of *Goethalsia* trees had maximum CO_2 uptake rates at high PAR of 7.5 mg/dm^2 per hour and *Cecropia* had a maximum CO_2 rate of 23 mg/cm^2 per hour. An understory species, *Croton,* had a maximum photosynthesis rate of 3 mg CO_2/dm^2 per hour. Net CO_2 uptake near midday for the simulated *Cecropia* system for 15 canopy layers was computed for 20 leaf PAR load classes (Fig. 6). The net CO_2 uptake rates in the low PAR peaks were much greater for the 30% and 60% diffuse cases than they were for the 10% diffuse solar radiation case. This difference occurs because the radiation loads in the shaded areas of the canopy are much lower in the 10% diffuse case than in the 30% or 60% diffuse cases, even after the reduction of total PAR with increasing light scattering by haze or cloud has been taken into account.

Figure 7 illustrates diurnal gross photosynthesis, net photosynthesis, and gross photosynthesis which could be supported by skylight sources alone, for 10, 30, 60, and 90% diffuse radiation, for both *Goethalsia* (lower curves) and *Cecropia* (upper curves). The model predicts that sky sources alone could support much of the photosynthesis in these species, especially with 30% or more diffuse radiation. With light curves that do not saturate in full sunlight, we would not expect skylight sources to be as effective when diffuse solar radiation increases.

Figure 8 illustrates CO_2 uptake for each of the 15 simulated canopy layers of a *Goethalsia* and *Cecropia* forest, respectively, with LAI = 3.3, where layer no. 1 is the canopy top and layer no. 15 the canopy bottom. The inputs for the bottom four layers were obtained from *Croton* leaf PAR response curves, and illustrate decreasing amounts of photosynthesis. In this simulation, between 0712 and 1612 apparent solar time, none of the layers had negative CO_2 uptake rates because the leaf respiration rates were low (0.68, 0.82, and 0.32 mg/dm^2 per hour for *Goethalsia, Cecropia,* and *Croton,* respectively). If the leaf respiration rates were higher, respiration would exceed photosynthesis, as it did in the maize simulations (Table 1).

Up to 60% diffuse radiation did not decrease canopy photosynthesis materially (Fig. 7). On a daily basis, the total PAR would be 257, 210, 138, and 109 cal/cm^2 for 10, 30, 60, and 90% diffuse radiation, respectively. A moderate amount of diffuse radiation (30 and 60%) gave a more favorable distribution of radiation for photosynthesis on leaves deep within the plant canopy.

Figures 3 and 5 showed that radiation was attenuated with depth into a plant canopy, and that CO_2 fixation decreased with depth and perhaps reached a point where respiration exceeded photosynthesis. Less radiant energy deep within a canopy also means less energy available to drive the

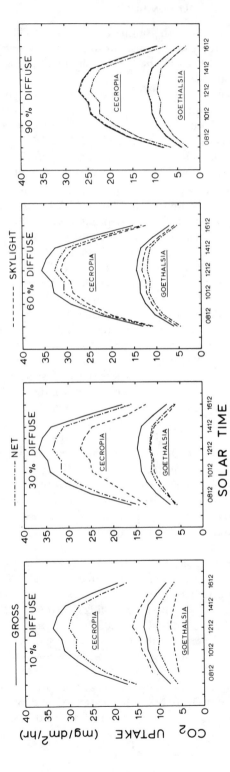

Figure 7. Daily course of predicted CO_2 uptake per unit ground area by *Goethalsia* and by *Cecropia* under 10, 30, 60, and 90% diffuse sky-source radiation. LAI = 3.3. In addition to the gross photosynthesis and net photosynthesis, the amount of gross photosynthesis that would be supported by skylight sources alone is shown. Simulations of Turrialba, Costa Rica condition, 14 Nov. 1967. (Allen et al., 1974).

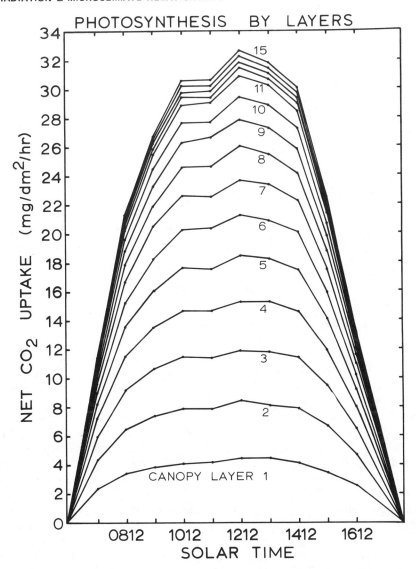

Figure 8. Diurnal course of simulated net photosynthesis per unit ground area for 11 layers of *Cecropia* leaves of a modeled forest at Turrialba, Costa Rica, 14 Nov. 1967. LAI = 3.3. The series of curves, from bottom to top of the figure, represent the added contributions from layer 1 (at the top of the canopy) to layer 15 (at the bottom of the canopy). The area between the curves represents the simulated net photosynthesis of the respective layers. (Allen et al., 1974).

processes of transpiration and sensible heat exchange with the atmosphere. Early experimental work by Begg et al. (1964) in bulrush millet (*Panicum* sp.) showed the source distribution of water vapor (Fig. 9). The greatest source of energy for evaporation is in the upper parts of the canopy.

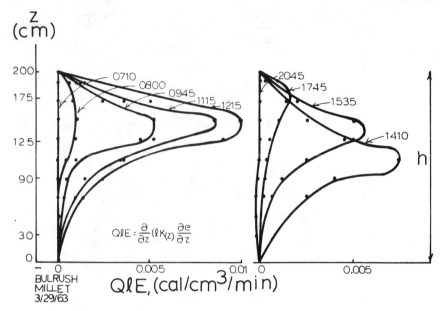

Figure 9. Latent heat source profiles on a leaf area basis, 29 March 1963. A. 0715 to 1215 hour. B. 1410 to 2045 hour. (Begg et al., 1964).

Table 1 also showed the source intensity distribution with height of water vapor (latent heat) and sensible heat for a SPAM simulation of maize. The maximum source intensity for water vapor was at a height slightly below that of CO_2 sink intensity in this simulation. The source intensities are lower at the top of the canopy because the leaf area density is low (Table 1), but the activity per unit leaf area (source or sink intensity per leaf area density) would be high. The information in Table 1, Figures 5 and 9, shows that the lower rates of exchange of CO_2, water vapor, and sensible heat occur in the bottom layers of plant canopies. The CO_2 environment does not change enough at the base of dense plant canopies to affect CO_2 uptake, because PAR, rather than CO_2, limits photosynthesis at the bottom of the canopy. Respiration in the soil or by the lower canopy vegetation raises the CO_2 concentration only slightly in open crops such as trees or maize (Allen & Lemon, 1975; Lemon, 1967; Lemon et al., 1971; Lemon & Wright, 1969). However, CO_2 concentration at the base of short dense crops such as red clover may be higher (Lemon, 1965).

Water vapor concentrations usually increase toward the base of all crops during the daytime (Allen & Lemon, 1975; Begg et al., 1964; Lemon, 1965, 1967; Lemon et al., 1971). Likewise, air temperature generally increases with depth in open crops, but it may decrease by as much as 5C in short, dense crops such as red clover (Lemon, 1965) or soybeans (Lemon, unpublished). The wind speeds and eddy diffusivities are usually lower at the base of short, dense crops than taller, more open crops (Lemon, 1966), and these factors cause larger microclimate modifications in the short, dense

crops. Foliar display, i.e., horizontal versus vertical leaf arrangement, influences radiation penetration and microclimate also (Lemon et al., 1973;
Shawcroft et al., 1974).

RADIATION QUALITY

Leaf pigments absorb more strongly in the PAR spectrum than in the
NIR spectrum, and this differential absorption causes shifts in the average
spectral quality of radiation with depth into plant canopies. Allen and
Brown (1965) reported percent transmission of radiation of PAR, NIR, and
SW radiation into a maize canopy. At midday, the NIR/PAR ratio at the
base of the canopy (at an LAI of 3.8) was 2:1, and by 1700 EST, the ratio
was 2.5:1 (Fig. 3). Sinclair and Lemon (1973) compared 730 nm/660 nm
ratios in maize for solar elevation angles ranging from 30° to 63° and reported ratios of up to 20:1 at low solar elevation angles (Table 2). NIR/PAR
ratios are comparable to 730 nm/660 nm ratios (Fig. 1).

Bimodal distributions of 660 nm and 730 nm radiation by Sinclair and
Lemon (1973) showed relative enrichment of 730 nm/660 nm radiation in
both sunflecks and shaded regions throughout the depth of a maize crop.
The irradiance ratio of 730 nm radiation was larger than the irradiance ratio
of 660 nm radiation at all sampling heights down within the canopy, both in
sunflecks and shadows. In fact, the irradiance ratio of 730 nm radiation in
sunflecks sometimes exceeded 1.0, especially in the upper midcanopy. Sometimes the NIR irradiance in sunflecks at 40 cm in maize exceeded NIR irradiance above the canopy (Yocum et al., 1964).

Theoretical computations of PAR and NIR radiation within a range of
plant canopies have been made using the SPAM computer simulation model.
Allen, Stewart, and Lemon (1974) analyzed a Costa Rican tropical rain
forest with 10, 30, 60, and 90% diffuse source of irradiance for leaf area indices of 0.33, 1.10, 2.20, and 3.30 (Table 3). The forest had a planophile,
regular distribution of leaves. The input leaf transmissivity for PAR and NIR
was 0.05 and 0.36, respectively, and the input leaf reflectivity for PAR and
NIR was 0.05 and 0.36, respectively, and the input leaf reflectivity for PAR

Table 2. The normalized ratio of 730 nm/660 nm irradiance at various heights in Cornell
M-3 maize on 11 Aug. 1969, at Ithaca, New York (Sinclair & Lemon, 1973)

Time	Solar elevation angle	Air mass	Height cm and LAI above sensor ( )			
			200 (0.32)	160 (1.09)	120 (1.94)	20 (3.26)
0900	44.3°	1.43	0.98	1.20	4.90	20.56
1045	60.8°	1.15	1.14	1.43	2.88	4.78
1215	63.3°	1.12	1.20	1.52	3.12	4.12
1315	60.2°	1.15	1.10	1.68	3.08	2.57
1415	51.4°	1.28	1.06	1.40	2.53	3.38
1515	40.7°	1.53	1.06	1.49	3.35	11.50
1615	29.5°	2.03	1.12	1.69	3.55	17.34

Table 3. The ratio of percent penetration of NIR to percent penetration of PAR
(normalized ratio of NIR/PAR irradiance) computed by the SPAM model for a
Costa Rican tropical rain forest based on 14 Nov. 1967 input data,
Turrialba, Costa Rica

Apparent solar time	Solar elevation	Air mass	LAI			
			0.33	1.10	1.98	3.30
		10% Diffuse				
0812	33.1	1.83	1.16	1.64	2.45	4.36
1012	55.6	1.21	1.13	1.50	2.04	3.24
1212	61.9	1.13	1.13	1.49	2.00	3.06
1412	47.25	1.36	1.13	1.51	2.08	3.24
1612	22.1	2.66	1.17	1.68	2.52	4.50
		30% Diffuse				
0812	33.1	1.83	--	1.63	2.62	4.12
1012	55.6	1.21	--	1.52	2.26	3.32
1212	61.9	1.13	--	1.51	2.22	3.19
1412	47.25	1.36	--	1.53	2.29	3.35
1612	22.1	2.66	--	1.65	2.72	4.41
		60% Diffuse				
0812	33.1	1.83	--	1.59	2.49	3.79
1012	55.6	1.21	--	1.55	2.34	3.46
1212	61.9	1.13	--	1.55	2.33	3.37
1412	47.25	1.36	--	1.56	2.34	3.44
1612	22.1	2.66	--	1.61	2.55	3.88
		90% Diffuse				
0812	33.1	1.83	--	1.57	2.38	3.55
1012	55.6	1.21	--	1.59	2.43	3.56
1212	61.9	1.13	--	1.59	2.44	3.56
1412	47.25	1.36	--	1.58	2.42	3.54
1612	22.1	2.66	--	1.54	2.33	3.45

and NIR was 0.075 and 0.26, respectively. The input ground level albedo
was 0.1 for both PAR and NIR. Generally NIR/PAR ratios increased with
depth (or cumulative LAI) into the canopy. The effect was greatest at low
solar elevation angles with clear skies (low diffuse radiation). Computer
simulation results were in general agreement with experimental observations.

The relative enrichment of 730 nm/660 nm radiation is much greater in
shade than in sunflecks. Normalized irradiance ratios measured on 14 Aug.
1961, at 1200 EST (a clear day) at the base of a maize crop were 7.75 and
1.05 in a shady spot and in a sunfleck, respectively (adapted from data of
Yocum et al., 1964). Another clear-day measurement on 27 Aug. 1961 at
1102 EST gave normalized 730 nm/660 nm irradiance ratios of 3.09 and 1.02
for shade and sunfleck, respectively. The relative enrichment of NIR to PAR
near midday at the 40-cm height in this maize canopy (Fig. 1) was 1.06 in a
sunfleck and 5.4 in a shady spot. SPAM simulations (Table 4) showed a
normalized NIR/PAR irradiance ratio in a sunfleck (at a cumulative LAI of
3.3) of about 1.14 during midday, clear-sky (10% diffuse) conditions. In
shade, the model predicted NIR/PAR to be about 10:1. Furthermore, under

Table 4. Percent NIR in sunflecks as a function of depth into a canopy (cumulative LAI) and the ratio of percent penetration of NIR to percent penetration of PAR (normalized ratio of NIR/PAR irradiance) computed by the SPAM model for a Costa Rican tropical rain forest based on 14 Nov. 1967 input data, Turrialba, Costa Rica

Apparent solar time	Percent diffuse	% Sunflect NIR	% NIR/% PAR (Sunfleck)	% NIR/% PAR (Shade)
		LAI 1.1		
0812	16.7	111	1.24	3.28
1012	10.0	114	1.20	4.13
1212	10.0	114	1.20	4.12
1412	10.0	114	1.20	4.15
1612	33.3	100	1.31	2.28
		LAI 2.2		
0812	16.7	101	1.19	5.12
1012	10.0	109	1.19	6.99
1212	10.0	109	1.19	7.06
1412	10.0	109	1.19	7.02
1612	33.3	100	1.30	3.93
		LAI 3.3		
0812	16.7	96	1.15	8.39
1012	10.0	102	1.13	9.75
1212	10.0	102	1.14	10.0
1412	10.0	102	1.13	10.0
1612	33.3	80	1.23	5.99

these clear-sky simulations, the amount of NIR in sunflecks at LAI = 1.1 was 14% greater than the above-canopy NIR.

Both experimental data and simulations not only showed relative enrichment of 730 nm (and NIR) irradiance with respect to 660 nm (and PAR) irradiance with depth into the canopy, but also showed that the relative enrichment is much greater in shady areas than in sunflecks. NIR does not contribute to photosynthesis, but it does contribute to the energy balance inputs to leaves; 730 nm/660 nm enrichment with depth into canopies may affect photomorphogenic processes differentially.

RADIATION FLUCTUATIONS

Radiation in plant canopies occurs across a wide range of periodicities and random fluctuations. Seasonal and diurnal cycles are obvious. Somewhat less obvious are variations due to cloudiness and the interaction of the daily progression of the sun across the sky with season, latitude, slope, row orientation, and plant geometry (Allen, 1974). Further down the scale are irradiance flickers due to wind movement of plant leaves. Figure 10 shows the type of irradiance fluctuations due to the interaction of the daily progression of the sun across the sky and crop geometry. These data were taken with fixed position net radiometers and averaged over 15 min, so the high

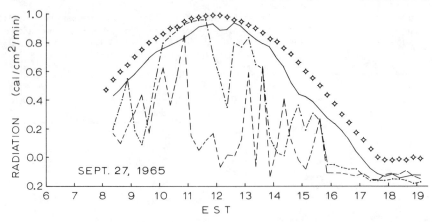

Figure 10. Diurnal course of 15-min average shortwave radiation above, net radiation above, and net radiation at two levels within a corn crop canopy at fixed positions. Legend: The symbol (O) is shortwave radiation above the crop; the solid line is net radiation at 300 cm above the crop; the dot-dash line is net radiation at 150 cm, and the broken line is net radiation at 80 cm. Each 15-min datum is an average of 7 points.

frequency fluctuations due to leaf flutter have been filtered out. Cumulus clouds cause irradiance fluctuations with periods of the order of 3 minutes, and the fluctuations are imposed externally. Here we will be mostly concerned with higher frequency fluctuations caused by wind flutter.

Garner and Allard (1931) conducted a classic experiment on the response of plants to intermittent irradiance of various frequencies of interruption. Rabinowitch (1956) illustrated that at interrupt frequencies of one per second or greater, plants may be able to utilize PAR twice as efficiently as they would with a daily photoperiod. Rabinowitch also illustrated a drop in effectiveness of irradiance with periods of 10 to 100 sec; however, this drop was probably associated with photoperiod effects, rather than light capture and enzyme kinetics effects. Rabinowitch's (1956) intermittency factors were constructed for equal periods of irradiance and *total* darkness. Under field conditions, light fluctuations do not decrease to total darkness. Therefore, his interpretations may not be strictly applicable to field conditions.

Figure 11 illustrates an irradiance fluctuation recording obtained using a photocell in maize at a 150-cm height at 1509 to 1514 EST, 4 Oct. 1963, near Ithaca, New York (Allen & Lemon, unpublished). In general, the photoexposure alternated back and forth between shaded and exposure conditions. Photocells mounted at four other locations showed conditions ranging from mostly fully exposed to mostly fully shaded. One photocell showed somewhat more rapid irradiance fluctuations than illustrated here.

The frequency of leaf flutter was related to wind speed. Since the skin-friction drag of flowing fluid on a flexible body is related to the square of fluid speed, the irradiance fluctuations of Figure 11 were analyzed over short time periods to relate fluctuation frequency to average wind speeds. Figure

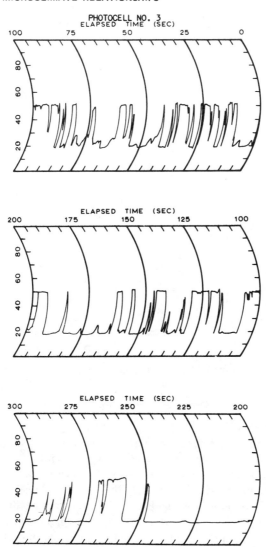

Figure 11. Light fluctuation in corn at a 150 cm height from 1509 to 1514 hour EST, 4 Oct. 1963. Ellis Hollow, Ithaca, New York.

12 shows leaf flutter frequency as a function of wind speed. A second-degree curve was drawn through the data of the form

$$f = b \; u^2 \tag{3}$$

where f = frequency (cycles/sec), u = wind speed (cm/sec), and b = 0.05.

Subsequently, Desjardins, Sinclair, and Lemon (1973) measured fluctuations of PAR at four levels in a maize crop with traversing sensors. Variance spectra were computed using both traversing and fixed sensors. In general,

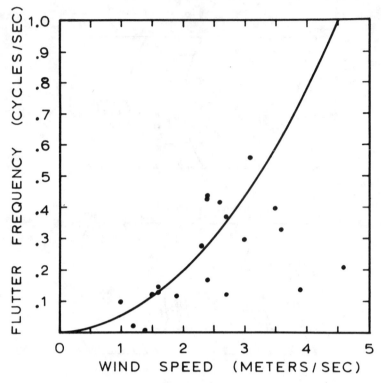

Figure 12. Frequency of corn leaf flutter at 150 cm as a function of wind speed at 300 cm. 1509 to 1514 EST, 4 Oct. 1963, Ellis Hollow, Ithaca, New York.

they found (i) more high frequency fluctuations at the top of the maize crop than at the bottom, (ii) more high frequency fluctuations with flexible leaf and stalk maize than with rigid leaf and stalk cultivars, and (iii) more high frequency fluctuations with high than with low wind. Mostly low-frequency fluctuations with periods from 100 to 10 sec occurred at the bottom of the maize canopy with above-crop wind speeds of 148 cm/sec, whereas almost all the variance was in periods shorter than 10 sec with wind of 305 cm/sec.

Light fluctuation effects on photosynthesis have been investigated by several researchers (McCree & Loomis, 1969; Huxley, 1969; Pollard, 1970; Ino, 1975; Kriedemann et al., 1973). Rapid fluctuations of radiation may have profound, yet unexplored, implications for plant growth and development. Rapid light fluctuations increase the quantum efficiency of CO_2 fixation by algae (Emerson & Arnold, 1932). However, efficiencies were increased at frequencies greater than 50 cycles/sec which is substantially greater than the rates observed in crop canopies (Norman & Tanner, 1969; Desjardins et al., 1973). McCree and Loomis (1969) found a 20% increase in the CO_2 assimilation rate of shade-adapted cucumbers (*Cucumis sativus* L.) by alternating 2 sec or less of saturating irradiance with periods of darkness of equal duration. This increase in CO_2 assimilation was not as great when low irradiances were substituted for the dark periods. Kriedemann et al. (1973)

observed over a 50% increase in the quantum efficiency of CO_2 assimilation for grape (*Vitis* sp.) leaves exposed to 0.5 sec of radiation alternated with 1.5 sec of darkness as compared with continuous radiation of equal quantity.

Stomata may also respond to alternating radiation differently than to steady irradiation. Virgin (1956) showed that the transpiration rate of wheat (*Triticum aestivum* L.) seedlings exposed to intermittent radiation with a period of 5 sec was equal to the transpiration rate under continuous radiation of equal quantity. Since stomatal pores typically open in radiation and close in darkness, apparently they have the ability to integrate the effects of radiation alternating at this frequency. Calculating stomatal resistance, based on the average effect of long-term irradiation alternating "on" and "off", would lead to higher estimated values than calculating stomatal resistance based on the average irradiance.

Radiation quality is also affected by rapid fluctuations in sunflecks and shade. Since the relative enrichment of 730 nm/660 nm radiation is much greater in shade than in sunflecks (Fig. 1 and Table 4), wind flicker of leaves should cause a reduction in the effects of far-red enrichment in the lower leaf canopy. Even though the proportion of area in sunflecks is small, about half the total solar energy at the base of the maize canopy illustrated in Figure 1 near midday appears in sunflecks. However, near the end of the day the proportion of energy in sunflecks is smaller so wind movement of leaves would not be as effective in changing the difference in 730 nm/660 nm relative enrichment between shaded and sunfleck leaves. On the other hand (Table 5) during low solar angle periods, the relative enrichment in shade may be less.

Table 5. Comparison of 80-cm row width model predictions of daily total direct-beam radiation penetration in erect-leaf and arch-leaf corn grown in Ellis Hollow near Ithaca, New York in 1970. Radiation units are cal/cm^2 per day (Allen, 1973)

Date and daily total irradiation	Height	Downward cumulative LAI Erect	Arch	Intercepted radiation Erect Daily total	Percent	Arch Daily total	Percent	Arch to erect ratio
	cm				%		%	
3 July	0	0.956	1.066	202	32.8	252	40.9	1.25
(617)	40	0.298	0.200	162	26.2	179	29.1	1.11
14 July	0	2.319	2.553	345	57.1	443	73.5	1.29
(604)	40	1.949	1.773	323	53.4	405	63.7	1.26
	100	0.308	0.099	196	30.7	39	6.1	0.20
19 July	0	2.868	3.223	382	64.3	481	80.9	1.26
(595)	40	1.966	1.950	365	61.3	456	76.6	1.25
	100	0.352	0.146	279	47.0	221	37.1	0.79
10 August	0	3.560	4.253	441	82.0	512	95.3	1.16
(538)	40	3.538	4.152	434	80.7	510	94.9	1.18
	100	3.132	3.022	352	65.4	464	86.3	1.32
	140	2.278	2.054	255	47.3	356	66.2	1.40
	160	1.342	0.820	125	23.3	203	37.8	1.62
	220	0.466	0.118	32	5.9	39	7.3	1.24

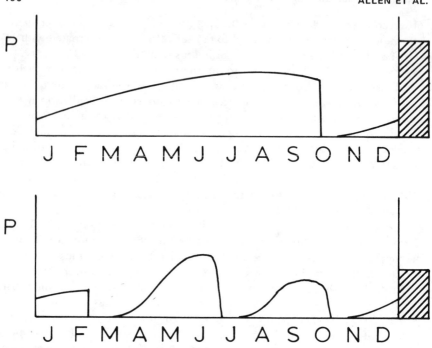

Figure 13. Illustration of theoretical photosynthesis or productivity, *P*, of a single, long-term crop as compared with three short-term sequential crops. The height of the bar graph at the end illustrates the relative total annual production of the area under the curves.

APPLICATIONS TO SEQUENTIAL CROPPING SYSTEMS

Sequential cropping systems offer a better total annual use of land than does the single crop system, when each of the component crops has a relatively short growing season. For example, maize followed by soybeans, followed by rye (*Secale cereale* L.) are three crops which effectively utilize the whole year in north Florida (G. M. Prine, 1975, personal communication; Prine et al., 1975; Guilarte et al., 1975).[2] However, the soil is not covered with an effective light-capturing, vegetative canopy during much of the growing season with this cropping system. In fact, for several weeks of prime growing season during the summer months—the time between senescence of one crop, and the development of an effective canopy by the sequential crop —much potential solar energy is not being utilized for photosynthesis. Not only is solar energy not being utilized during these periods, also more fuel is required for harvesting, land preparation, planting, and weed control for a subsequent crop. Theoretically, a long-season crop, which remained productive for much of the subtropical growing season from March to November,

---

[2]R. E. Perez-Levy, 1975. Relay crops after corn under irrigation in a multiple cropping system. M.S. Thesis, University of Florida. 56 p.

would be most effective in solar energy interception and biological conversion [sugarcane, kenaf (*Hibiscus cannabinus*), napiergrass (*Pennisetum purpureum*)]. Figure 13 illustrates the potential annual productivity of a long-term crop as compared with three short-term sequential crops. In this example, relative annual production, illustrated by the cross-hatched bar graph, could be about twice as large for the long-term as compared with the short-term crop.

Figures 14 and 15 show examples of interception, penetration, and percent penetration of direct-beam radiation to ground level in maize. These

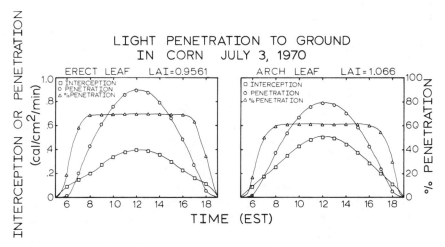

Figure 14. Comparison of model predictions of interception, penetration, and percent penetration of direct-beam radiation in erect-leaf and arch-leaf corn, 3 July 1970.

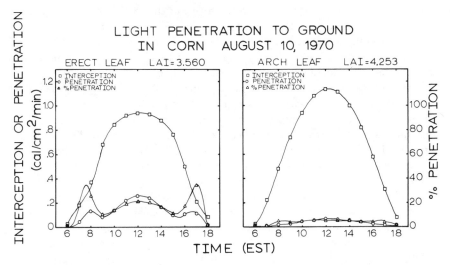

Figure 15. Comparison of model predictions of interception, penetration, and percent penetration of direct-beam radiation in erect-leaf and arch-leaf corn, 10 Aug. 1970.

figures are based on a light penetration model by Allen (1974) modified and presented by Allen (1973). The model showed good agreement with penetration data measured in the field with traversing sensors. Table 5 shows the percent of daily total radiation computed as intercepted by erect-leaf or arch-leaf maize canopies with LAI ranging from 0.96 to 4.25. With an LAI of about 1, about 60% of daily direct-beam radiation would be expected to reach the soil in 80-cm width rows. About 45 days (19 May to 3 July) were needed for this maize to achieve an LAI of about 1. By 19 July, 16 days later, the crop had quadrupled in leaf area and the light penetration model predicted that between 65% (erect-leaf) to 80% (arch-leaf) of direct-beam radiation would be intercepted daily. Mature maize canopies are capable of fixing about 80 mg CO_2/cm^2 per hour during peak daytime rates or about 700 mg/cm^2 per day (Baker & Musgrave, 1964). Furthermore, Baker and Musgrave (1964) showed that the maximum canopy photosynthesis rate for maize was about 6 mg/dm^2 per hour under full sunlight when the leaf area index was 0.36. Guilarte, Perez-Levy, and Prine (1975) pointed out that narrow row spacings and high plant populations enhanced yields of the first crop (maize) and the second crops [soybeans, peanuts (*Arachis hypogaea* L.), southern peas (*Pisum* sp.), or pigeon peas (*Cajanus cajan*)]. Clearly, ground cover is a limiting factor in maximizing yields in sequential cropping systems.

As an example, if we assume that about 1 month is lost between the senescence of one crop and the establishment to an LAI of 1.0 of the following crop, we can compute the photosynthesis potential that is not being utilized. Milaknovitch (see Hess, 1959, p. 133) computed daily solar radiation as a function of latitude and time of year assuming the atmosphere transmitted 0.7 of a vertical beam. Over 500 cal/cm^2 per day would impinge on the earth's surface during the month of July from 0 to 40°N latitude. Assuming 50% cloudiness with 50% reflectivity (London, see Hess, 1959, p. 134), about 375 cal/cm^2 per day would arrive at the earth's surface. Yocum, Allen, and Lemon (1964) computed about 6% conversion of total solar energy into biomass during the active growing season of maize. These figures translate into about 700 cal/cm^2 per month, or 180 quintals/ha per month of dry matter. These figures agreed closely with computations from data of Baker and Musgrave (1964), who found nearly 700 mg CO_2/dm^2 per day fixed (21 g/dm^2 per month). With a molecular weight ratio of CH_2O to CO_2 of 30/44 = 0.68, this would be a potential dry matter accumulation of 140 quintals/ha per month. Even if we assume that a canopy of leaves would utilize only a half or a third of the radiation as effectively as this example, we still see that much solar energy is *not* utilized during favorable periods of solar radiation, and usually, favorable periods of rainfall.

SPAM computer simulations of net photosynthesis were run at LAI values of 1.1, 2.6, and 4.3 for sugarcane, maize, soybeans, and rye under ideal radiation conditions. The same leaf photosynthetic response curve of maize and sugarcane were used (both are C_4 plants). Simulations at 800, 1000, 1200, 1400, and 1600 hours were summed to give 10-hour net photosynthesis rates. Daily net photosynthesis versus LAI curves were drawn, and applied to LAI versus data from planting curves for the crops such as those

Table 6. Summary of experimental data on productivity of sugarcane, maize, soybeans, and rye. Source of data or estimates are footnoted

Crop	Leaf photosynthesis rate	Crop growth rate	Yield of harvestable product
	mg CO_2/dm^2 per hour	g/m^2 per day	quintals/ha
Sugarcane	60*	25¶	140¶ (sucrose)
Maize	60†	25#	60‡‡ (grain)
Soybean	45‡	15#	25§§ (beans)
Winter rye	30§	5††	0¶¶ (grain)

* Tropical grasses, El-Sharkawy and Hesketh (1965); Irvine (1975).
† Hesketh (1963)
‡ Dornhoff and Shibles (1971).
§ Estimated from oat data, El-Sharkawy and Hesketh (1965).
¶ Bull and Glasziou (1975).
# Buttery (1970).
†† Estimated from winter rye production, Dunavin (1975).
‡‡ Guilarte et al. (1975).
§§ Hanway and Weber (1971).
¶¶ Winter rye does not have enough time to produce grain under subtropical Florida triple sequential cropping (R. E. Perez-Levy, 1975. Relay crops after corn under irrigation in a multiple cropping system. M.S. Thesis, University of Florida. 56 p.)

illustrated in Figure 13. The predicted CO_2 uptake for each crop was summed at 10-day intervals across the growing period for maize (120 days), soybeans (110 days), and rye (85 days), and at 30-day intervals for sugarcane (330 days). The predicted CO_2 uptake rates were converted to dry matter accumulation rates. These model simulations and assumptions yielded potential dry matter production of 1,000, 280, 170, and 30 quintals/ha for crops of sugarcane, maize, soybeans, and winter rye, respectively. (The predicted rye production rate was low because the growth period allowed was short (85 days) during the winter season). These simulations predict that potential dry matter productivity could be about twice as large with continuous plant cover by a vigorous crop as it could be with three sequential crops during the same annual cycle.

Experimental production data support the general conclusions of the simulations of CO_2 uptake (Table 6). Crop growth rates (dry matter production rates) of maize and sugarcane are similar during the maximum growth rate period (about 25 g/m^2 per day). Soybean growth rate is somewhat lower, about 15 g/m^2 per day and rye growth rate is estimated to be 5 g/m^2 per day. Maximum leaf photosynthesis rates (Table 6) would appear to support much larger crop growth rates, however part of the photosynthate is utilized in growth respiration and maintenance respiration.

Estimates of total harvest range from 140 quintals/ha of sugar from sugarcane, 60 quintals/ha of grain from maize, 25 quintals/ha of beans from soybeans and no grain from rye (the growing season is not long enough for rye to develop into grain, Dunavin, 1975).[3] The mass of harvestable product

---

[3] R. E. Perez-Levy, 1975. Relay crops after corn.

for the full season crop is still greater than for the sequential crops, although the relative difference is smaller than for the dry matter predictions from the SPAM simulations. However, the long-term crop appears to have the theoretical advantage in terms of light harvesting potential, although pests, diseases, weeds, or climate may change the advantages in reality.

As a corollary to the more efficient light capture of a long-term crop, crops with longer seed filling periods (Daynard et al., 1971) may be more productive at less expense than sequential crops.

Row orientation may influence direct-beam radiation interception in canopies, especially at higher latitudes (Allen, 1974).

Most of the introductory material on radiation interception, 730 nm/ 660 nm ratios, source and sink distribution of CO_2, and water vapor, and radiation fluctuations in canopies applied directly to sequential types of multiple cropping systems. Photomorphogenesis and weed germination may be mediated by the ratios of 730 nm/660 nm radiation in the predominantly shaded areas. Evapotranspiration should be less in developing crops than in fully mature crops, but with more water lost directly from the soil surface. Figure 16 shows that at LAI's less than 2, the loss of water directly from the soil may be important, whereas at LAI's above 2, the ground is shaded sufficiently to reduce soil water losses (Lemon et al., 1973; Shawcroft et al., 1974). Hence, sequential cropping which leaves a green blank in the middle of summer should have a lower overall water-use efficiency because of direct evaporation from the soil.

APPLICATION TO INTERCROPPING SYSTEMS

Intercropping systems are more complex than monocultures or sequential systems. The display of phytoelements will vary both in space and time depending upon interspecific competition as well as intraspecific competition. The system could vary as widely as overstory crops with coffee (*Coffea* sp.) or cacao (*Theobroma cacao*) (e.g., Jose, 1968) or legume-grass pasture mixtures (e.g., Kretchmer et al., 1973). Frequently, one crop will be taller and will tend to dominate the PAR environment. Sometimes the dominant (taller) species will be more or less permanent, although the cover will be broken and incomplete like in the shade production of coffee. Hart (1974) modified Odum's (1971) classification of interaction between two species populations as follows:

> *Commensalistic Polyculture:* the interaction between crop species has a positive net effect on one species and no observable effect (negative effect equals positive effect) on the other species.
>
> *Amensalistic Polyculture:* the interaction between crop species has a negative net effect on one species and no observable effect (negative effect equals positive effect) on the other species.
>
> *Monopolistic Polyculture:* the interaction between crop species has a positive net effect on one species and a negative effect on the other species.

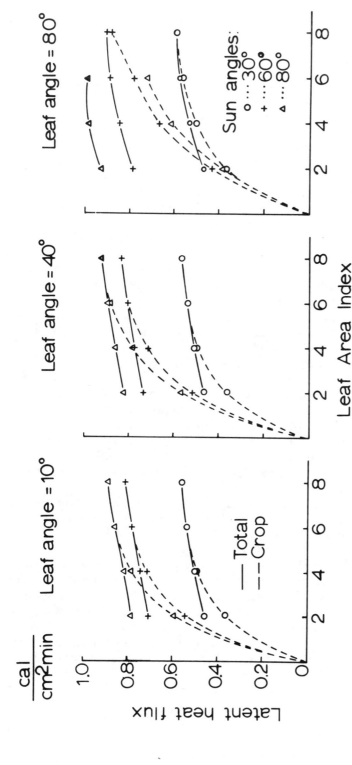

Figure 16. Simulation of corn crop leaf angle and leaf area (LAI) influence on evapotranspiration under various sun angles with other climate conditions held constant. Inputs for this simulation were: date, 18 Aug. 1968; 72.97°N for 30° sun angle; 42.70°N for 60° sun angle; 21.68°N for 80° sun angle; reference height temperature, humidity, and wind speed: 20.2C, 66% R.H., and 276 cm/sec; corn crop base level respiration rate: 15 mg CO_2/cm^2 per hour at temperature of 302.2K.

Inhibitory Polyculture: the interaction between crop species has a net negative effect on all species.

Radiation interception, which drives photosynthesis and evapotranspiration, will be more complex in these systems. The degree of success or failure of polycultures may reside in part on spatial and/or temporal display of phytoelements which minimizes competition for PAR.

Intercropping in mechanized agriculture is seldom found, except for certain tree crops, grass-legume pasture systems, and nurse crops for establishing seedlings. Even intercropping of varieties or cultivars of the same species is seldom practiced, although there might be some advantage in prevention of pathological disasters, if a cultivar is susceptible to certain diseases.

Since the dominant species in polycultures or intercropping systems seldom develops complete canopy closure, it is difficult to apply the previous material on radiation quality, photosynthesis, evapotranspiration, and radiation fluctuation to these systems. However, some qualitative inferences will be drawn.

First, lower canopy vegetation will receive less total solar radiation. Plants that are shade-intolerant are not as likely to thrive as shade-tolerant plants. The relative enrichment of 730 nm/660 nm radiation will be greater in the lower canopy than in the upper canopy. The relative enrichment may affect photomorphogenic processes (Hendricks & Borthwick, 1967). Their relative enrichment will be much greater near sunset than midday, and if the total plant is in the lower parts of the canopy, the effect on such plants may be amplified. This type of phytochrome mediated effect may be greater for intercropping systems in north-south rows than in east-west rows, because less radiation would be received near sunset between the rows in the north-south system (Allen, 1974) by shorter plants.

Less solar radiation beneath a taller canopy may make establishment of a shade-intolerant crop in an existing crop difficult or impossible. The C_4 plants are less likely to succeed than C_3 plants, unless they grow taller in a polyculture system.

Evapotranspiration would be expected to be less for the lower canopy under polyculture, as well as monoculture systems. This could lead to less water stress, unless the root system competition for water was more severe than the reduction of evaporative demand above ground.

Radiation fluctuations on lower level vegetation would vary depending upon leaf size, wind speed, and leaf dispersion (random, regular, or clumped) in the upper level vegetation. Cumulus clouds and the daily progression of the sun interacting with upper canopy gaps could also lead to PAR fluctuations. The type of photosynthesis or stomatal response (McCree & Loomis, 1969; Virgin, 1956) could influence the adaptability of lower level vegetation.

Finally, the success or failure of polycultures may depend heavily on photoperiod adaptability of the crops used in combination. Photoperiod has a large influence on some plants and may have an even greater influence in intercropping systems.

Most of the factors mentioned here for lower canopy vegetation would have less importance for upper canopy vegetation. Radiation loads would be heavier, potential for PAR-driven photosynthesis greater, evaporative and wind stresses greater, and 730 nm/660 nm irradiance ratios smaller in upper canopy vegetation.

DISCUSSION

Much work in monoculture or near monoculture canopies has been done to describe the radiation distribution and microclimate. Presently, renewed interest in multiple cropping has developed, both in high and low technology societies (Hart, 1974; Bradfield, 1972). Some aspects of sequential cropping seem very much like rotations, particularly in temperate climate agriculture. Sequential cropping attempts to gain more agricultural productivity by rapid replacement of monocultures. However, we indicate herein that much available solar energy is not utilized between the removal of one crop and the establishment of another in this system of sequential monoculture. One area for research would be the replacement of sequential monoculture with a monoculture with a long-term filling season, or methods of establishing a sequential or relay crop simultaneously with the first crop, or while the first crop is maturing. Growth analyses should be investigated in more detail to understand fundamental agroecological processes.

Intercropping seems much more complex than sequential monoculture. Relay cropping is intermediate to sequential monoculture and intercropping or polyculture. Relay crop establishment in the low light regime and high humidity regime at the base of another crop may have special problems not encountered in sequential monocultures or intercropping systems. Research should be extended to understand the competition for space and related microclimate entities. Research should extend beyond just determining which crops will work in a polyculture to the point of understanding reasons. Descriptive definitions of positive and negative results are not enough, but plant interactions, as a function of season, time of planting, stage of development, and climatic factors need to be determined. Understanding crop ecology of monoculture has not been rapid; understanding the crop ecology of polycultures has begun (e.g., Donald, 1963) but the permutations and combinations are numerous, and the problems of adapting polycultures to mechanized agriculture, or mechanized agriculture to polycultures, are great.

SUMMARY

Radiation source and source distribution (direct-beam, skylight) above crops, radiation quantity relationships to photosynthesis, microclimate, and the energy balance of crops, radiation quality in crops, and radiation fluctuations in crops were discussed in detail for monoculture systems. This information was applied to aspects of photosynthesis and yield in sequential cropping systems and intercropping systems.

Analyses of both experimental crop growth data and photosynthesis simulations showed that sequential crops would yield more per year than a single annual short-term crop. However, these analyses also showed that there was a significant loss of yield potential during the period between the harvest of one crop and the establishment of ground cover by a sequential crop due to the lack of a photosynthesizing ground cover. Also, these analyses showed that photosynthesis and yield potential were greater for continuous, long-term (one year) crops than for sequential crops. Increasing the length of seed-filling period (or other yield-filling period) and decreasing the period for establishing effective ground cover should utilize more effectively the radiant energy available in sequential cropping systems.

Radiation quality (730 nm/660 nm ratios) may affect morphogenesis responses of shorter plants in intercropped systems. Furthermore, the quantity of radiant energy to drive photosynthesis will also be less for shorter vegetation in these systems. Shade tolerance to both shifts in radiation spectral quality and to radiation quantity should be considered in choices of crops for intercropped systems.

LITERATURE CITED

Allen, L. H., Jr. 1973. Crop micrometeorology: A. Wide-row Light penetration. B. Carbon dioxide enrichment and diffusion. Ph.D. Thesis, Cornell University, 366 p. Univ. Microfilms Diss. Abstr. 73-14, 716.

Allen, L. H., Jr. 1974. Model of light penetration into a wide row crop. Agron. J. 66: 41-47.

Allen, L. H., Jr., and K. W. Brown. 1965. Shortwave radiation in a corn crop. Agron. J. 57:575-580.

Allen, L. H., Jr., and E. R. Lemon. 1972. Net radiation frequency distribution in a corn crop. Boundary-Layer Meteorol. 3:246-254.

Allen, L. H., Jr., and E. R. Lemon. 1976. Carbon dioxide exchange and turbulence in a Costa Rican forest. p. 265-308. In J. L. Monteith (ed.) Vegetation and the atmosphere. Vol. 2. Academic Press, London.

Allen, L. H., Jr., D. W. Stewart, and E. R. Lemon. 1974. Photosynthesis in plant canopies: Effect of light response curves and radiation source geometry. Photosynthetica 8:184-207.

Baker, D. N., and R. B. Musgrave. 1964. The effects of low level moisture stresses on the rate of apparent photosynthesis in corn. Crop Sci. 4:249-253.

Bazzaz, F. A. 1974. Ecophysiology of Ambrosia artemisiifolia: a succesional dominant. Ecology 55:112-119.

Begg, J. E., J. F. Bierhuizen, E. R. Lemon, D. K. Misra, R. O. Slatyer, and W. R. Stern. 1964. Dirunal energy budget and water exchanges in bulrush millet in an area of high solar radiation. Agric. Meteorol. 1:294-312.

Beuerlein, J. E., and J. W. Pendleton. 1971. Photosynthetic rates and light saturation curves of individual soybean leaves under field conditions. Crop Sci. 11:217-219.

Björkman, O., and P. Holmgren. 1966. Photosynthetic adaptation to light intensity in plants native to shaded and exposed habitats. Physiol. Plant. 19:854-859.

Bradfield, R. 1972. Maximizing food production through multiple cropping systems centered on rice. p. 143-163. In Rice, science, and man. IRRI, Los Banos, Philippines.

Bull, T. A., and K. T. Glasziou. 1975. Sugar cane. p. 51-72. In L. T. Evans (ed.) Crop physiology, Cambridge University Press.

Buttery, B. R. 1970. Effects of variation in leaf area index on growth of maize and soybeans. Crop Sci. 10:9-13.

Daynard, T. B., J. W. Tanner, and W. G. Duncan. 1971. Duration of the grain filling period and its relation to grain yield in corn, *Zea mays* L. Crop Sci. 11:45-48.

Desjardins, R. L., T. R. Sinclair, and E. R. Lemon. 1973. Light fluctuations in corn. Agron. J. 65:904-908.

Donald, C. M. 1963. Competition among crop and pasture plants. Adv. Agron. 15:1-118.

Dornhoff, G. M., and R. M. Shibles. 1970. Varietal differences in net photosynthesis of soybean leaves. Crop Sci. 10:42-45.

Dunavin, L. S. 1975. Production of rye and ryegrass forage with sulfur-coated urea and ammonium nitrate. Agron. J. 67:415-417.

Duncan, W. G., R. S. Loomis, W. A. Williams, and R. Hanau. 1967. A model for simulating photosynthesis in plant communities. Hilgardia 38:181-205.

El-Sharkawy, M. A., and J. D. Hesketh. 1965. Photosynthesis among species in relation to characteristics of leaf anatomy and CO_2 diffusion resistances. Crop Sci. 5:517-521.

Emerson, R., and W. Arnold. 1932. A separation of the reactions in photosynthesis by means of intermittent light. J. Gen. Physiol. 15:391-420.

Garner, W. W., and H. A. Allard. 1931. Effect of abnormally long and short alternations of light and darkness on growth and development of plants. J. Agric. Res. 42:629-651.

Guilarte, T. C., R. E. Perez-Levy, and G. M. Prine. 1975. Some double cropping possibilities under irrigation during the warm season in north and west Florida. Soil Crop Sci. Soc. Fla. Proc. 34:138-143.

Hart, R. D. 1974. The design and evaluation of a bean, corn, and manioc polyculture cropping system for the humid tropics. Ph.D. Dissertation, Univ. Fla. 158 p. Diss. Abstr. 75-19, 341.

Hanway, J. J., and C. R. Weber. 1971. Dry matter accumulation in soybean [*Glycine max* (L) Merrill] plants as influenced by N, P, and K fertilization. Agron. J. 63:263-266.

Hendricks, S. B., and H. A. Borthwick. 1967. The function of phytochrome in regulation of plant growth. Proc. Nat. Acad. Sci. USA. 58:2125-2130.

Hesketh, J. D. 1963. Limitations to photosynthesis responsible for differences among species. Crop Sci. 3:493-496.

Hesketh, J. D., and R. B. Musgrave. 1962. Photosynthesis under field conditions. IV. Light studies with individual corn leaves. Crop Sci. 2:311-315.

Hess, S. L. 1959. Introduction to theoretical meteorology. Holt, Rinehart and Winston, New York. 362 p.

Huxley, P. A. 1969. The effect of fluctuating light intensity on plant growth. J. App. Ecol. 6:273-276.

Ino, Y. 1970. The effect of fluctuating light on photosynthesis. p. 68-70. *In* Photosynthesis and utilization of solar energy. Level III. Rep. 1969, Jap. Nat. Subcomm. PP IPB.

Irvine, J. E. 1975. Relations of photosynthetic rates and leaf canopy characters to sugarcane yield. Crop Sci. 15:671-676.

Jose, B. M. 1968. Intercropping cacao with coconut. Coffee and Cacao J. 11:128-130.

Kretchmer, A. E., Jr., J. B. Brolmann, G. H. Snyder, and G. F. Gascho. 1973. Production of six tropical legumes each in combination with three tropical grasses in Florida. Agron. J. 65:890-892.

Kriedemann, P. E., E. Torokfalvy, and R. E. Smart. 1973. Natural occurrence of sunflecks by grapevine leaves. Photosynthetica 7:18-27.

Lemon, E. R. 1965. Micrometeorology and the physiology of plants in their natural environment. p. 203-227. *In* F. C. Stewart (ed.) Plant physiology, Vol. IV-A. Academic Press, New York.

Lemon, E. R. 1966. The impact of the atmospheric environment on the integument of plants. p. 57-69. *In* Proceeding Fourth International Biometeorology Congress, Rutgers University, New Brunswick, N. J. August 1966.

Lemon, E. R. 1967. Aerodynamic studies of CO_2 exchange between the atmosphere and the plant. p. 263-290. *In* Anthony San Pietro, F. A. Greer, and T. J. Army (ed.) Harvesting the sun: Photosynthesis in plant life. Academic Press, New York.

Lemon, E. R., D. W. Stewart, and R. W. Shawcroft. 1971. The sun's work in a cornfield. Science 174:351-378.

Lemon, E. R., D. W. Stewart, R. W. Shawcroft, and S. E. Jensen. 1973. Experiments in predicting evapotranspiration by simulation with a Soil-Plant-Atmosphere Model (SPAM). p. 57–76. In R. R. Bruce, K. W. Flack, and H. M. Taylor (ed.) Field Soil Water Regime. Spec. Pub. No. 5. Soil Sci. Soc. Am., Madison, Wis.

Lemon, E. R., and J. L. Wright. 1969. Photosynthesis under field conditions, XA. Assessing sources and sinks of carbon dioxide in a corn crop using a momentum balance approach. Agron. J. 61:405–411.

McCree, K. J., and R. S. Loomis. 1969. Photosynthesis in fluctuating light. Ecology 50: 422–423.

Moss, D. N. 1962. The limiting carbon dioxide concentration for photosynthesis. Nature 193:587.

Norman, J. M., and C. B. Tanner. 1969. Transient light measurements in plant canopies. Agron. J. 61:847–849.

Odum, E. P. 1971. Fundamentals of ecology. 3rd ed. W. B. Saunders Co., Philadelphia. 574 p.

Pollard, D. F. W. 1970. The effect of rapidly changing light on the rate of photosynthesis in large tooth aspens (Populus grandidentata). Can. J. Biol. 48:823–829.

Prine, G. M., T. C. Guilarte, and W. G. Duncan. 1975. Corn maturity dates for different Florida locations and planting dates based on Growing Degree Days. Soil Crop Sci. Soc. Fla. Proc. 34:134–137.

Rabinowitch, E. I. 1956. Time effects. II. Photosynthesis in intermittent light. p. 1433–1484. In Photosynthesis and related processes. Vol. II, Part 2. Interscience, New York.

Shawcroft, R. W., E. R. Lemon, L. H. Allen, Jr., D. W. Stewart, and S. E. Jensen. 1974. The Soil-Plant-Atmosphere Model and some of its predictions. Agric. Meteorol. 14:287–307.

Sinclair, T. R., and E. R. Lemon. 1973. The distribution of 660 and 730 nm radiation in corn canopies. Solar Energy 15:89–97.

Sinclair, T. R., and E. R. Lemon. 1974. Penetration of photosynthetically active radiation in corn canopies. Agron. J. 66:201–205.

Stephens, G. R., and P. E. Waggoner. 1970. Carbon dioxide exchange of a tropical rain forest. Part I. BioScience 20:1050–1053.

Stewart, D. W. 1970. A simulation of net photosynthesis of field corn. Ph.D. Thesis, Cornell Univ., Ithaca, New York. 132 p. Diss. Abstr. 10–17, 101.

Stewart, D. W., and E. R. Lemon. 1969. The energy budget at the earth's surface: A simulation of net photosynthesis of field corn. Tech. Rep. ECOM 2-68-I-6. Microclimate Investigations, USDA, Ithaca, New York. 132 p.

Tio, M. A. 1962. Effect of light intensity on the rate of apparent photosynthesis of coffee leaves. J. Agric. Univ. P. R. 46:159–166.

Uchijima, A., and K. Inoue. 1970. Studies of energy and gas exchange within crop canopies (9). Simulation of CO_2 environment within a canopy. J. Agric. Meteorol. (Japan) 26:5–18.

Virgin, H. L. 1956. Light-induced stomatal movements in wheat leaves recorded as transpiration. Experiments with the corona-hygrometer. Physiol. Plant. 9:289–303.

Waggoner, P. E. 1969. Environmental manipulation for higher yields. p. 343–373. In J. D. Eastin, F. A. Haskins, C. Y. Sullivan, and C. H. M. van Bavel (ed.) Physiological aspects of crop yield. Am. Soc. of Agron., Madison, Wis.

Wit, C. T., de. 1965. Photosynthesis of leaf canopies. Versl. Landbouwkd. Onderz. 663:1–57.

Yocum, C. S., L. H. Allen, Jr., and E. R. Lemon. 1964. Photosynthesis under field conditions. VI. Solar radiation balance and photosynthetic efficiency. Agron. J. 56: 249–253

Strip Intercropping for Wind Protection[1]

J. K. Radke and R. T. Hagstrom[2]

Strip intercropping (Andrews & Kassam, 1976) as a form of multiple cropping sometimes employs a tall crop to shelter a short crop from wind. These systems will be referred to as intercrop wind barriers. Intercrop wind barriers have received considerable attention in the northwest Corn Belt and the Great Plains.

The two main effects of interplanting a short and a tall crop are light-interception (shading) and wind protection. In this publication, L.H. Allen, Jr. et al. (1976) cover in detail the light interception aspect. This paper will discuss the wind-sheltering effects and related parameters, including plant response, plant-water relations, microclimate, wind structure, and turbulence.

The use of temporary wind barriers to benefit crops can be divided into three categories: to control wind erosion as practiced in Kansas (Hagan et al., 1972); Montana (Siddoway, 1970), and Texas (Fryrear, 1969); to harvest snow for soil water recharge, as practiced in North Dakota (George, 1971), Montana (Black & Siddoway, 1971; Siddoway, 1970), and Canada (Lehane & Nielson, 1961); and to alter crop response as practiced in western Minnesota (Radke & Burrows, 1970; Radke & Hagstrom, 1973); Canada (Lehane & Nielson, 1961; Moysey & McPherson, 1966), North Dakota (Frank et al., 1974; Frank & Willis, 1972; George, 1971), Kansas (Skidmore et al., 1974), and Nebraska (Brown & Rosenberg, 1970, 1971/72; Miller et al., 1973; Rosenberg, 1966; Rosenberg et al., 1967).

WIND BARRIER SYSTEMS

Various tall crops have been used as wind barriers (Aase & Siddoway, 1974; Radke & Burrows, 1970; Radke & Hagstrom, 1973, 1974; Rosenberg,

[1] Contribution from the North Central Soil Conservation Research Center, ARS, USDA, Morris, Minn. in cooperation with the Minnesota Agric. Exp. Stn., Sci. Journal No. 9237.

[2] Soil scientist, USDA, Morris, Minnesota and research associate professor, University of Minnesota; and electronics technician, USDA, Morris, Minnesota, respectively.

1966; Short & Kretchman, 1974) to shelter several short crops (Aase & Siddoway, 1974; Bagley & Gowen, 1960; Frank et al., 1974; Frank & Willis, 1972; George, 1971; Pelton, 1967; Radke & Burrows, 1970; Rosenberg, 1966; Rosenberg et al., 1967; Short & Kretchman, 1974; Skidmore et al., 1974). In western Minnesota, we have usually sheltered soybeans [*Glycine max* (L.) Merr.] with either double rows of corn (*Zea mays* L.) (Radke & Burrows, 1970; Radke & Hagstrom, 1973) as shown in Figure 1 or sunflowers (*Helianthus annuus* L.) (Radke & Hagstrom, 1974). We have also used constructed barriers such as snowfences and board fences (Radke & Burrows, 1970; Radke & Hagstrom, 1974).

Several factors must be considered when designing temporary wind barriers. The row direction of the sheltered and sheltering crops and the interval between successive wind barriers are important. Because prevailing summer winds in western Minnesota are generally south-southeasterly or northwesterly, the east-west oriented rows more effectively provide wind protection. The interval between successive wind barriers, if estimated by the rule of thumb sometimes used for shelterbelts, is approximately 10 times the effective height (10H) of the sheltering crop. Planting procedures and equipment must also be considered. In western Minnesota, an eight-row planter equipped with eight separate seed hoppers works well. By filling one end hopper with corn and the remaining seven with soybeans and going back and forth across the field in the conventional manner, two rows of corn are interplanted between every 14 rows of soybeans. With a 76-cm row spacing, the interval between successive wind barriers is approximately 11.4 m. Other factors must be considered too. For example, herbicides and pesticides must be chosen and applied so that they do not injure either the sheltered or sheltering crop.

Figure 1. Soybean field strip-intercropped with double rows of corn for wind protection.

In western Minnesota some farmers produce soybeans sheltered by corn wind barriers. Sometimes, planting arrangements are altered to fit particular equipment and farming procedures. For example, four rather than two rows of corn can be used for the wind barriers when farmers have four-row corn harvesting equipment.

Researchers in other U. S. areas have interplanted various crops for wind protection: corn to shelter sugar beets (*Beta vulgaris* L.) (Rosenberg, 1966); oats (*Avena sativa* L.) to shelter tomatoes (*Lycopersicon esculentum*) (Short & Kretchman, 1974); and tall wheatgrass (*Agropyron elongatum* L.) to shelter wheat (*Triticum aestivum* L.) (Aase & Siddoway, 1974). Extensive studies have been conducted with snowfence or slat fence to shelter crops including soybeans (Frank et al., 1974; Miller et al., 1973; Radke & Burrows, 1970); sugar beets (Brown & Rosenberg, 1970, 1971/72; Rosenberg, 1966); spring wheat (Frank & Willis, 1972; George, 1971; Pelton, 1967); snap beans (*Phaseolus vulgaris* L.) (Rosenberg et al., 1967); and others (Bagley & Gowen, 1960; George, 1971; Skidmore et al., 1974). Tree shelterbelts have been used to shelter many crops (Bates, 1911; Blundell, 1974; Caborn, 1957; Dickerson & Woodruff, 1975; Ferber et al., 1955; George, 1971; Gloyne, 1964/65; Lehane & Nielson, 1961; Lomas & Schlesinger, 1970; Marshall, 1967; Plate, 1971; Read, 1964; Shah & Kalra, 1970; Stoeckeler, 1962; Van der Linde, 1962; Van Eimern et al., 1964).

WIND SHELTERING EFFECTS

Soybean Response

Soybean rows near the interplanted corn rows were protected as soon as the corn plants were slightly taller than the soybean plants. These sheltered soybeans responded by growing slightly taller. As the effective wind barrier height increased, more soybean rows showed an increase in plant height over the unsheltered soybeans. Soybeans on the windward side of the wind barrier also receive some protection. A graph of soybean plant height between successive corn wind barriers would show a bowl-shaped curve which becomes shallower with time because the corn barriers protect more of the soybean rows. Sheltered soybeans remain about 2 to 5 cm taller than unsheltered soybeans, usually, until late August.

Dry matter production by the soybean tops increased when soybeans were sheltered by temporary wind barriers (Fig. 2). Dry matter production plotted as a function of row number typically shows double maxima between the wind barriers (Fig. 3). Shading effects and root competition with the corn caused the low soybean dry matter accumulation in the rows next to the corn wind barriers.

Soybeans sheltered by temporary corn wind barriers have a larger leaf area index than unsheltered soybeans. Leaf area index increased because of larger individual leaves and slightly more leaves per plant. A graph of leaf area index across rows is similar to that for dry matter production. Table 1

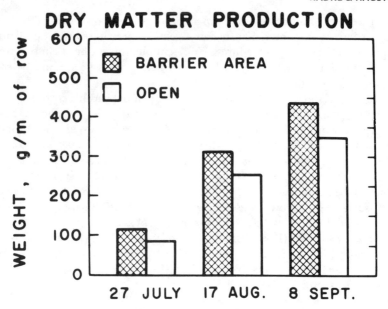

Figure 2. Soybean top dry weight taken on three dates in 1965 near Dumont, Minnesota. Data are significantly different at the 5% probability level for all dates.

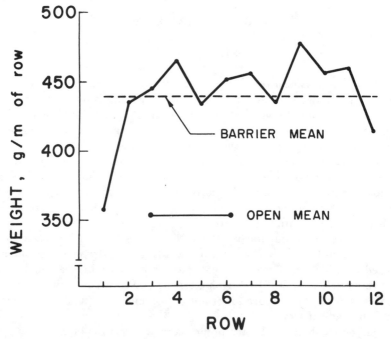

Figure 3. Soybean top dry weight as a function of row number in the barrier interval for 8 Sept. 1965. The Y-axis and row 13 represent corn rows. Among rows variation is significant at the 1.2% probability level.

Table 1. Soybean yields as affected by corn or snowfence wind barriers

Year	Location year no.*	Row spacing	Soybean/ barrier row ratio	Barrier spacing	Row direction	Soybean variety	Soybean yield Barrier area	Open area	Difference	Land equivalent ratio
		cm		m			—kg/ha—		%	
					Corn Barriers					
1963	1	102	11:1	12.2	East-west	Chippewa	2,190	1,820	20.3	1.17
1964	2	102	12:2	13.3	East-west	Chippewa	1,330	1,060	25.5	1.16
1964	3	102	12:2	13.3	East-west	Chippewa	1,430	1,280	11.7	1.06
1965	4	102	12:2	13.3	East-west	Chippewa	1,430	1,260	13.4	1.06
1966	5	102	12:2	13.3	East-west	Merit	920	720	27.8	1.19
1967	6	102	12:2	13.3	East-west	Traverse	1,920	1,930	-0.5	0.95
1967	7	102	12:2	13.3	North-south	Traverse	1,470	1,500	-2.0	0.96
1968	8	76	14:2	11.4	East-west	Chippewa	2,030	1,790	13.4	1.11
1968	9	76	14:2	11.4	North-south	Chippewa	1,380	1,250	10.4	1.06
1968	10	76	10:2	8.4	East-west	Hark	2,370	2,250	5.3	1.04
1968	11	76	22:2	17.5	East-west	Hark	2,400	2,150	11.6	1.10
1969	12	76	14:2	11.4	East-west	Chippewa	1,248	1,149	8.6	1.05
1969	13	76	22:2	17.5	East-west	Corsoy	2,197	2,042	7.6	1.07
1970	14	76	14:2	11.4	East-west	Clay	1,807	1,572	15.0	1.12
1970	15	76	22:2	17.5	East-west	Corsoy	2,593	2,492	4.1	1.03
					Snowfence Barriers					
1963	16	102	12:1	13.3	East-west	Chippewa	1,820	1,820	0.0	0.92
1964	17	102	13:1	14.3	East-west	Chippewa	1,410	1,280	10.2	1.02

* All experimental sites were located near Dumont, Minnesota in cooperation with the Tritz Bros. except location-years 10, 11, 13, and 15 which were located at the Southwest Minnesota Agricultural Experiment Station, Lamberton, in cooperation with the University of Minnesota.

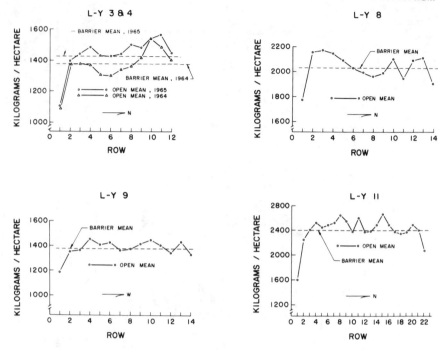

Figure 4. Soybean grain yield as a function of row number for several locations and years. Among rows variation and differences between open and barrier are significant at the 1% level for all five cases.

shows that grain yields of sheltered soybeans generally were greater than for unsheltered soybeans. Yields were decreased in 1966 because of a severe hailstorm. Lack of a yield increase by the sheltered soybeans for the two locations in 1967 might have occurred because (i) of an uneven fertilizer application, (ii) the herbicide applied injured the corn early in the season and the corn did not reach a protective height of 10H until 21 Aug. or (iii) this was the only year that 'Traverse' soybeans were planted.

Sheltered soybeans yielded significantly more than unsheltered soybeans in all years except 1967 (Table 1). Yields differed significantly among barrier rows in almost every case; whereas, there was no difference among open area rows. The soybean yield curves (Fig. 4) are similar to that for dry matter production (Fig. 3). The rows adjacent to the corn wind barriers had lower yields than the other rows, which varied cyclically between successive wind barriers.

Corn yields from the temporary corn wind barriers have generally been reduced over conventionally planted corn. Recently corn yields have been increased up to approximately 7,800 kg/ha by increasing the plant population and by side-dressing with additional fertilizer. This also produces a denser wind barrier (Fig. 5).

Other types of temporary wind barriers were also studied including snowfence (Radke & Burrows, 1970). In 1 year out of 2 snowfences sig-

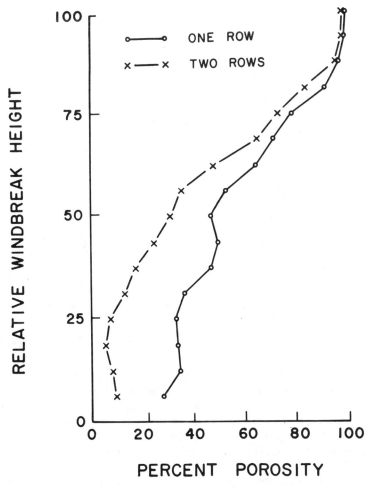

Figure 5. Percent corn wind barrier porosity at various corn height levels between the top of the soybean canopy and the top of the corn canopy.

nificantly increased yields. However, soybean yields were not increased enough to equal that obtained with temporary corn wind barriers. In 1972 through 1974, wind turbulence was measured around four different wind barriers: double rows of corn; double rows of sunflowers; a solid-board fence; and a snowfence (Radke & Hagstrom, 1974). The plots were not designed to evaluate yields, however, wind barrier effectiveness for yield increases of soybeans was corn > sunflowers > snowfence > solid board fence. The solid fence even reduced yields sometimes.

Figure 6 schematically represents the expected plant response or yield increases due to east-west porous wind barriers during a growing season with nearly equal southerly and northerly winds. The horizontal axis has not been designated because the response curves will depend on the type and the porosity of the barriers; however, the spacing would be of the order of 10 to

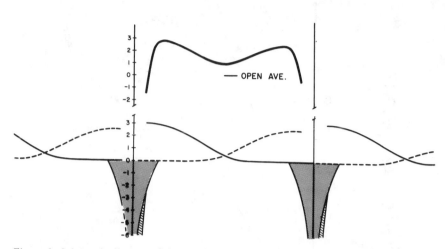

Figure 6. Schematic diagram of sheltered crop response to porous wind barriers with east-west orientation. The barriers are represented by the two vertical lines and the numbers represent relative increases of plant growth or yields. The solid and dashed curves in the lower part of the figure represent plant response to southerly and northerly winds, respectively. The light shaded areas represent negative plant response to root competition and the crosshatched areas represent additional decreases due to shading. The upper curve is the sum of the lower curves and represents the expected yield curve.

15H. The predicted yield curve is the combination of wind protection, root competition, and shading factors and is similar to the actual data curves obtained for dry matter and yields as shown in Figures 3 and 4.

Other researchers have also studied crop and artificial wind barriers (Table 2). Aase and Siddoway (1974) using tall wheatgrass to shelter winter wheat, found that yields increased in 1 year out of 2; approximately a 10% yield increase in 1971 and only a slight increase in the wet year of 1972. Short (1974), studied oats as wind barriers for seeded tomatoes and found that the sheltered tomatoes had greatly improved vigor and uniformity ratings. Rosenberg (1966), using corn rows to shelter sugar beets under irrigated conditions, found greater than 25% yield increases. Table 2 also shows that sheltered plants usually grow taller and produce more dry matter and larger leaves, while often exhibiting lower stomatal resistance.

Sheltered Microclimate

The effect of temporary wind barriers on micrometeorological factors are summarized by the diagram in Figure 7 which is similar to one originally presented by Marshall (1967). Daytime air temperatures behind wind barriers are generally slightly warmer than for unsheltered areas in some cases as much as 2C 20 cm above sheltered soybeans (Radke, unpublished data). Because sheltered soybean plants are generally taller and bushier with a larger

Table 2. Response of crops to shelter by crop and artificial wind barriers. For more complete data and statistics, see references cited

Reference	Barrier	Sheltered crop	Study years	Difference—shelter over open*				
				Yield	Height	Dry matter	LAI	Stomatal resistance
				%				
Crop Barriers								
Aase and Siddoway (1974)	Tall wheatgrass	Winter wheat	1971	10.0	8.5	10.0	59.8	
			1972	1.8	2.8	3.7	12.7	
Brown and Rosenberg (1971/72)	Corn	Irrigated sugar beets	1965	-5.5				
			1966	2.7				
Rosenberg (1966)	Corn	Irrigated sugar beets	1964	26.0				
Artificial Barriers								
Bagley and Gowen (1960)	Snowfence	Tomatoes	1959	63.3				
	Snowfence	Tomatoes	1959	16.3				
	Snowfence	Snap beans	1959	37.0				
Frank et al. (1974)	Slat fence	Soybeans	1971	31.8				
			1972	-4.0		-5.8		
	Slat fence	Irrigated soybeans	1971	19.2		31.0	45.2	7.0
			1972	25.1		17.5	9.4	-17.3
						1.3		
George (1971)	Slat fence	Spring wheat	1965-68	25.0				
Pelton (1967)	Snowfence	Spring wheat	1960-64	24.0-43.0				
Rosenberg (1966)	Snowfence	Irrigated sugar beets	1964	15.2				
Rosenberg et al. (1967)	Snowfence	Snap beans						
		'Tendercrop'	1964		37.2			-75.4†
		'Bush Blue Lake'	1964		42.9			-55.2†
Skidmore et al. (1974)	Slat fence	Winter wheat	1971		8.7		15.5	-47.5
			1972					
Skidmore, Hagen and Gwin§	Slat fence	Winter wheat	1973	34.3	21.1	25.8	72.8‡	

* Differences greater than or equal to 10% are significant at the 5% level.
† Percent differences obtained from stomatal aperture data.
‡ Percent difference obtained from area of Flag leaf.
§ Unpublished data (personal communication), data significant at the 5% level.

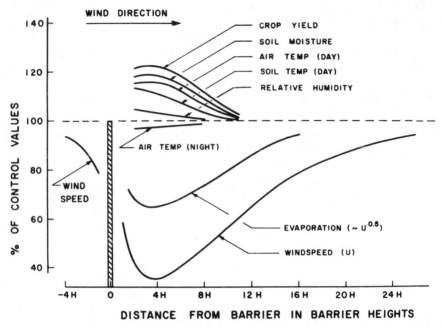

Figure 7. Summary diagram of the effect of wind barriers on micrometeorological factors. H = height of barrier. (Marshall, 1967).

leaf area, they may more completely cover the ground and change the energy balance. Night air temperatures usually differ little within and outside sheltered areas but are sometimes slightly cooler within the sheltered areas. Air temperatures in sheltered areas have increased diurnal amplitudes over that in unsheltered areas.

Relative humidity might increase slightly in sheltered areas (Fig. 7). The daytime water vapor pressure would probably increase more because of increased air temperatures in the sheltered area. In experiments with corn and soybeans, the relative humidity increased usually only a few percentage points (Radke, unpublished data). This was probably caused by a decrease in the removal rate of water vapor because of the lowered wind velocity and turbulence.

Soil temperature, soil heat flow, and net radiation generally do not differ greatly between sheltered and unsheltered areas if the soil surfaces are relatively dry. Any differences in these parameters likely reflect previous differences in plant response to the wind shelter. For example, a denser soybean canopy in the sheltered area would change the amount of radiation reaching the soil surface and thereby affect soil temperature and soil heat flow, as well as net radiation.

Under dryland conditions, evapotranspiration over sheltered and unsheltered areas, as measured by the energy balance method, generally do not differ greatly over an extended period. Differences can be significant over periods of a day or less, and often the evapotranspiration within the sheltered area is decreased. However, as unsheltered plants become water stressed and thus decrease their photosynthetic production rate, the sheltered crop will use more water for evapotranspiration and essentially catch up. Since the sheltered crop generally produces more dry matter and higher yields, it is using the available water more efficiently. Their transpiration to evaporation ratio is probably higher as compared with that of the unsheltered crop. We have never found a significant difference in the soil moisture for the sheltered versus the unsheltered areas under dryland conditions.

With a moist soil surface, evapotranspiration in sheltered areas is significantly decreased from unsheltered areas, which in turn may affect the soil moisture and temperature. If the soil does not become too dry before subsequent irrigation or rains, the sheltered areas may retain more soil moisture for a long time.

Microclimate changes behind snowfences or slat fences are similar to those behind crop wind barriers. The greatest changes are in the wind structure and turbulence components (Seginer & Sagi, 1972; Woodruff & Zingg, 1955). Other microclimatic parameter changes are much smaller and more variable as shown by several other researchers (Frank et al., 1974; George, 1971; Miller et al., 1974, 1973; Rosenberg, 1966; Rosenberg et al., 1967; Skidmore, 1969; Skidmore & Hagen, 1970; Skidmore et al., 1972).

Plant Water Relations

The general conclusion of most research is that shelter effects from crop wind barriers (Brown & Rosenberg, 1971/72; Radke & Hagstrom, 1973) or constructed barriers (Frank et al., 1974; Frank & Willis, 1972; Miller et al., 1973; Skidmore & Hagen, 1971) benefit plant water relations.

Figure 8 shows several parameters plotted as a function of row number between successive corn wind barriers for 2 days during a dry year. Net radiation in the sheltered area was the same as in the open except for the first point north of the barrier which was partially shaded and the point for interrow 7-8 which resulted from nonuniform ground cover on 20 Aug. Radiation for interrow 7-8 was not reduced on 21 Aug. because the wind deformed the soybean canopy differently. The average wind speed was reduced over most of the interval between successive corn barriers. The evaporimeters showed a similar trend; however, significant reductions occurred only over the first portion of the interval. Potential evaporation increased over the second portion of the barrier interval because of increased turbulent mixing and slightly increased air temperatures. Potential transpiration per unit dry matter (or leaf area index) measured with plant potometers (Radke & Hagstrom, 1973), and stomatal resistance as measured from leaf impressions varied inversely with each other over rows on 20 Aug. but not on 21 Aug. The shape of the potometer and stomatal resistance curves vary some during the day and considerably during the growing season. Stomatal resistance and plant-water stress depend not only on microclimate but also on several plant

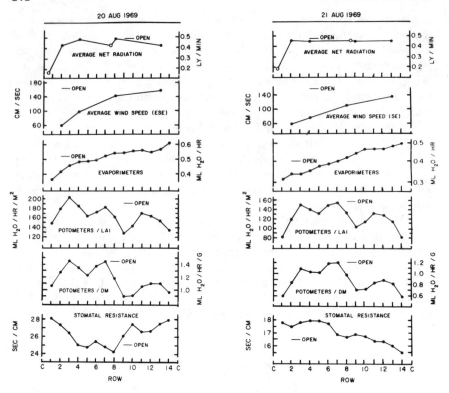

Figure 8. Micrometeorological and plant-water measurements as a function of row number north of a corn wind barrier compared with measurements in an open field for 20
and 21 Aug. 1969. Data points represent averages over the period during which measurements were taken.

factors, including type and variety of crop as well as the plant's history of
stress and its previous response to sheltered conditions. The potometer
curves (Fig. 9) show higher potential transpiration per unit leaf area and per
unit dry matter in the open than in the barrier for all times. The evaporim-
eter data were not different over time because, as shown in Figure 7, the first
portion of the sheltered interval had less potential evaporation but the remaining portion had more. For 1970, a wet year, plant-water measurements
differed somewhat but the same general trends were found (Radke & Hagstrom, 1973).

Wind Structure and Turbulence

Wind turbulence behind crop and constructed barriers in western Minnesota was studied using hot-film anemometers and a real time correlator.
Four barriers were used: double rows of corn, double rows of sunflowers, a
solid-board fence, and a snowfence. Each barrier was approximately 25 m

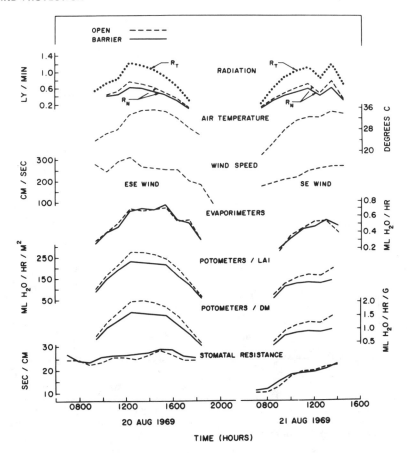

Figure 9. Micrometeorological and plant-water measurements as a function of time for 20 and 21 Aug. 1969. R_T and R_N are total solar and net radiation, respectively. Wind speed was measured 80 cm above the soybeans in the open area.

long and the barriers were placed end to end in a soybean field. Twelve rows of soybeans spaced 76 cm apart and oriented in an east-west direction were planted between two sets of barriers. Additional barriers were not constructed down wind because it had been previously determined that the wind structure and turbulence behind successive barriers was essentially the same as behind the first barrier if the barrier interval was 10H or greater. An open (check) area of more than 100 rows of soybeans was maintained south of the barriers. Measurements were made only on days with similar wind conditions.

Normalized wind velocity 20 cm above the soybean canopy was reduced for all four barriers (Fig. 10). Reduction patterns for the corn and sunflower barriers were similar but the solid barrier curve peaked between the barriers because the wind had to flow up and over the solid barriers. A smaller peak occurs in approximately the same place for the sunflower barrier. This peak

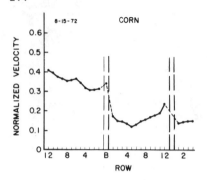

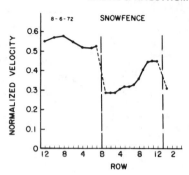

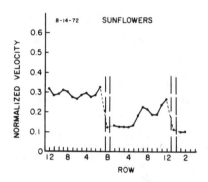

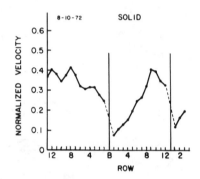

Figure 10. Normalized wind velocity 20 cm above the soybean canopy as a function of row number (76 cm row spacing) south or north of the four wind barriers. The wind velocities were normalized to a cup anemometer 320 cm above the open soybeans. The wind is southerly for each of the barriers.

indicates that some wind flows up and over the top of the sunflowers rather than all filtering through. This occurs because the sunflower barriers have only a 10% porosity compared with 40 and 50% for the corn and snowfence, respectively.

Turbulence, 20 cm above the soybean canopy, as measured by the root mean square of the turbulent component of the wind velocity, increases drastically about midway between the corn and snowfence barriers (Fig. 11). There is a large turbulence peak for the solid fence and a smaller peak for the sunflowers midway between the barriers. Figure 12 represents the wind energy at the given frequencies for the open area and behind the four wind barriers. Energy is greatly reduced by each of the four barriers compared to the open area; but, the corn and sunflower barrier curves have an energy bulge between 8 and 18 Hertz (Hz). Apparently, more energy was dissipated by the flexing stalks and fluttering leaves at the lower frequencies but an energy bulge remained in this range.

Calculation of energy distribution shows there is a large frequency shift upward for the first row and a smaller shift upward for the second row to the leeward of the porous wind barriers (Table 3). These and other turbulence

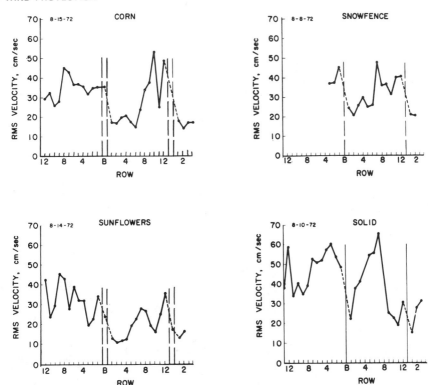

Figure 11. The root mean squares of the turbulent component of the wind velocity 20 cm above the soybean canopy as a function of row number north of the four wind barriers. Each datum point represents the average of several runs.

parameters indicate that porous barriers break the larger eddies into smaller eddies, decrease the wind velocities, and reduce the amount of energy more at lower than at the higher frequencies. The large flow of wind over the denser barriers and the increased turbulence between them is undesirable for crop production.

In a more detailed study of wind structure behind the four wind barriers, a field experiment was conducted patterned after a wind tunnel study by Spencer and Jones.[3] They put a horizontal divider plate in the throat of the wind tunnel midway between the floor and ceiling. The bottom half of the tunnel had a restrictor screen to reduce wind velocity below the plate. At the edge of the plate the high and low velocity air streams met and a mixing region developed downstream (Fig. 13). The points where the wind velocity profiles become vertical define the edges of the mixing region. Spencer and Jones developed the following empirical equation to describe the boundaries of this wake region

---

[3] B. W. Spencer and B. G. Jones, 1971. Statistical investigation of pressure and velocity fields in the turbulent two-stream mixing layer. AIAA 4th Fluid and Plasma Dynamics Conference, June. Paper No. 71–613.

$$b/(x - x_o) = K\,(1 - r)/(1 + r)$$

where b is the spread of the mixing region at a distance x from the reference point; x_o is the horizontal shift of the apex of the mixing region; K is a constant for a given wind barrier; and r is the ratio of the low velocity stream, U_b, to the high velocity stream, U_a.

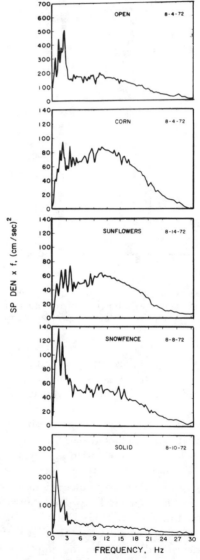

Figure 12. Power spectral density times frequency as a function of frequency measured 20 cm above the soybean canopy in the open area and the first soybean row behind each of the four wind barriers. The energy at low frequencies is somewhat reduced because measurements were made during periods with few, if any, low frequency wind gusts.

Table 3. F_{50} values representing the frequencies for different wind barriers at which 50% of the measured energy lies below and 50% lies above. The energy at frequencies below 0.15 Hz was not measured and thus is not represented. Rows are numbered sequentially leeward from the barriers. Data was obtained on the date indicated in 1972

| Rows | F_{50} values | | | |
	Corn 15 Aug.	Sunflower 14 Aug.	Solid 10 Aug.	Snowfence 8 Aug.
Open average	1.23	1.37	1.41	1.36
1	4.75	2.79	1.08	2.24
2	2.29	1.53	1.77	1.59
3	1.16	0.96	2.01	1.20
4	1.41	1.02	2.10	1.18
5	0.82	1.35	1.49	1.40
6	1.06	1.38	1.47	1.06
7	1.51	1.40	1.37	1.60
8	0.76	1.25	1.75	1.14
9	1.08	1.30	1.45	1.32
10	1.14	1.41	1.05	1.11
11	1.44	1.41	0.99	1.24
12	1.04	1.50	1.34	1.50

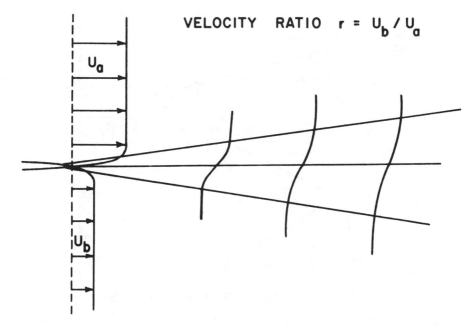

Figure 13. Diagram of the mixing region and wind velocity profiles of two parallel, uniform wind streams.

We assumed, as did Plate (1971), that our wind barriers behaved similarly to the wind tunnel experiment and used measured velocity profiles to determine the mixing regions behind corn, snowfence, and solid barriers (Fig. 14). Even though the corn is much taller than the snowfence, the bottom edge of the wake region for each barrier intercepts the soybean canopy approximately 525 cm behind the barrier, i.e., the wake spreads faster behind the corn. This distance corresponds to about midway between the wind

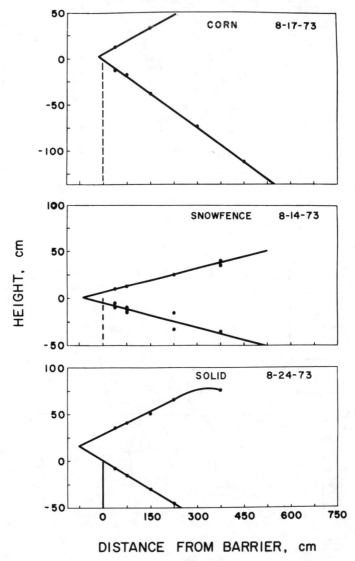

Figure 14. Wake regions generated by a corn barrier, a snowfence barrier, and a solid board fence. The vertical lines represent the barriers and the X-axis represents the top of the soybean canopy.

barriers. The wake region for the solid fence is radically different with a shift of the apex to the left (windward) and upward with the top edge of the wake region indicating a downward curl of the wind. The lower limb of the wake region intercepts the top of the soybean canopy only three rows behind the wind barrier.

In Figure 14, the area below and to the left of the lower limb of the wake region is the area of maximum plant response behind the corn and snowfence windbreaks. To the right of this lower limb is an area of increased turbulent mixing which is partially responsible for the increased evapotranspiration over the second portion of the sheltered area. Since the wake region depends on the velocity ratio of the high and low speed wind streams rather than on the velocity itself, the geometry of these wake regions are applicable for a rather large velocity range.

IMPLICATIONS FOR OTHER MULTIPLE CROPPING SYSTEMS

Research in the northwest Corn Belt as well as that for the Great Plain states indicates that plant growth often is increased by crop or constructed wind barriers. However, height and dry matter increases may not be desirable in all locations. For example, an increase in soybean height or dry matter in Illinois, where soybeans already grow bushy and tall, may cause lodging and reduce yields. Also, yield increases of some crops may cause decreases in quality. For example, sheltered sugar beets sometimes have a lower sugar concentration than unsheltered sugar beets (Rosenberg, 1966). However, usually, wind shelter will improve the quality of crops, especially vegetable crops that are easily damaged by wind (Short & Kretchman, 1974). In areas with light winds, barriers may not be desirable since they will even further reduce the wind velocity and lower the turbulent exchange (Allen, 1968; Brown & Rosenberg, 1971; Hagen & Skidmore, 1971, 1974; Skidmore & Hagen, 1970). If carbon dioxide is limiting to the crop, reducing turbulent exchange will aggravate the situation further. Also, if the winds are light, there is little advantage from wind protection and if intercropped plants compete for water and nutrients or have other antagonistic effects on each other, overall yields may be reduced.

Wind barriers benefit crops where there are strong winds and strong advection. Greatest benefits are obtained with vegetable and legume crops, especially soybeans and other beans. Wind-sheltered and irrigated crops may show yield increases over irrigated-only crops that are percentage-wise greater than for dryland conditions.

Though wind barriers generally cause desirable plant responses, not all of the reasons for such responses are known or understood. The complex interactions of wind barrier geometries, various types of crops, and microclimate may eventually be modeled on the computer but probably not before some more basic research has been done. Wind tunnel studies are being conducted with model wind barriers to further refine wind turbulence and structure parameters. Then additional field studies will probably be needed to determine the inputs of a computer model with enough accuracy to allow successful simulation of various intercropping systems.

SUMMARY

Crops sheltered by temporary wind barriers tend to grow taller, produce more dry matter, with a larger leaf area index and larger yield. Wind barriers alter the microclimate within them which in turn alters the plant-water relations of the sheltered crop.

Wind barriers are most effective when they are spaced at intervals from 10 to 15H and perpendicular to the prevailing wind. Porous wind barriers that allow the wind to filter through, rather than forcing it to go over the top, are more effective than solid or dense barriers. Of the porous barriers, the crop barriers are the most effective in causing desirable crop response because their flexing stalks and fluttering leaves better break up the wind eddies causing increased energy dissipation.

Strip interplanting tall and short crops has promise as an economical farming practice. If offers more flexibility in the farming operations than permanent shelterbelts while providing wind protection or it may be used to augment permanent shelterbelts.

LITERATURE CITED

Aase, J. K., and F. H. Siddoway. 1974. Tall wheatgrass barriers and winter wheat response. Agric. Meteorol. 13:321–338.

Allen, L. H., Jr. 1968. Turbulence and wind speed spectra within a Japanese Larch Plantation. J. Appl. Meteorol. 7:73–78.

Allen, L. H., Jr., T. R. Sinclair, and E. R. Lemon. 1976. Radiation and microclimate relationships in multiple cropping systems. p. 171–200. In R. I. Papendick, P. A. Sanchez, and G. B. Triplett (ed.) Multiple cropping. Spec. Pub. No. 27, Am. Soc. of Agron., Madison, Wis.

Andrews, D. J., and A. H. Kassam. 1976. The importance of multiple cropping in increasing world food supplies. p. 1–10. In R. I. Papendick, P. A. Sanchez, and G. B. Triplett (ed.) Multiple cropping. Spec. Pub. No. 27, Am. Soc. of Agron., Madison, Wis.

Bagley, W. T., and F. A. Gowen. 1960. Growth and fruiting of tomatoes and snap beans in the shelter area of a windbreak. 5th World Forestry Congr. Proc. 3:1667–1670.

Bates, C. G. 1911. Windbreaks—Their influence and value. USDA Forest Service Bulletin 86. Washington, D. C.

Black, A. L., and F. H. Siddoway. 1971. Tall wheatgrass barriers for soil erosion control and water conservation. J. Soil Water Conserv. 26:107–111.

Blundell, S. B. 1974. Evaporation to leeward of a shelterbelt. Agric. Meteorol. 13:395–398.

Brown, K. W., and N. J. Rosenberg. 1970. Effect of windbreaks and soil water potential on stomatal diffusion resistance and photosynthetic rate of sugar beets. Agron. J. 62:4–8.

Brown, K. W., and N. J. Rosenberg. 1971/72. Shelter-effects on microclimate, growth and water use by irrigated sugar beets in the Great Plains. Agric. Meteorol. 9:241–263.

Brown, K. W., and N. J. Rosenberg. 1971. Turbulent transport and energy balance as affected by a windbreak in an irrigated sugar beet field. Agron. J. 63:351-355.

Caborn, J. M. 1957. Shelterbelts and microclimate. Forestry Commission, Bulletin No. 29, Edinburgh Univ.

Dickerson, J. D., and N. P. Woodruff. 1975. Establishing windbreaks in semiarid areas by altering the microclimate or supplying additional water. Water Harvesting Symp. Proc. (Phoenix, Ariz.) USDA, ARS-W-22.

Ferber, A. E., A. L. Ford, and S. A. McCrory. 1955. Good windbreaks help increase South Dakota crop yields. Agric. Exp. Stn. and SCS, Brookings, S. D. Cir. 118, Sept.

Frank, A. B., D. G. Harris, and W. O. Willis. 1974. Windbreak influence on water relations, growth, and yield of soybeans. Crop Sci. 14:761-765.

Frank, A. B., and W. O. Willis. 1972. Influence of windbreaks on leaf water status in spring wheat. Crop Sci. 12:668-672.

Fryrear, D. W. 1969. Reducing wind erosion in the southern Great Plains. Texas A&M Univ., Sept. MP-929.

George, E. J. 1971. Effect of tree windbreaks and slat barriers on wind velocity and crop yields. USDA, ARS Production Res. Rpt. No. 121, Jan.

Gloyne, R. W. 1964/65. Some characteristics of the natural wind and their modification by natural and artificial obstructions. Sci. Hort. 17:7-19.

Hagen, L. J., and E. L. Skidmore. 1971. Turbulent velocity fluctuations and vertical flow as affected by windbreak porosity. Trans. Am. Soc. Agric. Engr. 14:634-637.

Hagen, L. J., and E. L. Skidmore. 1974. Reducing turbulent transfer to increase water-use efficiency. Agric. Meteorol. 14:153-168.

Hagen, L. J., E. L. Skidmore, and J. D. Dickerson. 1972. Designing narrow strip barrier systems to control wind erosion. J. Soil Water Conserv. 27:269-272.

Lehane, J. J., and K. F. Nielson. 1961. The influence of field shelterbelts on climatic factors, soil drifting, snow accumulation, soil moisture and grain yields. Research Station Bull., Swift Current, Saskatechewan. Jan.

Lomas, J., and E. Schlesinger. 1970. The influence of a windbreak on evaporation. Agric. Meteorol. 8:107-115.

Marshall, J. K. 1967. The effect of shelter on the productivity of grasslands and field crops. Field Crop Abstr. 20:1-14.

Miller, D. R., W. T. Bagley, and N. J. Rosenberg. 1974. Microclimate modification with shelterbelts. J. Soil Water Conserv. 29:41-44.

Miller, D. R., N. J. Rosenberg, and W. T. Bagley. 1973. Soybean water use in the shelter of a slat-fence windbreak. Agric. Meteorol. 11:405-418.

Moysey, E. B., and F. B. McPherson. 1966. Effect of porosity on performance of windbreaks. Trans. Am. Soc. Agric. Eng. 9:74-76.

Pelton, W. L. 1967. The effect of a windbreak on wind travel, evaporation and wheat yield. Can. J. Plant Sci. 47:209-214.

Plate, E. J. 1971. The aerodynamics of shelter belts. Agric. Meteorol. 8:203-222.

Read, R. A. 1964. Tree windbreaks for the central Great Plains. USDA Agric. Handbook No. 250.

Radke, J. K., and W. C. Burrows. 1970. Soybean plant response to temporary field windbreaks. Agron. J. 62:424-429.

Radke, J. K., and R. T. Hagstrom. 1973. Plant-water measurements on soybeans sheltered by temporary corn windbreaks. Crop Sci. 13:543-548.

Radke, J. K., and R. T. Hagstrom. 1974. Wind turbulence in a soybean field sheltered by four types of wind barriers. Agron. J. 66:273-278.

Rosenberg, N. J. 1966. Influence of snow fence and corn windbreaks on microclimate and growth of irrigated sugar beets. Agron. J. 58:469-475.

Rosenberg, N. J., D. W. Lecher, and R. E. Neild. 1967. Responses of irrigated snap beans to wind shelter. Am. Soc. Hort. Sci. Proc. 90:169-179.

Seginer, Ido, and Ram Sagi. 1972. Drag on a windbreak in two-dimensional flow. Agric. Meteorol. 9(5/6):323-333.

Shah, S. R. H., and Y. P. Kalra. 1970. Nitrogen uptake of plants affected by windbreaks. Plant Soil 33:573-580.

Short, T. H., and D. W. Kretchman. 1974. Windbreaks for direct-seeded tomatoes. Res. Summ. Ohio Agric. Res. Dev. Center., 72:7-8.

Siddoway, F. H. 1970. Barriers for wind erosion control and water conservation. J. Soil Water Conserv. 25:180–184.

Skidmore, E. L. 1969. Modifying the microclimate with wind barriers. p. 107–120. *In* Modifying the soil and water environment for approaching the agricultural potential of the Great Plains. March 17–19. Research Committee Great Plains Agric. Council Pub. No. 34.

Skidmore, E. L., and L. J. Hagen. 1970. Evaporation in sheltered areas as influenced by windbreak porosity. Agric. Meteorol. 7:363–374.

Skidmore, E. L., and L. J. Hagen. 1970. Evapotranspiration and the aerial environment as influenced by windbreaks. p. 339–368. *In* Evapotranspiration in the Great Plains, Seminar, March. Great Plains Agric. Council Pub. No. 50.

Skidmore, E. L., and L. J. Hagen. 1973. Potential evaporation as influenced by barrier-induced microclimate. p. 237–244. *In* Ecological Studies, Vol. 4. Physical aspects of soil, water, and salts in ecosystems. Springer-Verlag, N. Y.

Skidmore, E. L., L. J. Hagen, D. G. Naylor, and I. D. Teare. 1974. Winter wheat response to barrier-induced microclimate. Agron. J. 66:501–505.

Skidmore, E. L., H. S. Jacobs, and L. J. Hagen. 1972. Microclimate modification by slat-fence windbreaks. Agron. J. 64:160–162.

Stoeckeler, J. H. 1962. Shelterbelt influence on Great Plains field environment and crops. Prod. Res. Rpt. 62, Forest Service, USDA, Washington, D. C.

Van der Linde, Johan. 1962. Trees outside the forest. p. 141–208. *In* Forest Influences, FAO, Rome.

Van Eimern, J., R. Karschon, L. A. Razumova, and G. W. Robertson. 1964. Windbreaks and shelterbelts. Tech. Note No. 59, World Meteorological Organization (WMO) No. 147.

Woodruff, N. P., and A. W. Zingg. 1955. A comparative analysis of wind-tunnel and atmospheric air-flow patterns about single and successive barriers. Trans. Am. Geophys. Union 36:203–208.

Adapting Species for Forage Mixtures[1]

P. N. Drolsom and Dale Smith[2]

Donald (1963) reviewed research relative to competition for both cultivated and pasture plants. He followed the basic concepts of F. E. Clements, with modification to include animals. Besides competition per se, the review included equilibria in mixtures, grass and clover (*Trifolium* sp.) mixtures, plant arrangement, the influence of water, nutrient, and light availability, and species characteristics, such as shoot height, leaf area, and leaf arrangement. Donald stressed the density factor and how it related to competition, both from the mass or community standpoint, as well as to individual plant growth. Relative to density and competition, he warned of the risk "inherent in the assessment of any genotype at noncommercial spacing." He noted that competitive ability should be considered a heritable trait and that some investigators erroneously attempt to equate competitive ability and yield which is not necessarily true for forage species.

A competition model was proposed by de Wit, Tow, and Ennik (1966) to partition and quantify various aspects of plant associations. The term "interference" is preferred to "competition" by Harper (1961) and also is used by Hall (1974). They point out that competition lacks an independent scientific meaning and can be misinterpreted because of its common usage in human activities, as well as in economics. According to Hall (1974),

> Plant interference may be defined as the response of an individual plant or plant species to its total environment as this is modified by the presence and/or growth of other individuals or species. Competition itself is only one facet of interference between plants, although at times it may be a very dominating one.

A recent assessment of mixtures for crops in general was made by Trenbath (1974), but grass-legume combinations were not discussed. His review noted that mixtures of two species usually yield between the levels reported

[1]Contribution from the Dep. of Agron., Wis. Agric. Exp. Stn., Madison, Wis. Published with approval of the Director, Research Division, College of Agricultural and Life Sciences, Univ. of Wisconsin, Madison.
[2]Professors of agronomy, University of Wisconsin, Madison.

for the individual components, but instances were cited where a significant yield increase was obtained.

MIXTURES OF GRASSES AND LEGUMES WITH GRASSES

An objective of this paper is to summarize studies on forage species performance in mixtures of species and, in some instances, of cultivars within species. A review of competition among herbage grasses by Rhodes (1970) included grass response to competition, nature of competitive stress, the association of grass characteristics and competitive ability, and the effect of the environment. He questioned the possible yield advantage of a monoculture versus a mixed culture and cited studies that support each system. These suggest that local environments, including level of mineral nutrition, the species utilized, and the management techniques employed all interact to produce the end-product, yield. The complexity of these interacting components has made it impossible to formulate mixtures of broad adaption that farmers can accept as superior. This agrees with Rogers (1966), who pointed out that maximum production is not always achieved when management factors are applied in crop-mixture systems. He stated:

> In the future, varieties will be designed for a more precise management. Each variety will have clearly defined characteristics of growth and quality, and the management required for maximum production will also be defined. A combination of these varieties—each grown as a pure sward and either conserved or cut and carried—will make up the pattern of cropping on the farm.

This implies the application of advanced technology, a level which has not even been reached in developed countries. Land with less potential for tilled crops, such as hillsides, would appear to be best adapted for mixtures, particularly a grass and legume. Today the dimension of energy conservation, along with increasing costs, has placed additional emphasis on the value of legumes as a nitrogen source.

The interrelationships of white clover (*Trifolium repens* L.)-grass mixtures were reviewed by Chestnutt and Lowe (1970). Assuming environmental factors are favorable, it is evident that management principally determines the relative proportions of legume and grass in such mixtures when they are utilized as perennials. Important management variables include frequency and height of cutting, intensity of grazing (if this is practiced), and level of mineral nutrition. This assumes light energy, temperature, and moisture are adequate for growth and that insects and diseases are insignificant. Relative to minerals, the comparative responses of white 'Ladino' clover and alfalfa (*Medicago sativa* L.), when each were grown with orchardgrass (*Dactylis glomerata* L.), demonstrated the importance of mineral nutrition (Drake et al., 1974). Varying the levels of applied phosphorus and potassium directly influenced the yield contribution of each legume. Increasing levels of K maintained better stands of both alfalfa and Ladino clover, and the overall

N level in the forage increased, as well as the yields. For example, the N content in the alfalfa-orchardgrass forage increased from 2.4 (low K) to 3.2% (high K) (Drake et al., 1974). Another aspect of mineral response is the selection of plants more efficient in the use of minerals and more tolerant to undesirable soil conditions, such as low soil pH and certain associated soil toxicities (Foy, 1974). Progress has been reported for increased aluminum tolerance, e.g., in alfalfa (Dessureaux, 1969), and differences in response to aluminum were reported for ryegrass (*Lolium* sp.) (Vose & Randall, 1962).

A real advantage of the grass-legume association is the supply of N provided by the legume. A question still remains, however, whether or not production and species balance can be maintained without supplemental N. In addition, other grass species may respond differently than ryegrass, as Frame (1973) observed in the response of a tall fescue (*Festuca arundinacea* L.)-white clover mixture when harvested at differing frequencies and with or without supplemental N. Total yield was reduced the second harvest year, which was attributed to a decline in the white clover stand resulting from the addition of N. The grass species also was judged to be a factor, since it did not appear to have a high degree of compatibility. Studies with white clover, a low-growing and decumbent species, may not be directly applicable to upright legumes, such as alfalfa and red clover (*Trifolium pratense* L.).

PHYSIOLOGY AND MANAGEMENT

A grass-legume mixture involves the interaction of two or more species, each with an entirely different shoot morphology than when only grasses are associated or grown in pure stands. Initially, it is essential to understand the developmental morphology and physiology of perennial grasses (Jewiss, 1972; Langer, 1972; Ryle, 1974). More specifically, the formation of reproductive versus vegetative tissue is determined by external conditions. Species adapted to one climate may differ considerably in the factors resulting in floral formation. For example, timothy (*Phleum pratense* L.) will flower profusely when grown at 18.5 C with daylengths exceeding 15 to 16 hours; no short day or cold treatments are needed for flowering (Ryle, 1974). Perennial ryegrass (*Lolium perenne* L.), however, needs a combination of cool temperatures and short days to develop inflorescences, a situation somewhat similar to requirements of winter wheat (*Triticum aestivum* L.) and rye (*Secale cereale* L.) (Ryle, 1974). In all instances, certain levels of light energy, mineral nutrition, and moisture must be provided to sustain plant development. The relative amount of seed produced depends also upon availability of all essential factors, with N being a critical element.

The harvest of stems and leaves, as well as of reproductive tissue, adds another dimension to the plant-development complex. Differential responses have occurred when repeated clipping has been compared with pasturing. The frequency and degree of defoliation is important relative to the species recovery patterns, as well as to the environmental factors favoring regrowth.

Another aspect is the inherent recovery capacity of the species, i.e., some re-cover more rapidly than others. The basis of these differences is related to basal bud activity, which in part is controlled by natural growth regulators, i.e., apical dominance (Jewiss, 1972).

Specific attention to recovery after clipping has been summarized (Davies et al., 1972). Environmental factors, such as mineral nutrition, soil aeration and moisture, are related to plant development, including the re-covery potential. The date and height of cutting for the first spring clipping can influence markedly the amount of recovery growth, which is related to the status of food reserves in the plant and to the stage of development of the basal buds at the time of cutting (Davies et al., 1972; Smith, 1968).

BREEDING ASPECTS

A principal emphasis in this paper concerns improvement of genetic po-tential to increase herbage production of the species comprising grass-legume mixtures, with some discussion of problems involved in management so that the species seeded can be maintained in a desired balance for several years. Hutton (1971) discussed the performance of plant species in mixtures and noted that there are few data to substantiate the value of improved cultivars grown in mixtures. Nevertheless, he expressed optimism concerning the po-tential value of new cultivars which can increase animal production and cited supporting evidence (Hutton, 1971). Stage of growth and carbohydrate re-serves, cutting height and frequency, and plant competition all may be im-portant (R. W. Van Keuren, 1971. Management of grasses in pure stands and in mixtures with legumes. Presented at NCR–31 meeting, Mimeo, 5 p. and references). It also is recognized that problems arise when mixtures of grasses are to be maintained.

Rhodes (1971) found that a perennial ryegrass variety with long and erect leaf blades and with a sparse-tillering habit outyielded a short-leaved, prostrate, and densely-tillering variety under infrequent clipping, but not with frequent clipping. The reasons for such response were ascribed to dif-ferences in canopy structure, light interception, and leaf area index. This relates to the statement by Rogers (1966) that the management scheme should be specified as new varieties are developed. Another example of genotypic response to selection was shown by Harris and Brougham (1970). When they worked with two ryegrass varieties subjected to three systems of grazing for 5 years, differential survival of varieties occurred. Charles (1964) had similar results when he utilized cultivar mixtures of ryegrass, orchard-grass, and timothy. When mixtures within a genus were grown, one cultivar often became dominant within several years, and it was stressed that manage-ment factors influenced considerably the proportions of cultivars that per-sisted (Charles, 1964). Other studies have emphasized that selection of plant types should be oriented according to the management system utilized (Rhodes, 1973). Plant morphology, therefore, is an important aspect of herbage grass productivity, and it deserves greater emphasis in future breeding programs than has been given in the past. Physiological techniques also offer opportunities for selection, which should be helpful in increasing productivity (Cooper, 1974). With the current trend toward more intensive management, Simons, Davies, and Troughton (1973) demonstrated that an erect-growing perennial ryegrass clone in a dense sward had more growth and presumably was making better use of available light than a prostrate clone that developed faster in a less dense stand. Overall production potential was in favor of the erect-growing clone. Van Bogaert (1974) reported that improved competitiveness of meadow fescue (*Festuca pratensis* L.) should be attainable on the basis of progeny performance in mixture with perennial ryegrass.

ALFALFA-SMOOTH BROMEGRASS MIXTURES

Much of the forage grown in the U. S., especially in the northern dairy-producing areas, consists of grass-legume mixtures. Farmers are aware that such an association can provide an excellent energy-protein balance for ruminants. Other reasons for preferring mixtures rather than pure legume stands include: (i) the excellent soil-conserving features of the grass fibrous root system; (ii) protection against legume stand losses from winterkilling, heaving, and other hazards; (iii) ability of certain grasses to fill-in the stand when the legume is thinned; and (iv) the improved drying, or curing, qualities of mixtures.

A recommended perennial grass-legume mixture in the northern U. S. and in Canada is smooth bromegrass (*Bromus inermis* Leyss.) and alfalfa (Smith, 1975). Smooth bromegrass is well-adapted in temperate regions, having especially good winterhardiness (Fig. 1) and is nutritious forage

Figure 1. Winter damage in a space-planted nursery of timothy (front) compared with vigor shown by smooth bromegrass, when photographed in late spring.

(Smith, 1975; Winch et al., 1970) for cattle. When cut for hay or silage, two harvests per year (first cut near full bloom of alfalfa), the smooth bromegrass persisted very well, remaining competitive with the alfalfa in the mixture. Subsequently, management studies with improved alfalfa cultivars indicated that the highest yields of digestible dry matter and protein were obtained with three harvests per season rather than two and that the first cut should be with alfalfa in the late bud to first flower stage of growth (Smith, 1968). This management system resulted in less bromegrass, especially in the second and third harvests. Under some conditions, bromegrass stands were thinned and mainly alfalfa remained after the first harvest of the first year following establishment (Wolf & Smith, 1964). The response of timothy under such conditions was usually similar, but orchardgrass and reed canarygrass (*Phalaris arundinacea* L.) persisted well with alfalfa in the three-cut system (Fig. 2).

Investigations regarding growth patterns, including basal bud activity and food reserves, of smooth bromegrass help to explain the basic difficulties (Paulsen & Smith, 1968, 1969; Reynolds & Smith, 1962). When bromegrass is harvested three times annually and the first harvest coincides with the late bud to first flower stage of alfalfa, the bromegrass is low in total nonstructural carbohydrates. Under average climatic conditions for southern and central Wisconsin, this will be near 1 June. Often the bromegrass will have just completed stem elongation (jointing). According to Smith, Jacques, and Balasko (1973), grasses at this stage generally are low in food reserves, and

Figure 2. Row-seeded grasses in broadcast alfalfa after 2 years of cutting three times per year. Spring growth, after alfalfa was removed with a herbicide, shown for (left to right) reed canarygrass, orchardgrass, smooth bromegrass, and timothy.

Figure 3. Smooth bromegrass and alfalfa in late May, fertilized with 235 kg N/ha (210 lb N/acre) during the previous year and again in the spring. Left, no N, right, with N.

bromegrass, for example, has not yet produced new basal tillers from which is derived the recovery growth; in fact, basal tiller growth does not take place until the elongating shoots are near anthesis. Studies (Knievel et al., 1971; Paulsen & Smith, 1969; Sheard & Winch, 1966) have shown that activity of the basal tiller buds is correlated closely with regrowth yield and plant persistence. If growing conditions are not favorable, such as low soil moisture, then the bromegrass is at an even greater disadvantage, since it is competing for soil water and minerals with the tap-rooted alfalfa. Under such conditions, the bromegrass stand can be reduced or nearly eliminated.

There have been studies to develop management techniques to alleviate these difficulties. Approaches to establish and maintain a good grass-legume balance under a mechanical harvest system include (i) seeding rate adjustments (Kilcher, 1966) and (ii) management manipulations, such as time and height of cutting (Knievel et al., 1971; Paulsen & Smith, 1969; Smith et al., 1973), supplemental N fertilization (Newman & Smith, 1972; Paulsen & Smith, 1969; Smith, 1972; Smith & Jacques, 1973; Wolf & Smith, 1964), patterns of seeding (Newman & Smith, 1972; Smith & Jacques, 1973), and choice of species (Newman & Smith, 1972; Smith & Jacques, 1973; Smith et al., 1973; Wolf & Smith, 1964). Improved stands of smooth bromegrass, when associated with alfalfa and harvested three times annually, have been achieved by adding N fertilizer (Fig. 3) during the growing season (Smith, 1972) and by planting alfalfa in spaced rows or crossed rows, thereby reducing the competition from alfalfa for soil nutrients, water, and light (Smith &

Jacques, 1973). It is evident, however, that reduction of the alfalfa stand can be economical only to a point, that is, to where total herbage yields begin to decline. Time and height of cutting are important, especially for smooth bromegrass and timothy, and less so for orchardgrass and reed canarygrass (Smith et al., 1973). Although the latter two grasses persisted well over a range of cutting practices, their limitations include questionable palatability for reed canarygrass and marginal winterhardiness for orchardgrass.

Because bromegrass is winter-hardy and highly palatable, we studied germplasm for possible genetic variability to obtain persistence with alfalfa under a three cuts-per-year harvest schedule. Improved competitiveness appears to be a valid objective, even though emphasis has been placed primarily on the tropical grasses and legumes (Hutton, 1971). An earlier experiment showed that seeded rows of smooth bromegrass can be used to evaluate genotype response to cutting (Nielsen et al., 1969). It also has been suggested that basal axillary bud activity is closely associated with regrowth (Paulsen & Smith, 1969). It appeared, therefore, that regrowth potential of various genotypes warranted further research.

Selection Procedure

On 23 May 1969, seeds from 62 smooth bromegrass clones and two open-pollinated control strains were planted in one-row plots, 1 m apart and 12 m long. 'Vernal' alfalfa was overseeded at 7 kg/ha with a cultipacker seeder. The 62 clones represented germplasm selected for foliage and seedling disease resistance, vigor, leafiness, and satisfactory seed production characteristics. An incomplete block design with six replications was employed with three replications for three harvests per year and three replications for two harvests per year. On 29 August of the seeding year, when the alfalfa was approximately 40 cm tall, all topgrowth was clipped and removed. Regrowth height averaged 15 cm by late October, a height sufficient to catch snow during winter.

Harvests in the three-cut scheme were made on the following dates when alfalfa had reached late bud to first flower stages:

	1970	1971	1972
First harvest	5 June	3 June	5 June
Second harvest	9 July	15 July	18 July
Third harvest	26 Aug.	26 Aug.	7 Sept.

The forage was removed with a conventional flail-type harvester. One-half of each plot was clipped to a stubble height of 4 to 5 cm and the other half to approximately 10 to 12 cm. The two-cut schedule was followed in three replications during 1970 and 1971, but evaluation in late fall of 1971 showed a uniform and excellent recovery of all bromegrass genotypes. Consequently, this treatment was abandoned.

Table 1. Significance of mean squares for growth and persistence ratings† of 62 single-plant progenies and two cultivars of smooth bromegrass grown in association with alfalfa and harvested three times annually

			Stand		
Source of variation	Degrees of freedom	Amount of regrowth 15 Oct. 1970	27 Aug. 1971	26 Apr. 1972	28 Apr. 1973
Replication	2	**	**	**	**
Genotype	63	**	**	**	**
Height of cut	1	**	**	**	**
Height X replicate	2	**	**	**	NS‡
Height X genotype	63	NS	NS	NS	NS

** Significant at 1% level of probability.
† Scale: 5 = good, 1 = poor.
‡ NS = not significant.

RESULTS

The persistence of bromegrass genotypes was recorded at least once each year during 1970-73. A summary of analyses of variance for data recorded each year is shown in Table 1. The genotype component was highly significant for each growing season, regardless of when observations were recorded. The first order interaction, height X replication, was highly significant, except during 1973. In contrast, height X genotype never showed significance. Moisture was deficient only after the second harvest in 1971, resulting in little grass growth in the third cut. Since replicate differences were apparent before that time, drought conditions presumably were not related to this phenomenon. Generally, the poorest recovery and stand occurred in the second replicate, but there was no obvious explanation for this. The two control cultivars were among the slow-recovering genotypes.

In 1972 and 1973, genotypes with superior recovery growth and good persistence were observed closely (Fig. 4). The first removal of clones into isolation took place in 1972 when the best eight entries were removed as sod cores and planted in isolation. The method of propagation in isolation, i.e., removing sod cores from the rows established originally from seed, should be recognized as not comparable to clonal propagation. The main difference is that a clone theoretically is one genotype, while a seeded row of a naturally cross-pollinating species, such as smooth bromegrass, presumably represents a number of pollen parents. These selections were interpollinated in 1973, and the first progeny tests were established in 1974. The progeny test included a spaced-plant trial, as well as seeded-row plots established in a solid stand of alfalfa. Alfalfa was damaged, presumably from coverage by ice during winter 1974-75, so that clipping treatments to simulate recommended on-the-farm usage could not be initiated until 1976.

Figure 4. Single-plant progenies of smooth bromegrass grown in rows with broadcast-seeded alfalfa, showing good (right and left rows) and poor survival (center row) of the grass, after 2 years and three cuts per year.

CONCLUSIONS

Perennial grass-legume mixtures are used worldwide, because they make a nutritious and palatable feed for livestock. In the northern humid U. S., the alfalfa-smooth bromegrass mixture is used, but stands of bromegrass do not always persist.

Research shows that more persistent and quicker recovering types of smooth bromegrass can be selected. The initial evaluation of an experimental synthetic with this germplasm base has begun. Simultaneously, there will be evaluation for seed production potential, dry matter yield in mixture with alfalfa, disease resistance, and digestibility.

ACKNOWLEDGMENTS

Appreciation is expressed to K. J. Frandsen, A. Lazenby, and R. W. VanKeuren for many suggestions. Referral to literature by R. A. Bray, J. Nösberger, and P. Jacquard is acknowledged.

LITERATURE CITED

Bogaert, G. Van. 1974. The evaluation of progenies of meadow fescue (*Festuca pratensis* L.) in monoculture and in mixture with perennial ryegrass (*Lolium perenne* L.). Euphytica 23:48-53.

Charles, A. H. 1964. Differential survival of plant types in swards. J. Br. Grassl. Soc. 19: 198-204.

Chestnutt, D. M. B., and John Lowe. 1970. White clover/grass relationships: agronomy of white clover/grass swards: A review. Occasional Symposium No. 6, Br. Grassl. Soc. p. 191-213.

Cooper, J. P. 1974. The use of physiological criteria in grass breeding. p. 95-102. *In* Report of the Welsh Plant Breeding Station. 1973. Univ. College of Wales, Aberystwyth.

Davies, I., A. Davies, A. Troughton, and J. P. Cooper. 1972. Regrowth in grasses. p. 79-94. *In* Report of the Welsh Plant Breeding Station. 1971. Univ. College of Wales, Aberystwyth.

Dessureaux, L. 1969. Effect of aluminum on alfalfa seedlings. Plant Soil 30:93-97.

Donald, C. M. 1963. Competition among crop and pasture plants. Adv. Agron. 15:1-118.

Drake, M., W. G. Colby, H. Oohara, N. Yoshida, K. Fukunaga, and Y. Oohara. 1974. The effects of fertilizer phosphorus and potassium on yield and composition of alfalfa-orchardgrass and Ladino clover-orchardgrass mixture for the second 5-year period. Res. Bull. Obihiro Univ. 8:417-445.

Foy, C. D. 1974. Effects of aluminum on plant growth. p. 601-642. *In* E. W. Carson (ed.) The plant root and its environment. Univ. Press of Virginia, Charlottesville, Va.

Frame, J. 1973. The yield response of a tall fescue-white clover sward to nitrogen rate and harvesting frequency. J. Br. Grassl. Soc. 28:139-148.

Hall, R. L. 1974. Analysis of the nature of interference between plants of different species. I. Concepts and extension of the de Wit analysis to examine effects. Aust. J. Agric. Res. 25:739-747.

Harper, J. L. 1961. Approaches to the study of plant competition. Symp. Soc. Exp. Biol. 15:1-39.

Harris, W., and R. W. Brougham. 1970. The effect of grazing on the persistence of genotypes in a ryegrass population. N. Z. J. Agric. Res. 13:263-278.

Hutton, E. M. 1971. Plant improvement for increased animal production. J. Aust. Inst. Agric. Sci. 37:212-225.

Jewiss, O. R. 1972. Tillering in grasses—its significance and control. J. Br. Grassl. Soc. 27:65-82.

Kilcher, M. R. 1966. Fertilizers and seed ratios for controlling lucerne domination in mixtures. J. Br. Grassl. Soc. 21:135-139.

Knievel, D. P., A. V. A. Jacques, and Dale Smith. 1971. Influence of growth stage and stubble height on herbage yields and persistance of smooth bromegrass and timothy. Agron. J. 63:430-434.

Langer, R. H. M. 1972. How grasses grow. Studies in Biol. No. 34. The Inst. of Biology. 60 p. Edward Arnold, London.

Newman, R. C., and Dale Smith. 1972. Influence of two seeding patterns, nitrogen fertilization and three alfalfa varieties on dry matter and protein yields and persistence of alfalfa-grass mixtures. Wis. Agric. Exp. Stn. Res. Report 2377. 14 p.

Nielsen, E. L., P. N. Drolsom, and P. W. Voigt. 1969. Response of smooth bromegrass genotypes to cutting. Crop Sci. 9:785-787.

Paulsen, G. M., and Dale Smith. 1968. Influences of several management practices on growth characteristics and available carbohydrate content of smooth bromegrass. Agron. J. 60:375-379.

Paulsen, G. M., and Dale Smith. 1969. Organic reserves, axillary bud activity, and herbage yields of smooth bromegrass as influenced by time of cutting, nitrogen fertilization, and shading. Crop Sci. 9:529-534.

Reynolds, J. H., and Dale Smith. 1962. Trend of carbohydrate reserves in alfalfa, smooth bromegrass, and timothy grown under various cutting schedules. Crop Sci. 2:333-336.

Rhodes, I. 1970. Competition between herbage grasses. Herbage Abstr. 40:115–121.

Rhodes, I. 1971. Productivity and canopy structure of two contrasting varieties of perennial ryegrass (*Lolium perenne* L.) grown in a controlled environment. J. Br. Grassl. Soc. 26:9–13.

Rhodes, I. 1973. Relationship between canopy structure and productivity in herbage grasses and its implications for plant breeding. Herbage Abstr. 43:129–133.

Rogers, H. H. 1966. Breeding and blending. J. Br. Grassl. Soc. 21:102–107.

Ryle, G. J. A. 1974. The growth of the grass plant. p. 62–71. *In* Silver Jubilee Report, 1949–1974. Grassland Research Institute, Hurley, England.

Sheard, R. W., and J. E. Winch. 1966. The use of light interception, grass morphology and time as criteria for the harvesting of timothy, smooth brome and cocksfoot. J. Br. Grassl. Soc. 21:231–237.

Simons, R. G., A. Davies, and A. Troughton. 1973. The effect of spacing on the growth of two genotypes of perennial ryegrass. J. Agric. Sci. Camb. 80:495–502.

Smith, Dale. 1968. The establishment and management of alfalfa. Wis. Agric. Exp. Stn. Bull. 542. 22 p.

Smith, Dale. 1972. Influence of nitrogen fertilization on the performance of an alfalfa-bromegrass mixture and bromegrass grown alone. Wis. Agric. Exp. Stn. Res. Report R2384. 8 p.

Smith, Dale. 1975. Forage management in the north. 3rd ed. Kendall-Hunt, Dubuque, Iowa. 237 p.

Smith, Dale, and A. V. A. Jacques. 1973. Influence of alfalfa stand patterns and nitrogen fertilization on the yield and persistence of grasses grown with alfalfa. Wis. Agric. Exp. Stn. Res. Report R2480. 16 p.

Smith, Dale, A. V. A. Jacques, and J. A. Balasko. 1973. Persistence of several temperate grasses grown with alfalfa and harvested two, three, and four times annually at two stubble heights. Crop Sci. 13:553–556.

Trenbath, B. R. 1974. Biomass productivity of mixtures. Adv. Agron. 26:177–210.

Vose, P. B., and P. J. Randall. 1962. Resistance to aluminum and manganese toxicities in plants related to variety and cation-exchange capacity. Nature 196:85–86.

Winch, J. E., R. W. Sheard, and D. N. Mowat. 1970. Determining cutting schedules for maximum yield and quality of bromegrass, timothy, lucerne, and lucerne/grass mixtures. J. Br. Grassl. Soc. 25:44–52.

Wit, C. T. de, P. G. Tow, and G. C. Ennik. 1966. Competition between legumes and grasses. Versl. Landbouwk. Onderz. 687:1–30.

Wolf, D. D., and Dale Smith. 1964. Yield and persistence of several legume-grass mixtures as affected by cutting frequency and nitrogen fertilization. Agron. J. 56:130–133.

Adapting Varieties for Intercropping Systems in the Tropics

C. A. Francis, C. A. Flor, and S. R. Temple[1]

Intercropping is widespread on subsistence farms in developing countries of the tropics. Research in the tropics, however, has focused on the development of new technology directed toward the efficient production of single crops. With a shift to single crop systems, improved cultural practices, chemical fertilizers, pesticides, and other modern inputs the productivity of tropical soils has improved. Crop varieties have been developed for monocrop culture, and considerable progress has been made in increasing yield potential for those farmers who have put capital and available technology to work in the better agricultural regions.

We question the total validity of this approach to crop improvement. New technology has yet to reach small farmers who produce the food crops in many tropical countries. They insist on preserving traditional systems even when other alternatives, including new varieties best suited for monoculture cropping, become available. Although their decision-making criteria are poorly understood, diversity of diet and income source, stability of production, reduced insect and disease incidence, efficient use of family labor, and intensive production with limited land resources appear to be important. It is critical that we understand the farmer's production systems into which new varieties and other technological advances are to be introduced, and evaluate new varieties in a range of environments and systems in which food crops are produced.

[1]Agronomists and plant breeder, Centro Internacional de Agricultura Tropical (CIAT), Apartado Aéreo 6713, Cali, Colombia.

Varietal improvement methodology for intercropping systems in the tropics must reflect:

1. Previous varietal selection for these complex systems.
2. Need for a breeding program designed for complex cropping schemes.
3. Design of an efficient procedure for selection in more than one system.

PAST RESEARCH ON INTERCROPPING

Research attention has been given to intercropping in India (Aiyer, 1949; Kanwar, 1970; Mahapatra et al., 1973; Singh, 1970; Swaminathan, 1970), Taiwan (Chang, 1965; Kung, 1969), the Philippines (Bradfield, 1973; IRRI, 1972, 1973, 1974),[2] Nigeria (Andrews, 1972; Baker, 1974; Norman, 1974), Tanzania,[3] Uganda (Willey & Osiru, 1972), Mexico (A. Turrent and R. Laird, 1972. Report on the Puebla Project. Centro Internacional de Mejoramiento de Maiz y Trigo, CIMMYT, Mexico City. Unpublished data), Colombia (Higuita, 1971),[4] El Salvador (Chacón & Barahona, 1974), the Caribbean zone (Jolly, 1956), and Costa Rica, where a pertinent bibliography recently has been published (IICA, 1974). An excellent survey was published by Dalrymple (1971). In these papers the importance of multiple cropping for certain crops and regions has been described and at times quantified. In several reports, the differences among varieties of specific crops have been explored. Traits which have proven useful in intercropping systems also have been identified in traditional and improved varieties.

Prevalence of Intercropping Systems

It is estimated that 98% of cowpea (*Vigna* sp.), probably the most important legume in Africa, is grown in association with other crops (Arnon, 1972). A survey in northern Nigeria by Norman (1974) reports 83% of the crop land is in mixed cropping. In Colombia 90% of the bean (*Phaseolus* sp.) crop is grown in association with maize (*Zea mays* L.), potato (*Solanum tuberosum* L.) and other crops, while in Guatemala 73% of the bean production is from associated cropping, principally with maize (Gutiérrez et al., 1975). Eighty percent of the beans in Brazil are grown with other crops, principally maize (IICA, 1969). We estimate that in the Latin American

---

[2] W. T. Herrera, and R. R. Harwood, 1973. Crop interrelationships in intensive cropping systems. Seminar, 21 July, IRRI, Los Baños, Philippines, Mimeo. 24 p.

[3] R. C. Finlay, 1974a. Intercropping research and the small farmer in Tanzania. Field Staff Symposium, International Research Development Centre, Ottawa, Mimeo, 14 p.; 1974b. Intercropping soybeans with cereals. Regional Soybean Conference, Addis, Ababa, Mimeo, 20 p.

[4] C. A. Flor and C. A. Francis, 1975. Propuesta de estudio de algunos componentes de una metodología para investigar los cultivos asociados en el trópico latinoamericano. Paper presented at XXI Reunión Anual del Programa Cooperativo Centroamericano para el Mejoramiento del Cultivos Alimenticios (PCCMCA), San Salvador, El Salvador, 1974, Mimeo, 17 p.

tropics 60% of the maize is associated with other crops. Dalrymple (1971) concluded that multiple cropping is a widespread practice throughout the world.

Research Results on Intercropped Systems

Agronomic trials with intercropped systems have concentrated on such variables as relative plant population of component crops, planting dates, fertilizer treatments, and spatial orientation of the crops. High-yielding and early-maturing varieties have been used in these tests, at times with a preliminary screening to identify those varieties most suited to a given climate or system. Examples are varieties of sweet potato (*Ipomoea batatas* Lam.) in sugarcane (*Saccharum officinarum* L.) (Shia & Poa, 1964; Tang, 1963, 1964), mung beans (*Phaseolus aureus*), soybeans (*Glycine max* L. Merr.), cowpea, and sweet potato in maize (IRRI, 1972, 1973, 1974), beans with maize (Chacón & Barahona, 1974), and cotton (*Gossypium* sp.) associated with peanuts (*Arachis hypogaea* L.) (Rao et al., 1960).

Testing varieties in two or more systems has produced variable results. In a test of four sorghum (*Sorghum bicolor*) varieties in monoculture and intercropped with millet (*Setaria* sp.), yields of sorghum were consistently higher in the intercropped system and maintained about the same rank order in the two systems (Baker, 1974). In Tanzania, Finlay found that intercropping with maize, sorghum, and millet reduced yields of the soybeans to 37, 43, and 18% of the 15.2 quintals/ha monocrop yield (average of 12 varieties tested).[5] Yields of 12 mung bean varieties intercropped with maize in the Philippines were reduced to 37% of the monocrop potential in two seasons (IRRI, 1973). Relative yields of the varieties tested ranged from 24 to 43% of the monocrop. Highest-yielding cultivars suffered most from competition. Nine climbing bean varieties were tested in Boliche, Ecuador, by Buestan (1973), intercropped with normal (INIAP-515) and dwarf (Brachytic) maize. There were no differences in maize yields across the nine bean varieties, but four of the bean varieties showed significant yield differences between the contrasting maize plant types used as support.

Maize-bean intercropping in two seasons in El Salvador (Chacón & Barahona, 1974) showed highest total yields from a combination of the 'Sensuntepeque' bush bean variety and the maize hybrid H-3.

Plant Characteristics and Intercropping Systems

Photoperiod insensitivity allows the planting of a variety at any time during the year, and gives flexibility to new systems which require planting outside the traditional dates for a region and crop (Dalrymple, 1971; Swaminathan, 1970). *Early maturity* permits a more intensive organization

---

[5] Finlay, 1974b. Intercropping Soybeans with cereals. Mimeo.

and greater flexibility for intercropped or relay cropped systems (IRRI, 1972; Rao et al., 1960; Sindagi & Ansari, 1960).[6] *Short* and *nonlodging* plant types of some crops have been selected for nitrogen responsiveness and reduced foliage and light competition in crop associations (IRRI, 1972, 1973; Sindagi & Ansari, 1969; Swaminathan, 1970). *Population responsiveness* allows greater flexibility for varying the proportions of crops in a mixture according to present economic returns, and in obtaining the highest total field population of an intercropped system (IRRI, 1973; Swaminathan, 1970).

Selection of Crops for Intercropped Systems

Although certain characteristics of new varieties are helpful when these species are intercropped, there is only limited evidence that conscious selection has been made by plant breeders for intercropped systems. Most selection has been performed by farmers in the developing tropics who have grown crops under their specific systems for a number of years, and who have consistently chosen seed from individuals and varieties that performed best in the intercropped scheme.

IMPROVING PRODUCTIVITY OF INTERCROPPED SYSTEMS

The first step in improving crop species for intercropped systems is to decide if specific genetic selections are needed for specific cropping systems. An information base is needed on principal cropping systems and factors limiting production. The potentials for increasing intercropped yields with improved germplasm are a function of the corresponding monocrop potentials of each component and the relative reductions in yields when these crops are combined. Variety by system interactions may require more than a single breeding strategy for a specific crop. Using beans and maize as examples, we propose a scheme for developing improved varieties for farmers of tropical Latin America.

Predominant Cropping Systems in the Region

In Latin America certain crops are grown in monoculture, including sugarcane, sorghum, lowland rice (*Orysa sativa* L.), cotton, wheat (*Triticum aestivum* L.), and barley (*Hordeum vulgare* L.). Genetic improvement of these crops concentrates on evaluation in single-crop culture, although the same solution may not be appropriate for these crops in other areas, for example sorghum in Africa or sugarcane in Taiwan. Other basic food crops of the Americas—cassava (*Manihot esculenta*), maize, beans, potato, yams (*Dioscorea* sp.)—are most frequently found associated or intercropped. To improve these crops, researchers must consider the frequency of principal

---

[6]Herrera and Harwood, 1973. Crop interrelationships. Mimeo.

systems in which these crops are grown. This assessment should be *quantitative* with respect to crops and production-limiting factors, and *representative* of the country or region. Examples of such a survey are available for cassava and beans in Colombia (CIAT, 1975). Recent surveys (Gutiérrez et al., 1975; IICA, 1969) indicate that up to 80% of the total bean area in Latin America is intercropped.

Present Crop Yields and Potentials for Improvement

Reported experiment station yields for beans in Latin America are generally several times greater than those obtained in farmer's fields, where new varieties will be introduced into complex cropping systems. Dry bean production in Latin America, summarized by Gutiérrez et al. (1975) averages 600 kg/ha (Table 1). Data for Mexico, the second largest bean-producing country in Latin America, is from Lepiz (1974).

These national average yields are low compared to experimental results obtained by Howeler (CIAT, 1975; R. H. Howeler, 1975, personal communication, Bean Program, CIAT) in preliminary CIAT trials in four locations in Colombia and Ecuador (Table 2). Under good management at three altitudes,

Table 1. Dry bean production for Latin America countries reported by Gutiérrez et al. (1975), and Mexico reported by Lepiz (1974)

Country	Year	Area	Production	Yield
		ha	metric tons	kg/ha
Brazil	1970	3,484,778	2,211,449	635
Colombia	1971	68,000	39,000	583
El Salvador	1971	39,900	21,200	670
Guatemala	1971	185,269	61,154	331
Honduras	1971	72,700	55,400	762
Nicaragua	1969	59,635	44,054	738
Panama	1971	16,900	5,410	320
Peru (coast)	1971	60,750	47,993	790
Dominican Republic	1971	37,500	28,125	750
Mexico	1970	1,711,723	833,609	487

Table 2. Yields of superior varieties and selections of bush beans at four locations (CIAT, 1974; R. H. Howeler, 1975, personal communication, Bean Program, CIAT)

Location (season)	Plant density	Average yield of best five varieties
	1,000/ha	kg/ha
Popayán, Colombia (1974A)	280	2,702
Montería, Colombia (1974B)	213	1,196
Boliche, Ecuador (1974B)	280	2,986
Palmira, Colombia (1974A)	333	2,596
Palmira, Colombia (1974B)	333	2,404
Palmira, Colombia (1975A)	333	3,084

the best varieties produced over 2,500 kg/ha in Palmira (1,000 m), Popayan (1,600 m), and Boliche (14 m). Yields of 1,500 kg/ha were obtained with one variety in the lowland location Monteria (40 m). These are all early, black-seeded bush bean varieties. Varieties in these trials represent only our initial evaluation and preliminary selection of collections from Latin America. Although some varieties came from national programs, no crossing nor pure line selection using the more than 10,000 collections in the germplasm bank in CIAT was done prior to these initial trials.

The potential for yield improvement also is promising for climbing beans. Preliminary monocrop tests with artificial support and intensive management consistently have given experimental plot yields greater than 4,000 kg/ha (Y. Hayakawa and D. Laing, 1975, personal communication, Bean Program, CIAT) in trials at CIAT (Fig. 1). Experimental results from several seasons, varieties, and densities (Table 3) suggest that optimum densities vary with variety and season. High populations of climbing beans give high yields and profits at current prices. These preliminary results from diverse trials demonstrate a yield potential which has not been exploited, and these varieties were relatively unselected materials that have not as yet been improved in the breeding program.

Figure 1. High yields have been attained with monoculture climbing bean varieties at high densities and with elaborate support systems.

Table 3. Yields of climbing bean varieties grown with artificial support in CIAT,
Palmira, Colombia (CIAT, 1974; Y. Hayakawa and D. Laing, 1975,
personal communication, Bean Program, CIAT

Season	Variety	Density	Yield
		1,000/ha	kg/ha
1974A	Trujillo 3	1,000	5,650
	Trujillo 2	1,000	5,590
1974B	N-315-61-1-5-1	200	5,030
	PI 282-063	200	4,470
	Trujillo 2	200	4,100
	Trujillo 3	200	4,040
1975A	PI 310-739	400	4,500

Characteristics of the climbing types which distinguish them from the bush phenotype, and which may be related to yield potential, include taller plant structure, larger number of nodes and pods per unit land area, higher leaf area index, later flowering and maturity, and greater bean and total dry matter yields.

Effects of Intercropping

There is potential for increasing yields of monocrop beans, using improved varieties, high populations, and pathogen-free seed. Intercropping reduces bean yields in most seasons and systems when beans and maize are grown together (Lepiz, 1974). This is especially true for the commonly grown tall maize varieties (Fig. 2). In one CIAT trial, a 20% yield reduction was observed in bush beans grown with an evenly spaced maize population of 44,000 plants/ha (Table 4). A more traditional maize system, with three or four plants in widely-spaced hills, produced no significant reductions in bean yields. Maize yields were unaffected by the spacing treatments.

Relative planting dates of the two crops influence yields of the bush beans. Bean yields were reduced from 939 kg/ha in monocrop to less than 400 kg/ha when maize was planted before the beans (Table 5). A 15-day advantage for the beans gave highest yields, a result confirmed by small farmers in the vicinity who use this practice. Land equivalent ratios were highest when beans were planted after the maize.[7] Higher bean populations increased yields, but intercropping with maize reduced yields from the monocrop levels for a red bush bean variety, 'ICA Guali' (Table 6).

Yields of bush beans and climbing beans intercropped with normal and dwarf maize are reported in Table 7. Monoculture yields of the dwarf (brachytic-2) hybrid maize were higher than those of the normal hybrid

---

[7]R. T. Bantilan, and R. R. Harwood, 1973. The influence of intercropping field corn (*Zea mays* L.) with mung bean (*Phaseolus aureus*) or cowpea (*Vigna sinensis*) on the control of weeds. Paper presented at the IV Annual Scientific Meeting of the Crop Science Society of the Philippines, 21–23 May 1973, Cebu City, Philippines. Mimeo, 13 p.

Figure 2. Regional varieties of maize grown on the farm are often extremely tall, and do not permit growth of the associated bean crop.

Table 4. Yields of beans and maize with four planting systems, CIAT, 1973B (Flor & Francis, 1975. Propuesta de estudio de alqunos componentes. Mimeo)

Planting system*	Yield	
	Bean	Maize
	——— kg/ha ———	
Bean	1,330 a†	
Bean and maize (1 plant each 25 cm)	1,021 c	5,124 a†
Bean and maize (2 plants each 50 cm)	1,066 bc	5,290 a
Bean and maize (3 plants each 75 cm)	1,267 ab	4,518 a
Bean and maize (4 plants each 100 cm)	1,206 abc	4,446 a

* Bush bean variety 'ICA Guali' planted at 220,000/ha; yellow brachytic maize planted at 44,400/ha.
† Yields followed by same letter in each column not significantly different (5% level).

Table 5. Yields of beans and maize with varied planting dates, CIAT, 1974A (Flor & Francis, 1975. Propuesta de estudio de algunos componentes. Mimeo)

Planting dates*	Yield		LER†
	Bean	Maize	
	——— kg/ha ———		
Maize (monocrop)		7,270 a‡	
Maize 15 days before beans	365 c‡	5,730 bc	1.18
Maize 10 days before beans	400 c	5,840 bc	1.23
Maize 5 days before beans	394 c	5,040 c	1.11
Simultaneous planting	500 bc	5,710 bc	1.32
Beans 5 days before maize	483 bc	6,910 ab	1.46
Beans 10 days before maize	516 bc	7,230 a	1.54
Beans 15 days before maize	703 ab	6,760 ab	1.68
Beans (monocrop)	939 a		

* Bean variety 'ICA Pijao' (Linea 32) planted at 300,000/ha; maize hybrid 'ICA H-207' planted at 40,000/ha.
† Land equivalent ratio described by Bantilan and Harwood (1973. The influence of intercropping field corn. Mimeo).
‡ Yields followed by same letter in each column do not differ significantly (5% level).

Table 6. Yields of beans and maize with several planting systems, CIAT, 1974B (Flor & Francis, 1975. Propuesta de estudio de algunos componentes. Mimeo)

Planting system*	Bean density	Yield		LER
		Bean	Maize	
	1,000/ha	———kg/ha———		
Maize (monocrop)	--	--	3,767 a†	1.00
Maize with beans in same row	111	896 b†	4,139 a	1.78
Maize with beans in parallel row	111	693 c	4,162 a	1.63
Maize with beans in two parallel rows	222	1,008 b	4,239 a	1.88
Beans (monocrop)	222	1,326 a	--	1.00

* Bean variety ICA Guali, maize variety yellow brachytic at 44,400/ha.
† Yields followed by same letter in each column do not differ significantly (5% level).

('ICA H-207'), when each was planted at recommended densities. Total biological yields of maize did not differ significantly between these two hybrids nor among systems. Higher yields of dwarf maize resulted from higher harvest index (proportion of grain to total yield). Bush bean yields were reduced by 52 and 63% when intercropped with normal and dwarf maize, respectively. These yield reductions were the result of fewer racemes per plant (5 in intercrop vs. 9 in monocrop beans), fewer pods per plant (9 vs. 14), and reduced pod and stem weight per plant. Harvest indices of beans were not affected by the system. Yields were reduced 80% when climbing beans were grown with normal maize, and 90% when grown with dwarf maize, compared to monoculture climbing beans at the same plant densities.

Bean yield reductions due to competition from maize in the intercropped system are related to changes in yield components (Table 8). Plant

Table 7. Yields of bush and climbing beans with normal and brachytic maize, CIAT, 1975A

System	Density		Yield				LER
	Beans	Maize	Beans	Maize grain	Maize total	Maize harvest index	
	1,000 plants/ha		kg/ha				
Bush bean (ICA Pijao)	222	--	1,738 c*	--	--	--	1.00
Normal maize/Bush bean	155	44	845 d	7,631 bc*	14,268 a*	0.46 ab*	1.65
Brachytic maize/Bush bean	177	65	647 de	8,769 a	15,564 a	0.48 a	1.44
Climbing bean (PI 282–063)	44	--	2,148 b	--	--	--	1.00
Normal maize/Climbing bean	44	44	429 ef	7,318 c	15,839 a	0.40 bc	1.30
Climbing bean (PI 282–063)	65	--	2,456 a	--	--	--	1.00
Brachytic maize/Climbing bean	65	65	220 f	8,153 ab	15,634 a	0.45 abc	1.08
Normal maize (ICA H–207)	--	44	--	6,535 d	15,014 a	0.38 c	1.00
Brachytic maize (ICA H–210)	--	65	--	8,205 ab	15,796 a	0.45 abc	1.00

* Yields in same column followed by same letter do not differ significantly (5% level); bean yields with 14% moisture, maize grain yields with 15% moisture, and maize total dry matter yields based on absolute dry weight.

Table 8. Yield components of climbing beans grown in two densities and two systems, CIAT, 1975A (Yield components from 4-plant samples, final yield in kg/ha from complete plot harvest)

System	Plant height	Racemes per plant	Pods per plant	Leaves per plant	Branches per plant	Dry weights			Harvest index	Bean yield
						Stems	Leaves	Pods seed		
	cm					— g/plant —				
Climbing bean monocrop (44,400 plants/ha)	275 a*	27 a	46 a	52 a	3.8 a	18.5 a	25.2 a	55.0 a	0.56	2,148 b
Climbing bean monocrop (65,000 plants/ha)	247 a	19 b	37 a	38 b	2.8 b	14.2 b	20.0 b	37.8 b	0.53	2,456 a
Climbing bean Intercropped Normal Maize (44,400 plants/ha)	242 a	6 c	10 b	16 c	1.0 c	4.8 c	10.0 c	15.0 c	0.50	429 c
Climbing bean Intercropped. Brachytic Maize (65,000 plants/ha)	239 a	3 c	5 b	11 c	1.0 c	3.2 c	4.8 d	6.5 c	0.43	220 c

* Numbers in each column followed by same letter do not differ significantly (5% level).

Figure 3. High densities of climbing beans associated with maize produce reasonable bean
yields, with simultaneous planting dates and careful selection of the correct variety.

height of beans was unchanged, but lower numbers of racemes, pods, leaves,
and branches per plant were observed in the intercropped climbing beans.
Competition reduced dry weights of all bean plant components, but harvest
index was not altered substantially. Subsequent trials with higher bean populations, modified planting dates and physical orientation of the two crops
have reduced interspecies competition and increased bean yields (Fig. 3).

Yields of bush beans and soybeans were reduced by association with
maize, but were not affected when these legumes were intercropped with rice
(Table 9). There were no significant differences in maize grain, total biological yield, or harvest index. In all trials of spacing, densities, planting
dates, and physical orientation of intercropped systems, bean yields are low
compared to the experimental yields reported in Tables 2 and 3. Similar
trials are planned, using high yielding cultivars, pathogen-free seed, and the
best agronomic system based on results to date.

Variety by System Interactions

The decision to screen and select promising germplasm using more than
one system depends on the magnitude of variety by system interactions, as

Table 9. Yields of bush beans, soybeans, and maize in several combinations, CIAT, 1975A

System	Density		Yield		LER
	Legume	Maize	Legume	Maize	
	1,000 plants/ha		——— kg/ha ———		
Normal Maize (ICA H-207)		44	--	7,221 a*	1.00
Bush bean (ICA Pijao)	200	--	2,033 bc*	--	1.00
Soybean (ICA Pance)	200	--	2,910 a	--	1.00
Maize/Bush Bean	200	44	1,033 d	6,926 a	1.47
Maize/Soybean	200	44	1,550 c	6,525 a	1.44
Maize/Rice†	--	44	--	8,195 a	
Bush bean/Rice†	200	--	2,223 b	--	
Soybean/Rice†	200	--	3,025 a	--	

* Yields in each column followed by same letter do not differ significantly (5% level).
† Rice not yet harvested.

shown by the relative performance of different cultivars under two or more systems. Table 7 quantified the reduction in bush and climbing bean yields when each was grown with two types of maize, normal and dwarf. Germ-plasm testing in a high return monocrop system with artificial support would lead to selection of the climbing types, as compared to bush types. These climbers would not be optimum for planting with maize, where the bush types have shown a yield advantage in agronomic systems tested to date.

In Boliche, Ecuador, relative yields of nine climbing bean cultivars were determined from plantings with contrasting normal and brachytic maize (Buestan, 1973). The data summarized in Table 10 show significant yield differences among the bean varieties tested. A comparison of the bean yields between the two intercropped systems revealed nonsignificant correlations

Table 10. Yields of nine climbing bean collections associated with two contrasting maize types, Boliche, Ecuador, 1973B (Buestan, 1973)

Climbing bean variety	Beans associated with dwarf maize		Beans associated with normal maize	
	Rank	Yield	Yield	Rank
		——— kg/ha ———		
Panamito	1	1,343 a*	780 bc*	5
Puebla-421	2	1,025 b	695 cd	6
Aguascalientes-70	3	1,003 b	1,081 a	2
Pata de Paloma	4	954 b	991 ab	4
Guatemala-358	5	938 b	1,005 a	3
Puebla-163	6	882 bc	1,102 a	1
Guanajuato-113A	7	811 bc	669 cd	7
Puebla-151B	8	803 c	542 d	9
Aguascalientes-67	9	708 c	600 cd	8

* Bean yields in same column followed by same letter do not differ significantly (5% level); within a variety, yields connected by an underscore across the two systems do not differ significantly (5% level).

Table 11. Yield and rank order correlations for soybean production in different intercropping systems (Correlations for data reported by Finlay, 1974b. Intercropping soybeans with cereals. Mimeo)

Soybean systems	r (yield)	r (rank)
Monocrop vs. intercropped with maize	0.506	0.455
Monocrop vs. intercropped with sorghum	0.372	0.432
Monocrop vs. intercropped with millet	0.398	0.372
Intercropped with maize vs. intercropped with sorghum	0.595*	0.392
Intercropped with maize vs. intercropped with millet	0.444	0.336
Intercropped with sorghum vs. intercropped with millet	0.692**	0.601*

*,** Significant at the 5% and 1% probability levels, respectively.

for yield (r = 0.265) and for rank order (r = 0.361). Selection of a bean variety for one system would therefore not provide the best bean for a different system. In this trial the correlation coefficients were negative (nonsignificant) for yields of beans versus maize (r = –0.229 for normal, r = –0.509 for brachytic), which illustrates a differential competition between the two crops in these two systems with maize as support.

Using soybean data reported by Finlay, we calculated the simple correlations of yield and rank between monoculture soybeans and three intercropping systems with cereals (Table 11).[8] These correlations were not significant. Simple correlations between soybean yields and rank among pairs of intercropped systems with cereals were significant in two cases. Among the intercropped systems, yields of soybeans intercropped with sorghum were correlated with yields of soybean intercropped with the other two cereals.

Correlations of mung bean yields in monocrop versus maize associations (calculated from data of R. R. Harwood, IRRI, 1973, 1974) gave a negative, nonsignificant r-value for yield (r = –0.339) and rank order (r = –0.098) over two seasons in 1973. Similar calculations for 1974 gave positive, nonsignificant r-values for yield (r = 0.514) and rank order (r = 0.434). Monocrop yields of eight varieties common to the trials of both years showed a positive, nonsignificant r-value (r = 0.465) across years, with the same results for mung beans intercropped with maize (r = –0.045). This variety by season interaction complicates the selection of stable, high-yielding varieties.

Bean yields of seven varieties intercropped with maize (Chacón & Barahona, 1975) were not significantly correlated over two seasons (r = 0.218). There was no significant correlation of maize yields in two seasons across bean varieties (r = 0.318). Bean production was negatively correlated with maize production (r = –0.858, significant at 1% level).

The only significant association between intercropped and solo performance among varieties was found in the sorghum trial reported by Baker (1974). Monocrop sorghum yields were significantly correlated with yields of sorghum intercropped with millet (r = 0.947, significant at 1% level), although the trial included only four varieties.

---

[8] Finlay, 1974b. Intercropping soybeans with cereals. Mimeo.

This synthesis and analysis of existing data from intercrop studies confirms the importance of variety by system interactions. In reaching a decision on which system or systems to use in a breeding program, one must confront the circular problem inherent in the evaluation of genetic material in new systems. With a change in fertility, plant densities, or cropping system, selected materials with superior performance under a previous system may not be superior. It is necessary to select germplasm under the new conditions. As systems evolve and improve, it is necessary to test each cycle of promising selections under current cultural practices. Conversely, optimal populations, planting dates, soil fertility, physical orientation, and species balance in mixed crops should be confirmed regularly using the latest varieties.

The cost of implementing more than one system in a breeding program depends on the stage of germplasm development at which selection for intercropping is initiated. The relative advantage of moving large numbers of crosses and selections through one program, versus a reduced number through two programs, must be considered.

The decision on a breeding methodology depends on yield limitations in prevalent cropping systems, potentials of monocrop and intercropping, and variety by system interactions.

EVALUATION OF GERMPLASM FOR INTERCROPPED SYSTEMS

The importance of maize-bean intercropping in the Latin American tropics makes it essential that we consider these systems in the development of new germplasm. With evidence that variety by system interaction exists for maize-bean and other intercrop systems, CIAT has begun to test a number of promising varieties in two or more systems involving these two crops. The best agronomic recommendations from previous intercropping studies have been followed in planting the first cycle which is currently in the field. These evaluation procedures are described below.

Maize Evaluation in Three Cropping Systems

In addition to maize monoculture production in all parts of the Andean zone, Central America, and Brazil, there are large areas where maize is cultivated with bush beans (Brazil, Central America, and Mexico) and with climbing beans (highland areas throughout Latin America). The three systems included in this evaluation are:

a. Monoculture maize
b. Maize intercropped with bush bean
c. Maize intercropped with climbing bean

Bush Bean Evaluation in Two Cropping Systems

An evaluation of bush beans, in monoculture and intercropped with maize, includes the best local bean variety ('ICA Pijao'), the most promising variety from tests at several locations ('Porrillo Sintético'), and other promising selections:

a. Monoculture bush beans
b. Bush beans intercropped with maize

Climbing Bean Evaluation in Two Cropping Systems

Climbing beans evaluated in monoculture and intercropped with maize, include 'Trujillo,' PI 282-063, and other promising lines. The systems include monocrop on bamboo and wire trellises with twine guides to support the beans, and intercrop with a normal maize hybrid ('ICA H-207'):

a. Monocrop climbing beans with artificial support
b. Climbing beans intercropped with maize

In each evaluation, primary emphasis will be placed on yields of crop varieties in the comparison. However, if the yields of the uniform associated crop vary across the varieties under test, this will provide an additional measure of the total value of each cropping system.

From the results of these three tests, repeated in two seasons in each of two locations, decisions will be made on the need to evaluate segregating materials and conduct yield trials with more than one system. If there is little difference in relative performance under different systems, the most economical system can be chosen for breeding work on each crop. These least-cost systems are monoculture maize, monoculture bush beans, and climbing bean intercropped with maize. These methodological tests will be repeated in additional locations and in subsequent seasons with new and higher yielding materials to validate earlier conclusions. Exactly how different the results from contrasting systems must be to justify the cost of two evaluations, and determining the point in an improvement scheme where the two systems should be introduced, are difficult questions that still must be answered. This procedure is designed to give the researcher an objective evaluation of new germplasm in the systems into which it will be introduced.

GENETIC IMPROVEMENT OF VARIETIES FOR INTERCROPPING

As an integral part of this breeding procedure for one or more cropping systems, the desirable characteristics for each crop must be included as selection criteria. If different varietal characteristics are needed for different systems, they must be identified and given priority. Several characteristics are discussed in relation to their importance in monocrop versus intercropped systems.

1. Photoperiod insensitivity is associated with adaptation across latitudes and planting dates, and permits accurate prediction of maturity and allows planting throughout the year. The development of photoperiod insensitive materials is an objective of international programs that are developing cereals, legumes, and tuber crops for a wide range of climatic and cultural conditions (Dalrymple, 1971; Swaminathan, 1970), although there may be situations where sensitivity is desirable for a specific crop.

2. Maturity objectives depend on crop and system. Intensive intercrop or relay systems may require early and uniform varieties (IRRI, 1972),[9] but there is often a trade off between yield potential and maturity. Where increased yield depends on late maturity in a crop such as beans, the breeding objectives for monoculture versus intercropping may be different.

3. Short and nonlodging plant types are desirable where the objective is yield response to nitrogen and more efficient production per unit leaf area. Reduced foliage and competition for light, and greater seed or tuber production efficiency, are desirable for component species in an intercropped system (IRRI, 1972, 1973; Swaminathan, 1970). Certain systems require a tall and competitive crop variety, such as a rice variety to compete with weeds, or a strong maize variety to support climbing beans. In tests with sorghum varieties (Baker, 1974), increases in yields of sorghum intercropped with millet, as compared with monocropped sorghum, were correlated with sorghum varietal height ($r = 0.921$, significant at 5% level).

4. Population response is critical for increasing yields in monoculture and intercropping, especially to exploit dwarfness and more efficient plant types. Competition for light and nutrients can be maximized and highest yields achieved when the density of a responsive variety is increased beyond densities used with traditional varieties.

5. Uniformity of flowering and maturity is desirable in intensive intercrop schemes where two or more crops occupy a limited available time and space (IRRI, 1973), but this creates a high-risk situation when adverse conditions occur during flowering—a short drought or continuous rains at a critical time reduce yields of most crops.

6. Insect and disease resistance are objectives of most breeding programs, and the relative importance of specific resistance factors varies with the cropping system and the production area under consideration.

7. Fertility response is typical of the new dwarf cereal varieties, and valuable for intercropped species. The precise response to specific major elements will depend on species mix and soil type, and site and system specificity make this a difficult characteristic for which to select.

8. Yield potential is a product of these factors and others, and the prime objective of nearly all breeding programs.

CONCLUSIONS

An understanding of present and potential cropping system is essential to successful genetic improvement of crop species. The research procedure includes a study of predominant systems and factors limiting production, a consideration of alternative strategies to solve these problems, and a breeding

---

[9] Herrera and Harwood, 1973. Crop interrelationships. Mimeo

program designed to remove yield limitations by means of improved varieties. The method described to determine the system or systems for selecting improved maize and bean varieties is an example which may be modified for other cropping systems and climatic zones. Success in plant breeding, agronomic research, and other activities of international and national programs, is measured by increased production at the farm level. The final step in this research process is farm testing of new varieties and cultural practices, and an evaluation of their impact on farm income and family nutrition. This is the potential contribution of crop improvement programs to intercropping systems in the tropics.

LITERATURE CITED

Aiyer, A. K. Y. N. 1949. Mixed cropping in India. Indian J. Agric. Sci. 19:439–543.

Andrews, D. J. 1972. Intercropping with sorghum in Nigeria. Exp. Agric. 8:139–150.

Arnon, I. 1972. Crop production in dry regions. Vol. 2. Leonard Hill, London.

Baker, E. F. I. 1974. Research into intercropping aspects of farming systems in Nigeria. Mixed cropping with cereals—a system for improvement. p. 287–301. *In* Proceedings of the Farming Systems Workshop. ICRISAT, Hyderabad, India.

Bradfield, R. L. 1973. Multiple cropping on rice farms. World Farming. December 28–31.

Buestan, H. 1973. Programa de Leguminosas de Grano. Informe Anual 1973. Estación Experimental Boliche, Instituto Nacional de Investigaciones Agropecuarias (INIAP), Guayaquil, Ecuador.

Chacon, A. E., and M. A. Barahona. 1974. Granos básicos en multicultivo. p. 63–77. *In* XXI Reunión del Programa Cooperativo Centroamericano para el Mejoramiento de Cultivos Alimenticios (PCCMCA), San Salvador, El Salvador, 1974.

Chang, H. 1965. Rotation and intercropping systems of sugarcane in Taiwan. Taiwan Sugar 12(1):17–22.

Centro Internacional de Agricultura Tropical. 1974. Annual Report 1975. CIAT. Cali, Colombia.

Dalrymple, D. F. 1971. Survey of multiple cropping in less developed nations. USDA, Washington, D. C. FEDS. 108 p.

Gutiérrez, U., M. Infante, and A. Pinchinat. 1975. Situación del cultivo de fríjol en América Latina. CIAT, Cali, Colombia, Boletín Informe. ES–19. 36 p.

Higuita, M. F. 1971. Siembras múltiples intercaladas. Bogotá, Instituto Colombiano Agropecuario (ICA). Boletín de Divulgación No. 42.

Instituto Interamericano de Ciencias Agricolas. 1969. Reunión técnica sobre programación de investigación y extensión en frijol y otras leguminosas de grano para América Central. IICA, Turrialba, Costa Rice. IICA Publ. ZN. 112–65. Vol. 2.

Instituto Interamericano de Ciencias Agricolas. 1974. Bibliografía sobre sistemas de agricultura tropical. IICA, Turrialba, Costa Rica. Documentación e Información Agrícola No. 27. 145 p.

International Rice Research Institute. 1972. Annual report 1972. Multiple cropping. IRRI, Los Baños, Philippines. p. 21–34.

International Rice Research Institute. 1973. Annual report 1973. Multiple cropping. IRRI, Los Baños, Philippines. p. 15–34.

International Rice Research Institute. 1974. Annual report 1974. Cropping systems program. IRRI, Los Baños, Philippines.

Jolly, A. L. 1956. Mixed farming in the Caribbean. Corona, October:385–388.

Kanwar, J. S. 1970. Multiple cropping: trends and problems. Indian Farming 20(7):5–7.

Kung, P. 1969. Multiple cropping in Taiwan. World Crops, May–June, 1969.

Lepiz, I., R. 1974. Asociación de cultivos maíz-fríjol. INIA, SAG, México, Folleto Técnico No. 58.

Mahapatra, I. C., D. M. Leeuwrik, N. K. Singh, and Dayanand. 1973. Green revolution through multiple cropping in India. Agric. Mech. in Asia. Spring:37–42.

Norman, D. W. 1974. Rationalizing mixed cropping under indigenous conditions: the example of northern Nigeria. J. Devel. Studies 10:3-21.

Rao, M. R., P. N. Rao, and S. M. Ali. 1960. Investigation on the type of cotton suitable for mixed cropping in the northern tract. Indian Cotton Grow. Rev. 14:384-388 (Field Crop Abstr. 1962, 15:377).

Shia, F. Y., and T. P. Pao. 1964. On the yields of sugarcane interplanted with different varieties of sweet potato. Rep. Taiwan Sugar. Exp. Stn. 1964. No. 35:55-63. (Field Crop Abstr., 1965, 18:306).

Sindagi, S. S., and Z. A. Ansari. 1969. A dwarf mutant in castor (*Ricinus communis* Linn.). Mysore J. Agric. Sci. 3:231-232. (Field Crop Abstr. 1970, 23:1584).

Singh, A. 1970. Multiple Cropping in Uttar Pradesh. Indian Farming 20(7):15-17.

Swaminathan, M. S. 1970. New varieties for multiple cropping. Indian Farming 29(7): 9-13.

Tang, C. F. 1963. A study on interplanting sweet potato with sugarcane. I. Date of interplanting, variety of sweet potato and row width of autumn plant cane. Rep. Taiwan Sugar Exp. Stn. 1963. No. 31:27-55.

Tang, C. F. 1964. A study on interplanting sweet potato with sugar cane. II. Effects on some important agronomic characteristics of different cane varieties. Rep. Taiwan Sugar Exp. Stn. 1964. No. 35:43-53 (Field Crop Abstr. 1965, 18:305).

Willey, R. W., and D. S. O. Osiru. 1972. Studies on mixtures of maize and beans (*Phaseolus vulgaris*) with particular reference to plant population. J. Agric. Sci. 79: 517-529.

Land Preparation and Seedling Establishment Practices in Multiple Cropping Systems[1]

P. W. Unger and B. A. Stewart[2]

With multiple cropping systems, as with any other cropping system, a most critical period in a plant's life cycle is that of seed germination and seedling establishment. At this time, the seed must break dormancy and send forth its roots and shoot and the seedling must become established. It is also a time when the seed and seedling are greatly influenced by environmental conditions. This report will illustrate that planting and seedling establishment in multiple cropping systems can be accomplished by both conventional land preparation and management practices and reduced or no-tillage practices. "Conventional tillage" includes primary and secondary tillage operations normally performed for a given crop in a given geographical area. For this report, "seedlings" are defined as young plants that subsist basically upon stored foods of the seed. Because of this restricted definition, the "seedling zone" is that zone occupied by the seedling roots. While this zone undoubtedly varies greatly depending upon plant species and environmental conditions, the seedling zone arbitrarily is considered to be about 20 cm deep and 10 cm in diameter for individual seeds. For rows of close-planted seeds, the zone would be 10 cm wide along the seeded row.

REQUIREMENTS FOR GERMINATION AND SEEDLING ESTABLISHMENT

Basic requirements for germination are oxygen, water, and temperature. To assure seed germination and seedling establishment, some secondary requirements must be met also. These include:

1. Adequate soil aeration for gaseous exchange in the seed and root zone.

---

[1]Contribution from the Soil, Water, and Air Sciences, Southern Region, Agricultural Research Service, USDA, in cooperation with the Texas Agric. Exp. Stn.
[2]Soil scientist and research leader, respectively, USDA Southwestern Great Plains Research Center, Bushland, Texas.

2. Adequate seed-soil contact to permit water flow to seeds and seed-ling roots.
3. A noncrusted soil to permit seedling emergence.
4. A low density soil that permits root elongation and proliferation.
5. An environment that provides adequate light to the seedling.
6. An environment that affords protection against wind and water erosion.
7. A pest-free or pest-controlled environment.

Through the years, various practices and systems have been developed to reduce potential hazards to crop production during seed germination and seedling establishment. With annual cropping or alternate crop-fallow systems, time generally is adequate to prepare a desirable seedbed well in advance of crop seeding.

Time may be adequate for preparing seedbeds in multiple cropping systems when the growing season is long. However, time is critical for establishing a second crop when delays may reduce yields through freeze damage, failure of day length sensitive plants to mature, and potential droughts, insect buildups, and disease outbreaks. The importance of time is illustrated in Figure 1 for double cropping systems involving grain sorghum (*Sorghum bicolor* L.) and sunflowers (*Helianthus annuus* L.) planted after wheat (*Triticum aestivum* L.) harvest on the Texas High Plains where frost may occur before the second crop matures.

Because of limited and erratic precipitation, double cropping on the Texas High Plains is practical only with irrigation. The average harvest date for irrigated winter wheat is late June, making 1 July a reasonable planting

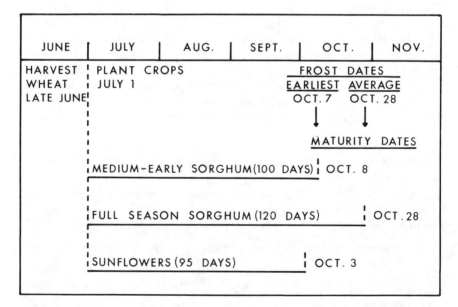

Figure 1. Illustration showing the influence of planting date and frost dates on the possibility of three crops having different lengths of growing season to mature before frost.

date for a second crop. A medium-early season grain sorghum planted on 1 July would mature grain before frost most years. A full season grain sorghum planted on that date would fail to mature grain before frost about one-half of the years. Sunflowers, which have a shorter growing season, would always escape frost damage when planted on 1 July.

Planting by 1 July on the Texas High Plains is possible most years when limited- or no-tillage methods are used for the second crop. With conventional-tillage, delays are possible, thus increasing the risk of frost damage.

Allen et al. (1975) double-cropped grain sorghum after wheat for 5 years on the Texas High Plains, using conventional (clean) and no-tillage methods. Grain sorghum on no-tillage plots emerged sooner, grew more rapidly, and matured up to 5 days earlier than sorghum on clean tillage plots. Killing frost reduced yields in 2 of the 5 years, but because of earlier emergence, faster growth, and more advanced maturity at frost, grain yields were higher with no-tillage than with clean-tillage all 5 years. Yields averaged 5,690 and 5,070 kg/ha with no- and clean-tillage, respectively, a 12% advantage for no-tillage.

When soybeans (*Glycine max* L. Merr.), corn (*Zea mays* L.), or grain sorghum are double cropped after wheat, timely planting is important. In Illinois, soybean yields declined 50 kg/ha (0.75 bu/acre) each day planting was delayed in June or early July (Hoeft et al., 1975). Major factors contributing to yield reductions of late-planted soybeans were uncertainty of rainfall in late June and early July for good germination and early growth, and frost before crop maturity (McKibben & Pendleton, 1968). To permit earlier soybean planting, Hoeft et al. (1975) suggested harvesting wheat at 19 to 22% moisture, which allowed planting 4 to 7 days earlier than with normal harvesting.

No-tillage planting has been widely accepted for double cropping in the soft wheat belt in Illinois because the crops can be planted in wheat straw without delay, thus insuring prompt germination and maturity before frost (G. E. McKibben, 1975. Personal communication). Also, the wheat straw mulch conserves water present in the soil and impedes runoff, thus permitting more time for rainfall infiltration and minimizing erosion. In comparison, conventional-tillage is difficult because of the straw. Also, tillage may reduce soil water in the tillage zone, causing delayed and erratic germination or even death of the seedlings (Hoeft et al., 1975).

ADVANTAGES AND DISADVANTAGES OF NO-TILLAGE METHODS FOR ACHIEVING THE REQUIREMENTS FOR GERMINATION AND SEEDLING ESTABLISHMENT

Oxygen

Oxygen required for germination, defined as breaking of the seed coat by the shoot or radicle, varies among plant species (Morinaga, 1926; Vlamis & Davis, 1943), but was low for corn (Unger & Danielson, 1965). Corn germinated at 0.0 cm Hg O_2 pressure. Apparently, enough O_2 was supplied to the seeds during an initial 17-hour imbibition period in aerated water or was retained in seed tissues to permit germination. Continued radicle growth and root and shoot development required greater O_2 pressures. Radicle growth was maximum at about 20 cm Hg O_2 pressure, a slightly higher O_2 pressure than in air.

Any soil condition that permits ready access of air to seeds and roots should supply adequate O_2 for near optimum germination and seedling development. Tillage method should have little or no influence on O_2 supply, except possibly for poorly drained and dense or crusted soils.

Water

Soil water, undoubtedly more often than any other factor, determines whether seeds will germinate and seedlings become established. Generally, too little rather than too much water causes problems with conventional systems. With multiple cropping, seed zone water may be even more critical because the second crop must be established rapidly to avoid possible yield reductions due to frost. Also, because of depletion by the preceding crop, soil water contents at planting of subsequent crops in multiple cropping systems may be low as compared to planting following a fallow period. Hence, any technique that results in higher water contents throughout the season should be beneficial in multiple cropping systems.

Numerous reports showed higher water contents at planting with no-tillage than with conventional-tillage (Blevins et al., 1971; Greb et al., 1970; Jones et al., 1968, 1969; Moody et al., 1963; Unger et al., 1971; Unger & Phillips, 1973). With no-tillage, surface residues absorbed raindrop energy, and thus reduced soil dispersion, surface sealing, and runoff, and enhanced infiltration. Surface residues also reduced evaporation.

Water contents in the seed zone or near the soil-residue interface were greater for surface mulches or no-tillage systems than for bare soil or conventional-tillage systems. For the 0- to 8-cm depth of the Donerail soil in Kentucky, volumetric water contents were 40 and 31% for no- and conventional-tillage methods, respectively. For the same depth of Maury soil, water contents were 39 and 23% for the respective tillage methods. These measurements were made after killing bluegrass (*Poa pratensis* L.) with herbicides or tillage (Blevins et al., 1971).

In a residue placement study with Pullman clay loam, Unger and Parker (1968) found greater water contents immediately beneath residue layers than at greater depths in the soil (Table 1). Residues were placed on the surface, mixed with surface soil, or placed in a layer 2.5 cm below the surface. The determinations were made when 40% of the water held between matric potentials of –1/3 and –15 bars had evaporated.

Many reports showed or mentioned that seed zone water contents generally were higher with no-tillage than with conventional-tillage. Of equal and possibly greater importance was that water contents remained higher

Table 1. Effect of residue placement on soil water distribution (Unger & Parker, 1968)

	Residue treatments		
Soil depth	On surface	Mixed	Below surface
cm		— % water by weight —	
0.0- 2.5	†	13.5 c†	4.5 e
2.5- 5.0	24.6 a*	26.5 ab	†
5.0- 7.5	24.5 a	27.3 a	31.0 a
7.5-10.0	24.2 a	26.2 ab	29.5 b
10.0-12.5	23.6 b	25.7 ab	27.9 c
12.5-15.0	22.9 c	25.2 b	26.5 d

* Mean values within a column followed by the same letter or letters are not significantly different at the 5% level.
† Residue layer or mixed soil-residue layer.

longer with no-tillage than with conventional-tillage because of slower drying by evaporation. This provided favorable conditions for seeding for a longer period, permitted more rapid early growth, helped plants to better withstand short-duration droughts, and often resulted in higher crop yields, provided other conditions were favorable (Allen et al., 1975; Blevins et al., 1971; Unger & Phillips, 1973).

High soil water contents are undesirable in areas with poorly drained soils or frequent rainfall. In such cases, surface residues delay soil drying and planting. However, crops were planted soon after rainfall when sod provided traction for planting equipment under conditions where planting was not possible on tilled areas (Allis-Chalmers. No nonsense guide to no-till farming), and Young (1973) planted sod fields by no-tillage methods during rain with excellent results.

Temperature

Surface residues associated with reduced- and no-tillage systems often result in lower soil temperatures than those for bare soil, especially at planting time in early spring. Later in the season, the temperature differences may be slight. Because of lower spring soil temperatures, favorable temperatures for germination and emergence may occur up to 7 days later in no-tillage seedbeds as compared with that in conventional-tillage seedbeds in the northern U. S. (Fig. 2).

The temperature lowering varies, among other factors, with location, soil slope, average temperature, residue level, and soil water content. Early corn growth in Iowa, Minnesota, and Ohio was decreased by a straw mulch, whereas the mulch did not appreciably influence growth in South Carolina where soil temperatures were considerably higher. The data supported earlier work which showed that corn growth increased as soil temperature increased from 10 to 30 C, was little influenced from 30 to 32 C, and decreased at 32 to 44 C (Van Wijk et al., 1959).

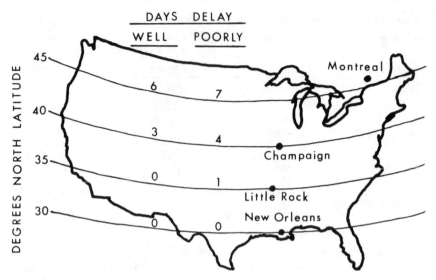

Figure 2. Approximate number of days delay (additional time) to reach a mean soil temperature of 15.6 C (60 F) in well-drained and poorly drained soils with heavy sod cover as compared with that in a conventionally-tilled seedbed. (Adapted from Chevron Chemical Company, Ortho Division, No-Tillage Farming.)

Reduced maximum temperatures under a mulch in summer or in warm climates may improve germination and seedling establishment. In Nigeria, the temperature was 41 C at the 5-cm depth 2 weeks after planting grain sorghum in clean-tilled soil. Where the sorghum was no-tillage planted through 1 to 2 cm of crop residue, the temperature reached only 31 C. The high temperatures reduced germination and seedling vigor, and yields were 50% greater with no-tillage than with clean-tillage because lower temperatures reduced plant water stress (Rockwood & Lal, 1974).

Hot, dry weather often occurs in late June and early July on the Texas High Plains when wheat is harvested and the second crop is planted in a double cropping system. Allen et al. (1975) double cropped grain sorghum after wheat by planting sorghum after clean-tillage or into standing wheat stubble. In 1968, maximum air temperatures averaged 38 C during the seedling emergence period. Lower temperatures within wheat stubble contributed to reduced evaporation, causing the soil surface to remain moist longer and improving the microclimate for germination and seedling emergence. Seedlings emerged sooner and grew more rapidly on no-tillage than on clean-tillage plots. In 1973, soil surface temperatures reached 37 C on clean-tillage plots, but only 32 C on no-tillage plots. Higher temperatures on bare soil contributed to poor sorghum germination, emergence, and seedling vigor.

Different optimum temperatures for various crops suggest the possibility of adapting crops to prevailing conditions in multiple cropping systems where timing and temperatures are critical rather than adapting cropping systems to the crops. Shorter season soybean or sorghum varieties may be used rather than full season varieties. Also, crops with shorter growing seasons, e.g., sunflowers, may be substituted for a longer growing season crop such as sorghum. While all aspects must be considered when contemplating crop substitutions, the above possibilities are some ways that multiple cropping may increase overall production in areas where planting time and temperatures are critical.

Soil Aeration

Soil aeration concerns the interchange of O_2 and carbon dioxide between soil and atmosphere. Oxygen must be supplied for germination and root growth while CO_2, a respiration product, suppresses plant growth when excessive amounts are present in the root atmosphere.

Aeration may limit germination and seedling development under poorly drained soil conditions or when a surface crust is present, especially one with a high water content. While some O_2 may be carried to seeds and roots along with infiltrating water, most gaseous interchange occurs by mass flow or diffusion through soil pores.

Poorly drained soils may retain excessive water in the seed and root zone after rains and, thus, restrict aeration. On such soils, producer acceptance of and success with no-tillage has been lower than on well-drained soils (Griffith et al., 1973). Often seedling establishment is delayed and more difficult on poorly drained soils with no-tillage as compared with conventional-tillage.

While soil water contents, especially near the surface, often are higher with no-tillage than with conventional-tillage, aeration evidently is not a problem with no-tillage on well-drained soils. In fact, aeration in no-tillage soil often is better than in tilled soil where dense layers or crusts form after intense rainfall or irrigation for germination and seedling emergence (Allen et al., 1975; Batchelder et al., 1966; Sanford et al., 1973, 1974). There is some evidence that aeration is reduced under soil crusts, but O_2 diffusion was limiting for wheat emergence only where the crusts had a high water content (Grable, 1966).

Seed-Soil Contact

For rapid water imbibition, seeds must adequately contact moist soil. Good seed-soil contact also prevents seeds from being pushed out of the soil by the elongating radicle and makes seedlings stand upright so that roots will become anchored in soil. Adequate seed coverage, an aspect of seed-soil contact, also reduces bird, rodent, and insect damage to seeds and seedlings.

Poor seed-soil contact has been a major problem of no-tillage crop production where crops are planted through surface residues or into sod. Conventional planters are designed to operate in loose soil essentially free of surface residues. In no-tillage systems, planters must cut through surface residues or sod, open a slot in the soil, place the seed at the proper depth, pro-

Table 2. Influence of wheat planting method, date, and rate on grain yields of wheat that
was double cropped after soybeans (Sanford et al., 1974)

Planting method, date, and seeding rate	Wheat yield at 10% moisture
	— kg/ha —
Before soybean harvest (3 Oct.)	
67 kg/ha, overseeded at leaf drop	2,480 b*
134 kg/ha, overseeded at leaf drop	3,320 a
202 kg/ha, overseeded at leaf drop	3,347 a
After soybean harvest (10 Nov.)	
101 kg/ha, broadcast, covered with sweep cultivator	3,037 ab
101 kg/ha, disk, harrow, plant with grain drill	2,688 b
101 kg/ha, broadcast, disked lightly	2,802 b

* Means not followed by the same letter are significantly different at the 5% probability level.

vide good seed coverage, and firm soil over the seed. For good seed-soil contact, excessive amounts of residue must not be pressed into the slot with the seed (Harrold et al., 1970). To overcome planting problems in rice (*Oryza sativa* L.) straw in Japan, Brown and Quantrill (1973) successfully planted wheat and barley with a drill that extracted soil cores and placed the seeds in the holes thus formed.

To overcome the disadvantages of delayed planting, Sanford et al. (1974) planted wheat by airplane on 3 Oct. 1973, before soybean harvest (at leaf drop). Wheat planting by more conventional methods after soybean harvest was delayed until 10 Nov. (Table 2). Although seed-soil contact was low for airplane-planted wheat, this was overcome by timely rainfall, which resulted in germination within 5 days after planting. Good plant populations were obtained also for the late-planted wheat.

A distinct grain yield advantage for timely planting of rye (*Secale cereale* L.) and wheat in North Carolina was shown by Clapp (1974). Small grains were overseeded in standing soybeans with a hand seeder and drilled in a conventionally-prepared seedbed on the same date after soybean harvest. About 25% of the soybean leaves had dropped at overseeding. Overseeding rye and wheat before soybean harvest resulted in higher grain yields than conventional planting, either at the same date or after soybean harvest (Table 3). Poor seed-soil contact resulting from overseeding did not reduce rye and wheat grain yields. Evidently, rye and wheat seeds germinated and seedlings became established without soil covering, probably because of good soil water conditions under fallen plant leaves and within the plant canopy.

Because of better water conditions near the soil surface and the possibility of lower soil temperature, shallower planting with no-tillage than with conventional-tillage is sometimes recommended, but at higher planting rates to offset losses from birds and rodents (Clapp, 1972; Gregory et al., 1975).

Table 3. Influence of seeding method on average rye and wheat grain yields
(Clapp, 1974)

Seeding method	Rye planted at 125 kg/ha	Wheat planted at	
		84 kg/ha	168 kg/ha
	kg/ha		
Overseeded	2,389 a*	2,641 a	3,058 a
Conventional	1,906 b	2,278 b	2,580 b
Conventional-late	1,561 c	1,539 c	1,747 c

* Means within a column not followed by the same letter are significantly different at
the 5% probability level.

Soil Crusts

The major adverse effect of soil crusts is in preventing seedling emergence (Grable, 1966). Crusts with a high water content may also reduce germination and root activity through reduced soil aeration.

Surface crusts develop when raindrops strike bare soil (except possibly sandy soils), thus causing dispersion and reorientation of soil particles. Crusts also develop when irrigation or flood waters disperse low-stability soil aggregates or deposit sediments. In contrast, surface residues dissipate raindrop energy and reduce movement of water-borne particles, thus greatly reducing the incidence of crusting.

Seedlings of different species vary widely in their ability to emerge through crusts. Corn seedlings often emerge by lifting large portions of crusts (Grable, 1966) whereas cotton (Gossypium hirsutum L.) emergence is highly dependent on crust strength (Bennett et al., 1964; Wanjura, 1973).

Sanford et al. (1973) planted grain sorghum and soybeans in conventional- and no-tillage plots and obtained variable results among years for emergence. In 1970, 2.2 cm of rainfall occurred 5 days after planting. Both crops emerged sooner on conventional-tillage plots. In 1971, crops on no-tillage plots emerged sooner when there was 10 cm of rainfall after planting. In 1972, there was 8 cm of intense rainfall after planting. Subsequent hot, dry winds resulted in a dense crust on conventional-tillage plots. Grain sorghum seedlings emerged through the crust, but soybean seedlings did not. In contrast, a near-perfect soybean plant population was obtained on the no-tillage plots.

Besides affecting seedling emergence, crusts along with concomitant surface sealing reduced rainfall infiltration (Batchelder et al., 1966). While not expressly stated in the many reports showing higher water contents with no-tillage than with conventional-tillage, the condition of the surface (residue protected vs. crusted and sealed) undoubtedly contributed to the water content differences.

Soil Density

For efficient water and nutrient utilization by plants, extensive root systems generally have been considered essential. For deep root development, low density soils are important and tillage has been widely used to remove restricting layers near the surface. Recent research, however, has shown that plants grew and produced relatively high yields when the idealized seedbed conditions once considered essential were not provided (Gill & Trouse, 1972). Improved conditions created by tillage are often negated by subsequent tillage when traffic is not restricted to specific zones. This situation has been aggravated by using larger tractors with larger or additional tires. Consequently, when crops are planted, much of the surface has been traversed by a tractor or implement with resultant increases in soil density. Thus, reducing field operations or restricting field traffic to specified zones should maintain better soil conditions for planting and seedling establishment.

Under normal conditions, about 16 field operations are required to produce dryland cotton on sandy soils of West Texas, with nine operations performed between harvest of one crop and establishment of the next crop, thus resulting in potentially high soil densities (D. W. Fryrear and P. T. Koshi, 1973, Texas Tech-SCS Conservation Workshop report). However, Koshi and Fryrear (1973) also showed that seedbed soil density could be maintained at relatively low levels after chiseling by limiting subsequent traffic to specified zones. Bulk densities at the 0- to 7.5-cm depth of Acuff loam averaged 1.40, 1.60, and 1.65 g/cm^3 under the crop row (chiseled) and in the nontraffic and traffic zones, respectively. At the 7.5- to 15.0-cm depth, the respective densities were 1.50, 1.65, and 1.75 g/cm^3.

Similar reductions in density were reported by Gill and Trouse (1972) for Norfolk sandy loam in Alabama. Because of traffic in the interrow space, bulk density averaged 1.80 g/cm^3 in the surface layer, while density in nontrafficked soil averaged 1.48 g/cm^3. The soil was loosened to a 36-cm depth with a chisel plow.

While soil of sufficient density reduces or restricts root growth (Taylor et al., 1967), the restriction depends on soil water content. Because of generally high water contents with no-tillage as compared with conventional-tillage, higher densities apparently are not as critical with no-tillage as with conventional-tillage. Besides, higher water contents near the surface suggest that deep rooting is less essential in no-tillage than in conventional-tillage areas. The natural improvement of soil structure in no-tillage systems is also important. Freezing and thawing, root decay, and reduced traffic with no-tillage may maintain low soil densities as effectively as tillage when subsequent traffic is not controlled. Shear and Moschler (1969) found no significant differences in bulk densities at 10- to 12- and at 40- to 42-cm depths of Lodi loam in Virginia after six corn crops were produced by conventional- and no-tillage methods.

Light

Seeds of only a few plant species require light for germination. However, all green plants require light for photosynthesis. When water and nutrients are available in adequate amounts so that competition ceases for these factors, then light becomes the factor that limits production (Donald, 1963). In multiple cropping systems, no competition for light should occur if tillage precedes planting of successive crops. If successive crops are overseeded before crop maturity, planted between rows of growing crops, or no-tillage planted in standing residues, then competition for light may occur. When considering multiple cropping under these conditions, the light requirements of the succeeding crop and the shading effect of the present crop must be considered. For successful multiple cropping under low light conditions, it may be necessary to grow crops that require or tolerate low light conditions or that will effectively compete for light with existing plants through rapid growth. An alternative would be to remove or reduce existing vegetation to such heights that the second crop would not be adversely affected due to competition for light.

Erosion and Pests

Erosion (wind and water) and pests (weeds, plant diseases, and insects) are important aspects of any cropping system, beginning with land preparation and continuing through crop maturity. While important for land preparation, erosion and pests are covered in other chapters of this publication. Hence, they are not discussed in this report.

EXPERIENCES REGARDING LAND PREPARATION IN MULTIPLE CROPPING SYSTEMS

In this section, land preparation methods for multiple cropping under various climatic conditions in the world and their effects on crop establishment and yield are discussed.

Humid, Subhumid, and Irrigated Regions

Humid and subhumid climatic conditions prevail from the tropics where year-round crop production is possible to temperate zones where growing seasons for many crops are limited by frost. While crops in these regions are largely dependent upon precipitation, irrigation is sometimes used during short, dry periods.

Cool-season grasses formed the basis for grass-grain multiple cropping systems used extensively for corn production in the U. S. Numerous comparisons between conventional- and no-tillage practices for planting corn in the southeastern U. S. showed that grain yields with no-tillage generally equaled or exceeded those obtained with conventional tillage (Bennett et al., 1973; Jones et al., 1968; Lillard & Jones, 1964; Moschler et al., 1972; Young, 1973). Grain yields decreased with no-tillage when sod was not killed by herbicides, thus resulting in competition between corn and grass for water and plant nutrients (Adams et al., 1970; Carreker et al., 1972, 1973). When corn was harvested for silage, orchardgrass (*Dactilis glomerata* L.) and red clover (*Trifolium pratense* L.) reestablishment was better after no-tillage than after conventional-tillage corn (Moschler et al., 1969).

Warm-season grasses also have been used in grass-grain multiple cropping systems. Corn planted after plowing under a bermudagrass (*Cynodon dactylon* L.) sod and small grains (wheat and rye) drilled into bermudagrass sod performed well in Oklahoma (Brensing & Lynd, 1965; Elder & Tucker, 1969). Bermudagrass regrowth after grain harvest provided hay or grazing for cattle.

For year-round forage production in East Texas, Matocha (1975) drilled small grains (wheat and rye) and ryegrass (*Lolium multiflorum*) into dessicated or nondessicated bermudagrass sod or after preparing a seedbed by disking. Sod dessication increased early season forage yields of the small grains and ryegrass, which also were related to average minimum temperatures in November and time of first frost. Forage production on prepared seedbeds was greater than when sod-planted into bermudagrass. Differences generally were larger in fall than in spring. Bermudagrass regrowth in spring decreased as the amounts of dessicant [paraquat (1,1'-dimethyl-4,4'-bypyridinium ion)] applied in the fall increased. Delayed planting of winter forages increased bermudagrass regrowth in spring.

To improve pastures for greater forage production, Sprague (1952) substituted chemicals for tillage. To control unwanted sod grasses, chemicals with no or a few diskings were more successful in pasture renovation than 7 or 12 diskings. The potential for erosion was also reduced by not disturbing the sod. Greater success in pasture renovation with no-tillage than with more intensive seedbed preparation was also reported by McClellan and Baylor (1972) and Van Keuren and Triplett (1972). Other approaches to increase forage production for livestock included seeding *Brassica* species in pastures in New Zealand (Leonard, 1973) and in Wales (Evans, 1973), and after cereal crops in England (Toosey, 1973). Forage production generally was greater when using no-tillage rather than conventional seedbed preparation methods.

For grain production in western Australia, Stonebridge and Fletcher (1973) direct drilled (Spray-Seed method) wheat after killing weeds and regenerating pasture grasses with a mixture of bipyridyl herbicides or after conventional tillage. Grain yields averaged 1,480 and 1,460 kg/ha for the direct-drilled and conventional cropping systems, respectively.

Another common multiple cropping practice is to plant soybeans, corn, grain sorghum, or other summer crops after harvesting small grains. Because the second crop must be established quickly to permit maturity before frost, no-tillage methods are widely used. In double-cropping systems, soybeans have been readily established by no-tillage methods (Jeffers et al., 1973; McKibben & Oldham, 1973; Sanford et al., 1973, 1974; Triplett et al., 1971) whereas establishment by conventional methods was difficult because of soil crusting after rainfall (Sanford et al., 1973, 1974) or poor soil water conditions (Jeffers et al., 1973). Double-cropped soybeans generally yielded as much or more with no-tillage as with conventional-tillage (Jeffers et al., 1973; Sanford et al., 1973, 1974; Triplett et al., 1971) but were lower with no-tillage when weed control by herbicides was poor (Sanford et al., 1973, 1974).

Corn was successfully double-cropped after wheat in Illinois (Hoeft et al., 1975; McKibben & Pendleton, 1968) and after grazed-out rye in Texas (Fowler, 1972; Fowler & Ikard, 1974) by using no-tillage planting methods. Yields were high when weed and volunteer crop plants were adequately controlled with herbicides. Corn grain yields were reduced by 4,580 kg/ha by improperly using herbicides in Illinois (McKibben & Pendleton, 1968).

Comparisons of tillage methods for double-cropping sorghum after wheat indicated grain yields with no-tillage equaled or exceeded those obtained with conventional-tillage. Irrigated grain sorghum yields in Texas averaged 5,690 and 5,070 kg/ha during 1969 to 1973 for no-tillage and tillage (disking, listing, or rotary tilling) treatments, respectively (Allen et al., 1976).

With adequate rainfall and good weed control, grain sorghum yields in Mississippi were 5,072 and 4,335 kg/ha with no- and conventional-tillage, respectively, in 1971. For 1970 and 1972, sorghum with no-tillage yielded 85% as much as conventional-tillage sorghum. The lower yields resulted from weed competition and lack of water during flowering and fruiting in August 1972 (Sanford et al., 1973).

Double-cropped sunflowers after wheat yielded 1,960 kg/ha with no-tillage and 1,758 kg/ha with clean (disk and rebedding) tillage on the Texas High Plains in 1974. Volunteer wheat control methods had little effect on sunflower yields (Unger et al., 1975).

In Idaho, potatoes (*Solanum tuberosum* L.) planted in 1970 after winter wheat on sandy soils after rototilling, disking, or without tillage yielded 33.0, 35.9, and 30.7 metric tons/ha, respectively. In 1971, potatoes under sprinkler irrigation yielded 29.2 metric tons/ha when planted directly in winter rye with every other row of grain left throughout the season, 34.9 metric tons/ha when planted in 38-cm rows of rye (killed at potato emergence to remove residual rye), and 32.7 metric tons/ha when planted in a solid stand of rye (killed at potato emergence to remove residual rye). Increasing the N application rate from 84 to 140 kg/ha generally increased potato yields on tilled plots and decreased yields on no-tillage plots. A possible reason for lower potato yields with no-tillage was poorer weed control. As with potatoes, sugar beets (*Beta vulgaris* L.) yielded less with no-tillage than with tillage, apparently because of competition from wheat (Cary et al., 1975).

Dry peas (*Pisum sativum* L.) in southern Idaho usually are harvested by the first of August, which leaves the land bare and unproductive for the last third of the growing season. Cary (1971) studied the potential of forage production after harvesting peas in late July. Alfalfa (*Medicago sativa* L.) planted with peas had little effect on dry pea yield, but turnips (*Brassica rapa*) planted with peas reduced pea yield (Table 4). Forage yields by alfalfa and turnips after harvesting peas were higher than forage yields of corn and wheat. Highest forage yields were obtained with second crop peas and turnips, which better tolerated cool weather late in the growing season.

Musick et al. (1972) in Texas planted winter wheat with a single-disk grain drill in standing grain sorghum stubble or on seedbeds prepared by rotary tillage (with bed-shaper attached). An emergence-irrigation resulted in excellent plant populations on both areas. Shredding sorghum stubble did not affect no-tillage wheat and may be disadvantageous in seasons when snow could be trapped in standing stubble. No-tillage planting increased early spring wheat growth in the 1968 to 1969 season when soil water was limited, snow trapping in stubble was significant, and temperatures were above normal. Hail destroyed the wheat before grain harvest, but potential yields were about equal with both tillage methods. Wheat growth from late fall to early spring was decreased by no-tillage planting in the 1969 to 1970 season when soil water was adequate and air temperatures were below normal. Grain yields were 3,750 and 3,670 kg/ha with no- and conventional-tillage, respectively.

In some countries, bushfallow is used in which the soil's productivity is maintained by alternating short cropping periods with long fallow periods under natural regrowth vegetation. Because of increasing population pres-

Table 4. Dry peas and forage yields as influenced by method of establishing the peas and forage crops (Adapted from Cary, 1971)

First crop	First crop yield (dry peas)*	Second crop	Second crop yield (forage)†
	kg/ha		kg/ha
Peas	3,200	Corn‡ + peas§	2,460
Peas	3,200	Wheat‡ + peas§	2,690
Peas	3,200	Peas§	3,800
Peas	3,200	Turnips‡	6,050
Peas + alfalfa	3,158	Alfalfa¶	3,360
Peas + turnips	2,744	Turnips¶#	5,150

* Field dry weight basis.
† Oven-dry weight basis.
‡ Planted 1 Aug.
§ Volunteer peas (no volunteer peas emerged in alfalfa or turnip plots).
¶ Planted 25 March.
# Includes roots and tops.

sures on land in Ghana, cropping periods are increasing and soil regeneration periods are often too short. To derive maximum benefits from the cover crop occupying the land during fallow and to achieve soil conservation, Kannegieter (1967) managed the tropical kudzu (*Pueraria phaseoloides* or *P. javonica*) cover crop before planting corn by (i) removing the cover followed by tillage, (ii) burning the cover and incorporating the ash, (iii) slashing the cover and incorporating the trash, and (iv) killing the cover with 2,4-D [(2,4-dichlorophenoxy) acetic acid] and planting by no-tillage methods. Corn grain yields for the respective treatments were 818, 1,792, 1,523, and 1,915 kg/ha. Although quite low, no-tillage corn yields equaled or exceeded those obtained with other treatments. In addition, the killed cover crop provided excellent protection against erosion.

A year-round growing season, short-season crops, and intensive cropping systems permit growing of four or more crops per year in the Philippines (Bradfield, 1969). For maximum production with multiple cropping, Bradfield (1969) attempted to minimize days that the land was idle and maximize days it was producing crops. To attain these goals, he recommended:

1. Bedding the land to accelerate drying of the bed tops.
2. Keeping tillage operations and the volume of soil stirred to a minimum.
3. Using early maturing crop varieties with the capacity to produce high yields per hectare per day.
4. Growing rattoon crops when feasible.
5. Transplanting slow growing vegetable crops.
6. Directly seeding rice in unpuddled soil.
7. Growing some crops each season which can be harvested in an immature state.
8. Intercropping whenever possible.

Using some of these principles, he squeezed a five-crop system requiring 413 days of growing season into a 12-month period by intercropping. Two major land preparation operations were used annually. Average yields were: rice, 5.0 metric tons/ha; sweet potatoes (*Ipomoea batatas*), 25.0 metric tons/ha; soybeans (dry), 2.5 metric tons/ha; sweet corn, 40,000 ears/ha; and soybeans (green pods), 6.0 metric tons/ha.

In another system, Bradfield (1969) produced 22.6 metric tons/ha of grain in 12 months. Individual crop yields were: rice, 5.0 metric tons; sorghum, 5.5 metric tons; sorghum (first rattoon), 6.6 metric tons; and sorghum (second rattoon), 5.5 metric tons. Rattoon crops did not require additional land preparation.

Semiarid Regions

The winter wheat-fallow system often used in the Great Plains, where one wheat crop is produced in 2 years, generally results in low precipitation storage as soil water and low water-use efficiency. A major reason for low precipitation storage is low residue production by the dryland crops.

Since precipitation storage as soil water often is highest during the early part of fallow, recent attempts to intensify crop production on dryland have involved shorter fallow periods (10–11 months) than those (about 16 months) of the wheat-fallow system. A wheat-grain sorghum-fallow system (two crops in 3 years) increased grain production over that obtained with the wheat-fallow system, but residue production still was too low to greatly increase water storage during fallow (Johnson et al., 1974; Ramig & Smika, 1964; Unger, 1972). Stubble-mulch tillage generally was satisfactory for land preparation.

Greb, Smika, and Black (1967, 1970) illustrated the influence of increased surface residue levels on water storage during fallow for the Central and Northern Great Plains. Increases in surface residues from 0 to 6,720 kg/ha increased the precipitation storage efficiency from 16 to 37%. Dryland crops in West Texas generally do not produce adequate residues to obtain high precipitation storage efficiencies, but irrigated wheat produced 11,000 kg/ha of residue (Unger et al., 1971). During fallow after wheat harvest in July 1968, soil water storage totaled 7.8 cm when disk tillage was used for weed control and 14.1 cm when atrazine [2-chloro-4-(ethylamino)-6-(isopropylamino)-s-triazine] and 2,4-D were used. Water storage efficiencies were 22 and 39% for the respective treatments.

During fallow in Texas from wheat harvest in 1970 to grain sorghum planting in 1971, water storage from 20.6 cm of precipitation and a 7.6-cm preplant irrigation was 26 and 52% for disk and chemical fallow treatments, respectively (Unger & Phillips, 1973). Subsequent sorghum grain yield for the chemical fallow treatment with 15.2 cm of growing season irrigation was 5,900 kg/ha, which almost equaled the 6,090 kg/ha yield for the disk treatment with 30.5 cm of irrigation. The study showed that the irrigation water requirement of a crop is reduced when water storage during fallow is adequate and that intensive land preparation is not necessary when other conditions for crop growth are favorable.

SUMMARY AND CONCLUSIONS

In multiple cropping systems, as with conventional cropping systems, various basic and secondary seedbed conditions must exist or be established for rapid seed germination and seedling establishment. With conventional systems, adequate time is available to establish satisfactory seedbed conditions with tillage operations. However, in multiple cropping systems, time is critical for establishing the next crop. Delays may result in lower yields because of frost, unfavorable climatic conditions, and deviation from the optimum growing season for the particular crop. To establish the next crop quickly, reduced- and no-tillage systems are highly successful and widely used.

Most seedbed requirements can be met by using no-tillage cropping practices. Surface residues maintained by no-tillage systems are especially beneficial for increasing soil water contents. Residues also are effective for controlling wind and water erosion, and for reducing soil crusting, thus enhancing seedling establishment. Soil temperatures may be lower under residues, which may delay seed germination in cooler regions. In addition, insect and disease problems may be more severe with reduced-tillage systems. However, at many locations, even with lower soil temperatures and potentially greater insect and disease problems, no-tillage crop yields equaled or exceeded those obtained with conventional-tillage. Yield increases with no-tillage generally were attributed to better seedling emergence due to reduced soil crusting and to higher soil water contents at planting and throughout the growing season, which permitted plants to withstand short-duration droughts that were detrimental on conventionally-tilled areas.

LITERATURE CITED

Adams, W. E., J. E. Pallas, Jr., and R. N. Dawson. 1970. Tillage methods for corn-sod systems in the southern Piedmont. Agron. J. 62:646-649.

Allen, R. R., J. T. Musick, F. O. Wood, and D. A. Dusek. 1975. No-till seeding of irrigated sorghum double cropped after wheat. Trans. ASAE 18:1109-1113.

Batchelder, A. R., M. J. Rogers, and J. P. Walker. 1966. Effects of subsoil management practices on growth of flue-cured tobacco. Agron. J. 58:345-347.

Bennett, O. L., D. A. Ashley, and B. D. Doss. 1964. Methods of reducing soil crusting to increase cotton seedling emergence. Agron. J. 56:162-165.

Bennett, O. L., E. L. Mathias, and P. E. Lundberg. 1973. Crop responses to no-till management practices on hilly terrain. Agron. J. 65:488-491.

Blevins, R. L., Doyle Cook, S. H. Phillips, and R. E. Phillips. 1971. Influence of no-tillage on soil moisture. Agron. J. 63:593-596.

Bradfield, Richard. 1969. Training agronomists for increasing food production in the humid tropics. p. 45-63. *In* J. Ritchie Cowan and L. S. Robertson (ed.) International agronomy training and education. Spec. Pub. No. 15, Am. Soc. of Agron., Madison, Wis.

Brensing, O. H., and J. Q. Lynd. 1965. Corn grown with bermudagrass in eastern Oklahoma. Oklahoma Agric. Exp. Stn. Bull. No. 643.

Brown, I. A., and R. A. Quantrill. 1973. The role of minimal tillage in rice in Asia, with particular reference to Japan. Outlook Agric. 7:179-183.

Carreker, J. R., J. E. Box, Jr., R. N. Dawson, E. R. Beaty, and H. D. Morris. 1972. No-till corn in fescuegrass. Agron. J. 64:500-503.

Carreker, J. R., S. R. Wilkinson, J. E. Box, Jr., R. N. Dawson, E. R. Beaty, H. D. Morris, and J. B. Jones, Jr. 1973. Using poultry litter, irrigation, and tall fescue for no-till corn production. J. Environ. Qual. 2:497-500.

Cary, J. W. 1971. Double cropping dry peas and forage in southern Idaho. Idaho Agric. Exp. Stn. Current Information Series No. 167.

Cary, J. W., R. A. Kohl, D. T. Westermann, and R. W. Rickman. 1975. Row cropping sandy soils under sprinklers using a winter grain cover to control wind erosion. Idaho Agric. Exp. Stn. Bull. 549.

Clapp, J. G. 1972. No-tillage soybean production. North Carolina Agric. Ext. Serv. Cir. No. 537.

Clapp, J. G., Jr. 1974. Overseeding small grain in standing soybeans vs. conventional planting methods. Agron. J. 66:463-465.

Donald, C. M. 1963. Competition among crop and pasture plants. Adv. Agron. 15:1-118.

Elder, W. C., and B. B. Tucker. 1969. Over-seeding small grains in bermudagrass sod. Oklahoma State Univ. Ext. Facts No. 2017.

Evans, Tonlas. 1973. New approaches to increasing fodder production 2. Swedes and turnips in upland situations. Outlook Agric. 7:171-174.

Fowler, Lehman. 1972. Experience with no-tillage—Winrock Farms. p. 108-112. *In* Proceedings No-Tillage Systems Symposium, Columbus, Ohio. Ohio State University, Ohio Agric. Res. Dev. Center, and Chevron Chemical Co.

Fowler, Lehman, and Charles Ikard. 1974. Minimum and no tillage farming with sprinkler irrigation. p. 46-49. *In* Proceedings Limited and No-Tillage Crop Production Systems Symposium, USDA Southwestern Great Plains Research Center, Bushland, Texas.

Gill, W. R., and A. C. Trouse, Jr. 1972. Results from controlled traffic studies and their implications in tillage systems. p. 126-131. *In* Proceedings No-Tillage Systems Symposium, Columbus, Ohio. Ohio State Univ., Ohio Agric. Res. Dev. Center, and Chevron Chemical Co.

Grable, A. R. 1966. Soil aeration and plant growth. Adv. Agron. 18:57-106.

Greb, B. W., D. E. Smika, and A. L. Black. 1967. Effect of straw-mulch rates on soil water storage during summer fallow in the Great Plains. Soil Sci. Soc. Am. Proc. 31: 556-559.

Greb, B. W., D. E. Smika, and A. L. Black. 1970. Water conservation with stubble mulch fallow. J. Soil Water Conserv. 25:58-62.

Gregory, W. W., J. W. Herron, and J. H. Herbek. 1975. 1975 No-tillage recommendations. Univ. of Kentucky Coop. Ext. Serv. ID-1.

Griffith, D. R., J. V. Mannering, H. M. Galloway, S. D. Parsons, and C. B. Richey. 1973. Effect of eight tillage-planting systems on soil temperature, percent stand, plant growth, and yield of corn on five Indiana soils. Agron. J. 65:321-326.

Harrold, L. L., G. B. Triplett, Jr., and W. M. Edwards. 1970. No-tillage corn—characteristics of the system. Agric. Eng. 51:128-131.

Hoeft, R. G., John Wedberg, M. C. Shurtleff, A. G. Harms, R. A. Hinton, Randall Nelson, W. O. Scott, G. E. McKibben, H. J. Hirning, M. D. Thorne, D. E. Millis, H. A. Cate, J. C. Siemens, and F. M. Sims. 1975. Double cropping in Illinois. Univ. of Illinois Coop. Ext. Serv. Cir. No. 1106.

Jeffers, D. L., G. B. Triplett, and J. E. Beuerlein. 1973. Double-cropped soybeans. Ohio Rep. 58:67-69.

Johnson, W. C., C. E. Van Doren, and Earl Burnett. 1974. Summer fallow in the Southern Great Plains. p. 86-109. Chapter 5. *In* Summer fallow in the western United States, USDA-ARS Conserv. Res. Rep. No. 17.

Jones, J. N., Jr., J. E. Moody, and J. H. Lillard. 1969. Effects of tillage, no tillage, and mulch on soil water and plant growth. Agron. J. 61:719-721.

Jones, J. N., Jr., J. E. Moody, G. M. Shear, W. W. Moschler, and J. H. Lillard. 1968. The no-tillage system for corn (*Zea mays* L.). Agron. J. 60:17-20.

Kannegieter, A. 1967. Zero cultivation and other methods of reclaiming *Pueraria* fallowed land for food crop cultivation in the forest zone of Ghana. Trop. Agric. 123:51-73.

Koshi, P. T., and D. W. Fryrear. 1973. Effect of tractor traffic, surface mulch, and seedbed configuration on soil properties. Soil Sci. Soc. Am. Proc. 37:758-762.

Leonard, W. F. 1973. New approaches to increasing fodder production 1. Direct drilling of chou moellier in New Zealand. Outlook Agric. 7:168-170.

Lillard, J. H., and J. N. Jones, Jr. 1964. Planting and seed-environment problems with corn in killed-sod seedbeds. Trans. ASAE 7:204-206, 208.

Matocha, J. E. 1975. No-till and seedbed production of small grains and ryegrass mixture for forage in East Texas. Texas Agric. Exp. Stn. Bull. No. 1155.

McClellan, W. L., and J. E. Baylor. 1972. A new ripple in pasture renovation. p. 81-82. *In* Proceedings No-Tillage Systems Symposium, Columbus, Ohio. Ohio State Univ. Ohio Agric. Res. Dev. Center, and Chevron Chemical Co.

McKibben, G. E., and M. G. Oldham. 1973. Double cropping soybeans in small grain stubble. Ill. Res. 15:10-11.

McKibben, G. E., and J. W. Pendleton. 1968. Double cropping in Illinois. Ill. Res. 10: 6-7.

Moody, J. E., J. N. Jones, Jr., and J. H. Lillard. 1963. Influence of straw-mulch on soil moisture, soil temperature and the growth of corn. Soil Sci. Soc. Am. Proc. 27:700-703.

Morinaga, T. 1926. Favorable effect of reduced oxygen supply upon the germination of certain seeds. Am. J. Bot. 13:159-166.

Moschler, W. W., G. D. Jones, and G. M. Shear. 1969. Stand and early growth of orchard-grass and red clover seeded after no-tillage corn. Agron. J. 61:475–476.

Moschler, W. W., G. M. Shear, D. C. Martens, G. D. Jones, and R. R. Wilmouth. 1972. Comparative yield and fertilizer efficiency of no-tillage and conventionally tilled corn. Agron. J. 64:229–231.

Musick, J. T., R. R. Allen, D. A. Dusek, and F. O. Wood. 1972. No-till seeding of wheat and barley after grain sorghum harvest. Texas Agric. Exp. Stn. Prog. Rep. No. 3043.

Ramig, R. E., and D. E. Smika. 1964. Fallow-wheat-sorghum: An excellent rotation for dryland in central Nebraska. Nebraska Agric. Exp. Stn. S. B. No. 483.

Rockwood, W. G., and R. Lal. 1974. Mulch tillage: A technique for soil and water conservation in the tropics. Span 17:77–79.

Sanford, J. O., D. L. Myhre, and N. C. Merwine. 1973. Double cropping systems involving no-tillage and conventional tillage. Agron. J. 65:978–982.

Sanford, J. O., D. L. Myhre, and N. C. Merwine. 1974. Double-cropping: Aerial seeding of wheat before soybean harvest. Mississippi Agric. and For. Exp. Stn. Research Highlights 37(10).

Shear, G. M., and W. W. Moschler. 1969. Continuous corn by the no-tillage and conventional tillage methods: A six-year comparison. Agron. J. 61:524–526.

Sprague, M. A. 1952. The substitution of chemicals for tillage in pasture renovation. Agron. J. 44:405–409.

Stonebridge, W. C., and I. C. Fletcher. 1973. "Spray-seed": The Western Australia direct sowing system. Outlook Agric. 7:155–161.

Taylor, H. M., G. M. Roberson, and J. J. Parker, Jr. 1967. Cotton seedling taproot elongation as affected by soil strength changes induced by slurrying and water extraction. Soil Sci. Soc. Am. Proc. 31:700–704.

Toosey, R. D. 1973. New approaches to increasing fodder production 3. Stubble catch-cropping with brassicae. Outlook Agric. 7:175–178.

Triplett, G. B., Jr., D. L. Jeffers, D. M. Van Doren, Jr., and C. R. Weaver. 1971. Double cropping wheat and soybeans. Ohio Rep. 56:24–27.

Unger, P. W. 1972. Dryland winter wheat and grain sorghum cropping systems—Northern High Plains of Texas. Texas Agric. Exp. Stn. Bull. No. 1126.

Unger, P. W., R. R. Allen, and A. F. Wiese. 1971. Tillage and herbicides for surface residue maintenance, weed control, and water conservation. J. Soil Water Conserv. 26:147–150.

Unger, P. W., and R. E. Danielson. 1965. Influence of oxygen and carbon dioxide on germination and seedling development of corn (*Zea mays* L.). Agron. J. 57:56–58.

Unger, P. W., O. R. Jones, and R. R. Allen. 1975. Sunflower experiments at Bushland on the Texas High Plains—1974. Texas Agric. Exp. Stn. Prog. Rep. No. 3304.

Unger, P. W., and J. J. Parker, Jr. 1968. Residue placement effects on decomposition, evaporation, and soil moisture distribution. Agron. J. 60:469–472.

Unger, P. W., and R. E. Phillips. 1973. Soil water evaporation and storage. p. 42–54. *In* Proceedings National Conference Conservation Tillage. Soil Conserv. Soc. of Am., Ankeny, Iowa.

Van Keuren, R. W., and G. B. Triplett. 1972. No-tillage pasture renovation. p. 69–80. *In* Proceedings No-Tillage Systems Symposium, Columbus, Ohio. Ohio State Univ., Ohio Agric. Res. Dev. Center, and Chevron Chemical Co.

Van Wijk, W. R., W. E. Larson, and W. C. Burrows. 1959. Soil temperature and the early growth of corn from mulched and unmulched soil. Soil Sci. Soc. Am. Proc. 23:428–434.

Vlamis, J., and A. R. Davis. 1943. Germination, growth and respiration of rice and barley seedlings at low oxygen pressures. Plant Physiol. 18:685–692.

Wanjura, D. F. 1973. Effect of physical soil properties on cotton emergence. USDA-ARS Tech. Bull. No. 1481.

Young, H. M. 1973. 'No-tillage' farming in the United States—its profit and potential. Outlook Agric. 7:143–148.

Soil Fertility Management in Tropical Multiple Cropping[1]

D. D. Oelsligle, R. E. McCollum, and B. T. Kang[2]

Multiple cropping has been practiced for centuries in many parts of the world, but the scientific community's interest in multicrop systems as a means of increasing food production per unit of land area is more recent in origin. Such systems are particularly prevalent on small farms in tropical latitudes where seasonal fluctuations in temperature are minor and crops can be grown year-round if other environmental factors are favorable. Whatever their reasons for doing so (wider food variety, risk reduction, greater barter potential), operators of small land holdings in the tropics have learned that total production is usually increased by following planting schedules which are more intense than those possible in temperate-zone agriculture.

Whether this intensification is in time, in space, or some combination of space and time—generally achieved by associating economic species with differing growth habits or nutritional requirements on the same land—the practices followed fall within the scope of "multiple cropping" as used in this symposium (Andrews & Kassam, 1976). The challenge for soil and crop scientists is to determine how food production under traditional systems can be increased by better management and develop new systems that will out-produce the old ones. To meet this challenge, scientists need not only a thorough knowledge of the basic principles of soil and crop management but also how these principles apply as cropping intensity approaches environmental or practical limits.

In developing any practice that has not been extensively researched, an evaluation should be made of the "state of the art." However advanced the

[1]Paper No. 4952 of the Journal Series of the North Carolina Agric. Exp. Stn., Raleigh, North Carolina.
[2]Former visiting assistant professor and associate professor, North Carolina State University, and soil scientist, International Institute of Tropical Agriculture, Ibadan, Nigeria.

art of multiple cropping, it seems fair to conclude that the *science* of fertilizing multicropped soils with concentrated inorganic chemicals is comparatively primitive (Dalrymple, 1971). This is not surprising, for many of the cropping systems being considered here originated, and continue to persist, under subsistence farming. High-analysis fertilizers, if available at any price, frequently constitute a direct cost input that is beyond the means of the marginal farmer.

Many soils of the tropics are inherently acid and relatively infertile in their native state, and mineral nutrition is a principal concern for any cropping system. Fertilization practices for insuring adequate nutrients and their availability are perhaps even more rigorous when soils are multicropped. Multicrop researchers in the Philippines (Bradfield, 1970; IRRI, 1972), who were studying cropping systems per se, determined the rate(s) of fertilization by summing the estimated requirement for each crop to insure that fertility was not a limiting factor. While technically sound, this approach may not be the most efficient in production agriculture. High fertilizer prices in developing countries dictate that this input be used efficiently. When developing fertilization practices for multiple cropping patterns, particularly for the marginal farmer, it is important that the economics of the practices be considered simultaneously with their biological potential.

ADAPTING EXISTING INFORMATION TO MULTIPLE CROPPING

Beyond its potential for increasing production, another reason for multiple cropping is to use native and applied nutrients more efficiently. At the present time, direct information about fertilization practices for multiple cropping is scarce. However, there is available certain basic information from sole cropping which can be applied to multiple cropping situations. By studying the characteristics of the soil and of the crops to be grown on it, some basic concepts can be established which should be helpful in determining fertilization schedules for a particular multiple cropping pattern.

Soil Characteristics

INITIAL FERTILITY

The first step in determining any fertilization practice is an evaluation of the inherent soil nutrient supply. The commonly accepted method for estimating native soil fertility is a routine soil analysis. Considerable soil-test correlation data and interpretations related to sole cropping are available, but few examples of similar approaches with multicrop systems have been reported. Del Valle (1975) found that "critical" soil-test values of phosphorus and potassium established for sole crops of corn (*Zea mays* L.) and edible beans (*Phaseolus vulgaris*) also applied when these two species were intercropped.

"Multiple cropping" and "shifting cultivation" are not synonymous, but a high percentage of the land managed by this traditional system is also multicropped. Unlike continuous cultivation systems, the fertility status of soil under shifting cultivation changes drastically with time. Prior to clearing, most of the nutrients are held in a closed cycle between the soil and the vegetation on it (Nye & Greenland, 1960). When the vegetation is burned, nonvolatile nutrients (P, K, Ca, and Mg) are added to the A horizon and result in a marked, but usually short-lived, rise in nutrient availability (Lal et al., 1974; North Carolina State University, 1973, 1974). In acid soils, base saturation is increased and exchangeable aluminum is usually reduced to non-toxic levels. On soils near neutrality, however, this addition of bases may raise the soil pH to such high levels that deficiencies of iron and other micro-nutrients are induced. During the cropping period, nutrient losses by leaching, removal in harvested crops, or by runoff and erosion usually deplete the available supply quite rapidly. Special attention must therefore be given to the dynamics of nutrient supply and nutrient availability under shifting cultivation, not only for assessing fertilizer needs but also in selecting the crops to be grown. In practice, farmers tend to adapt to these changes in fertility by planting the most-demanding crops (cereals) during the early part of the cut-and-burn cycle and following them with species [cassava (*Manihot* sp.), plantains (*Plantago* sp.)] that are more tolerant to low-fertility regimes. Where multiple cropping is practiced, species with tolerance to low fertility are frequently relay interplanted into the less-tolerant species.

FERTILITY MAINTENANCE

Whatever the geographic location of a soil or the cropping system employed on it, chemical amendments will ultimately be essential if a permanent agriculture is to evolve. In tropical latitudes, fertility maintenance through applications of fertilizers or lime usually becomes necessary more quickly than elsewhere; and soil characteristics which influence the availability of applied nutrients are likely to become critical at any earlier date. Most such influences are well documented, and many practices favoring the maintenance of fertilizer-applied nutrients in plant-available forms are known. It is our opinion, however, that some of these practices become particularly pertinent when soils are multicropped. After deciding what nutrients are needed and in what amounts, decisions relative to the source, timing, and placement of fertilizer additions are needed to insure their continued availability. To paraphrase Mengel (1969), it is not only necessary to supply the soil with sufficient quantities of nutrients; care must be taken that these nutrients are available to the plant roots in sufficient amounts during the growing season.

SOIL PHYSICAL PROPERTIES

The physical properties of a soil has a bearing on the timing of fertilizer applications as well as which fertilizer is applied. Soil that can be worked under varying moisture regimes allows more flexibility for fertilizer incorporation. Furthermore, the water holding capacity of soils indirectly determines the rate at which nutrients are lost by leaching. Under high rainfall, for example, nitrates may move past the rooting zone in soils which retain low amounts of water. Root-restricting layers are equally as critical for multiple cropping as for sole cropping.

Crop Characteristics

Fertilizer responses are governed perhaps as much by differences among crop species as by the variability among soils. It is therefore important to know as much as possible about the nutritional requirements and the growth characteristics of the crops which are to be grown in a specific cropping pattern.

DIFFERENCES IN NUTRIENT REQUIREMENT

The amounts of nutrients which a given crop species requires and can extract from the soil to complete a productive life cycle is valuable information in designing fertilization practices for any cropping system. Since plant species differ widely in nutrient requirements, each crop which will be included in a given cropping system should be studied in respect to its nutritional needs. In Costa Rica, for example, the addition of phosphorus to rice (*Oryza sativa* L.) grown on soils with 4 ppm of soil-test P (modified Olsen extract) gave no economic return; but when corn was grown on soils with the same soil-test levels, phosphorus additions were necessary to make it an economic venture (Cordero & Miner, 1974). Juntaken, Asher and Edwards (personal communication) observed that cassava grown in solution culture has a much higher requirement for substrate phosphorus than corn, soybeans (*Glycine max* L. Merr.), or cotton (*Gossypium* sp.) in comparable media. Under field conditions, however, cassava seldom responds to phosphorus application, indicating that this crop has the capacity to extract sufficient phosphorus from soils with low native supplies. Increasing fertility levels in two multiple cropping patterns in Costa Rica caused an increase in yields of beans and corn, a moderate increase in yields of cassava, no change in soybean yields, and a decrease in sweet potato (*Ipomoea batatas* Lam.) yields (Table 1). Where such results are consistent, it would seem appropriate to apply fertilizer to those crops which responded to it and little or none to the nonresponding crops.

Information such as the above can be used in grouping crop species into categories such as nonresponsive, moderately responsive, or highly responsive to specific plant nutrients. Such groupings may not always agree with estimates based on total nutrient removal, however, because some species are more efficient than others in extracting nutrients from the soil. In any case, data on total nutrient removal would be a good place to start when estimating nutrient requirements and determining fertilization practices to satisfy

Table 1. Yields from two intercropping patterns, each at three levels of N–P–K fertilization in Costa Rica (North Carolina State University, 1974)

Cropping pattern	Level of fertilization (kg N-P$_2$O$_5$-K$_2$O/ha)		
	0-0-0	212-63-109	424-126-218
	metric tons/ha		

Corn			
Cassava			
Beans	Sweet potato		
Corn	0.77	1.26	1.13
Cassava	9.30	12.80	13.80
Beans (climbing)	0.61	1.49	2.25
Sweet potato	10.20	9.70	6.40
Corn			
Cassava			
Beans	Soybeans		
Corn	0.77	1.26	1.13
Cassava	12.80	12.10	15.50
Beans (bush)	1.04	2.04	2.44
Soybeans	0.86	0.90	0.90

them. Consideration should also be given to the variety, yield, length of growing season, and climate under which the information on total nutrient requirement was obtained.

PATTERNS OF GROWTH AND NUTRIENT ACCUMULATION

Rates of nutrient uptake vary with plant age, and the period of maximum nutrient demand for one species may not coincide with that of another. Within a given species, furthermore, the uptake curve for one element may differ from that of another. Growth and nutrient-accumulation patterns can thus be invaluable information in determining the time of fertilizer application as well as the amounts of specific elements that need be applied. Publications such as "How a Soybean Plant Develops" (Hanway & Thompson, 1971) are available for many species, and they should be used. Invaluable as such information is, certain limitations in its applicability should be recognized, especially when the crops are grown in highly competitive situations. For example, Dalal (1974) observed that dry matter production by pigeon peas (*Cajanus cajan*) in a corn-pigeon pea intercrop was less than one-half that of sole-cropped pigeon peas during the first 16 weeks (Table 2). Once the corn matured, however, its competitive influence was reduced; and growth of the interplanted pigeon peas between 16 and 24 weeks was sufficient to produce seed yields comparable with the sole crop. The pattern of nutrient accumulation seemed to parallel growth (Table 2).

Ideally, if a given multiple cropping pattern is agronomically and economically sound for an area, data on nutrient and dry matter accumulation for the crop species included would provide good information in determining

Table 2. Yields of dry matter, grain, and nutrients by pure and interplanted stands of corn and pigeon peas (adapted from Dalal, 1974)

Treatment	16 weeks*		24 weeks† (PP)	24-week total (C + PP)
	C‡	PP‡		
	kg/ha			
Total dry matter				
Corn	6408	--	--	6408
Pigeonpeas	--	822	5127	5127
Mixed intercrop	4004	221	3808	7811
Row intercrop	4718	340	4893	9611
Grain				
Corn	3130	--	--	3130
Pigeonpeas	--	--	1871	1871
Mixed intercrop	2025	--	1710	3735
Row intercrop	2606	--	1854	4460
Nitrogen				
Corn	66.2	--	--	66.2
Pigeonpeas	--	17.1	119.4	119.4
Mixed intercrop	44.6	3.7	99.8	144.4
Row intercrop	48.6	5.7	126.8	175.4
Phosphorus				
Corn	13.2	--	--	13.2
Pigeonpeas	--	1.0	6.4	6.4
Mixed intercrop	9.0	0.2	5.4	14.4
Row intercrop	10.9	0.3	6.5	17.4
Potassium				
Corn	50.8	--	--	50.8
Pigeonpeas	--	10.1	36.9	36.9
Mixed intercrop	34.6	2.1	32.2	66.8
Row intercrop	42.8	3.7	33.0	75.8
Magnesium				
Corn	12.3	--	--	12.3
Pigeonpeas	--	2.5	13.5	13.5
Mixed intercrop	8.0	0.9	7.8	15.8
Row intercrop	7.4	1.2	12.3	19.7

* Corn harvest
† Pigeonpea harvest
‡ Corn = C and pigeonpeas = PP.

fertilization practices for that pattern. It seems especially important, however, that fertilizer applications either coincide with or precede periods of rapid growth and nutrient uptake.

Sole-crop data on nutrient requirements and accumulation patterns are probably directly applicable to the less-intensive forms of multiple cropping, e.g., sequential cropping, strip intercropping, and in certain instances, relay intercropping. The likelihood is, however, that existing data will not apply for the most intensive multiple cropping schemes because total nutrient up-take and nutrient removal in harvested products must be greater under multiple cropping if yields are significantly increased by the practice. In Costa Rica, the "yield" of nitrogen in the grain of interplanted corn and beans was greater than either crop grown alone (Table 3). Investigations in the Philippines (IRRI, 1974) have also demonstrated increased nitrogen uptake when corn and rice were grown together as compared to either of the respective sole crops, and Dalal's (1974) data support the view that the demand for all nutrients will be greater if yields are increased by intercropping (Table 2). In any event, the conditions under which the various forms of multiple cropping provide for increased nutrient-utilization efficiency need to be identified and described.

ADAPTABILITY TO SEASONAL VARIATION

All crops cannot be grown at all times of the year, even if adequate moisture is available. Temperature, rainfall, solar radiation, and even slight changes in day length will affect total growth as well as growth responses to added fertilizers. Although important in sole cropping, the influence of light and temperature on plant growth becomes even more critical when crops are grown together. The well known influence of solar radiation on yield, nitrogen response, and nitrogen uptake by rice (DeDatta & Zarate, 1970) is probably similar for other crops and other systems of management.

The capacity of a species to withstand short or extended dry periods is an important crop characteristic, and information about the influence of fertilization on drought tolerance is essential. Crops such as beans which can complete their life cycle during dry periods, may produce higher yields if fertilizer is applied early enough to permit some movement of the mobile nutrients into the soil profile. With an adequate nutrient regime throughout the profile, plant roots may penetrate deeper and thus be in a position to take advantage of subsoil water. Practices which promote good root penetration could thus be especially pertinent for the corn-bean relay intercropping pattern so common in the tropics.

Table 3. Nitrogen removal in the grain of sole-cropped or interplanted corn and beans with apparent recovery of fertilizer-applied nitrogen (Oelsligle & Pinchinat, unpublished)

Nitrogen applied	Corn		Beans		Corn and beans (interplanted)	
	N in grain	Apparent recovery	N in grain	Apparent recovery	N in grain	Apparent recovery
kg/ha	kg/ha	%	kg/ha	%	kg/ha	%
0	45	--	36	--	45	--
100	55	10	66	30	75	30
200	62	8	87	25	95	25
300	56	4	109	24	113	23

ADAPTABILITY TO LOW FERTILITY

Some tropical areas are so remote, and their soils so infertile, that fertilization with inorganic nutrient sources is prohibitive. Where such adverse soil conditions prevail, it may be easier and more economical to select crops adapted to low nutritional regimes than to amend the soil. Recent studies have suggested the existence of important differences among species and among varieties of the same species in tolerance to high soil acidity or high aluminum (Foy, 1974; Spain et al., 1974), low levels of extractable soil phosphorus (Salinas & Sanchez, 1975), high salinity, and micronutrient deficiencies or toxicities (Ponnamperuma & Castro, 1972). The matching of species compatible with each other and with low fertility is an aspect of multiple cropping which requires more research.

FERTILIZATION PRACTICES OF SPECIFIC SYSTEMS

The discussion above suggests that information already available can frequently be tailored to multiple cropping practices. The extent to which this is possible will be dictated by the intensity of competition for nutrients, light, and water within a particular system. Several of the prevailing multiple cropping schemes will be considered from a soil fertility management aspect, the perspective being the degree of competition between the crops growing within each system.

Sequential cropping, e.g., double or ratoon crops, fits into the definition of multiple cropping by virtue of the fact that more than one crop is generally harvested from a specified area within a one-year period. Andrews and Kassam (1976) also consider strip cropping a form of multiple cropping; but the reasons for using such systems are seldom related to fertility management, and interspecific competition for nutrients is not likely to be intense. For these systems, soil fertility problems should not differ greatly from those of sole cropping because there is only one crop growing on a specified area at any one time. The principal difference between these systems and sole cropping is a higher land use intensity.

Strip Cropping

From the viewpoint of fertility management, growing two or more crops in separate strips does not appear different from sole cropping. If the strips are sufficiently wide for independent cultivation, each of them can be managed as a sole crop.

Double Cropping

Except for the shortened time lapse between crops, and hence between fertilizer applications, the fertility management of double cropped soil should not differ significantly from yearly rotations. Green manure crops could be an advantage in this system because it would still allow at least one cash crop to be harvested per year. However, the beneficial effects of green manure are short-lived and rarely extend beyond the second following crop (Webster & Wilson, 1966). Consequently, the green manure crop must be grown rather frequently in the rotation if yields of the cash crop are to be maintained at reasonable levels.

For corn-groundnut (*Arachis hypogaea*) and sorghum (*Sorghum bicolor*)-groundnut rotations, Sarma and Patil (1971) reported that yields of groundnuts varied with the variety or hybrid of sorghum that preceeded them, the fertilizer rates applied to the sorghum, and sorghum yields. Other work (Jones, 1974) has shown that the crop which precedes corn may influence the optimal rate of nitrogen for the following corn crop. When corn followed cotton, the nitrogen response was maximal with 84 kg/ha; but corn following sorghum, groundnuts, or cowpeas (*Vigna* sp.) required 168 kg N/ha to achieve maximum yields.

The importance of previous history in a rotation is thus apparent, but quantifying residual effects of previous crops and fertilizers applied to them for complex cropping patterns will require additional work. In one attempt to resolve this problem, workers in India have derived regression equations which are proposed to predict levels of N, P, and K in soils following harvests of rice and wheat (*Triticum aestivum* L.) (IARI, 1972). Their estimates are based on initial soil-test levels, amounts of fertilizer added, and yields of the previous crop.

Ratoon Cropping

In their review of ratoon cropping, Plucknett et al. (1970) provide good information relevant to fertility management. Ratooning is perhaps the most intensive form of sequential cropping; and fertilization practices may be different for ratooned crops because of residual effects, the existence of a fairly well developed root system at the start of regrowth, or earlier maturity of the ratoon relative to the original planting for crops like sorghum and rice. Fertilizer practices which have proved successful for forages in the tropics (Vicente-Chandler et al., 1974) should also provide a good guide for ratoon cropping.

Relay Intercropping

Many practices appropriate to crops in rotation should pertain to relay cropping. A relay system is essentially a rotation with an overlap of the harvest and seeding of the two respective crops. Depending on the amount of time overlap between seedings, there may be an increased efficiency in nitrogen recovery when late N applications are made on the first crop.

Relay intercropping is a common practice in wet-dry climates where the wet season is not sufficiently long for two full-season crops. The corn-bean relay is a major association in Central America. Corn is grown through the wet season, and beans are planted as the corn approaches physiological maturity. The bean crop then completes its growth cycle during a period of dry weather. Preliminary data show that beans cropped in relay with corn respond to high rates of N fertilization (D. D. Oelsligle, J. J. Nicholaides, and G. Ramirez, unpublished data). Bean yields of 0.68, 0.85, 1.19, 1.31, and 1.55 metric ton/ha, respectively, were obtained when 0, 50, 100, 150 or 200 kg N/ha were applied to beans planted in maturing corn. The response data suggest that residual effects of nitrogen applied to the corn were nil, but there were no control treatments to support this conclusion.

Row Intercropping

Because row intercropping is one of the more extreme and perhaps least researched means of intensifying land use, the concept deserves special consideration with regard to fertility management. In considering the various aspects of supplying nutrients as inorganic fertilizers (i.e., rate, placement, sources, and timing of applications), it seems a foregone conclusion that the set of practices which maintains adequate fertility at the lowest possible cost is best. Although the nutrients in plant residues are not "fertilizers" in the sense used above, they may contribute a significant proportion to the total nutrient supply. Residue management thus becomes an integral part of any fertilization program.

FERTILIZER RATES

When two or more crops are associated in an intercropping pattern, their fertilization becomes more complex. A first approximation for deciding on the amounts of fertilizer to apply can be arrived at by the "balance sheet" approach where the amounts of nutrients gained and lost are estimated. Several examples of this approach are given by Cooke (1969). Stanford (1973) suggested that,

> for making optimum N recommendations for corn the following information was needed: 1) the internal N requirement of the crop for expected attainable yield, 2) the amount of soil N mineralized during the cropping season, 3) the amount of residual mineral N present in the root zone early in the cropping season, and 4) the expected efficiency of recovery of the plant available N supply.

Without specific data from field trials, this is the logic used in determining fertilizer rates for monocultures, and the same approach could be applied for intercropping. The question which must be answered is: what, if any, are the increases in utilization efficiency of the different nutrients when compared to sole cropping?

When horsebeans (*Vicia faba equina*) and wheat were planted together in lysimeters, Ibrabim and Kabesh (1971) found that uptake of N, P, K, and

Ca was increased by 29, 33, 39, and 32%, respectively, over the monocultures. Working with intercropped corn and sugarcane (*Saccharum* sp.), Bhoj and Kapoor (1970) found that an extra 112 kg N/ha and three extra irrigations were required to eliminate the competitive effect of corn on the sugarcane. Chang et al. (1969) interplanted sweet potatoes or peanuts (*Arachis hypogaea* L.) in sugarcane and followed the recovery of fertilizer-applied P and K as influenced by crop association and fertilizer placement. Measurable effects of crop and fertilizer placement on recovery patterns for ^{32}P and ^{86}Rb were observed. Particularly relevant to intercropping, however, was their conclusion that the soil layer(s) from which sugarcane extracted the bulk of its nutrients, especially during latter stages of growth, differed from that of sweet potatoes or peanuts. Presumably, sugarcane was postulated to extract P or K from lower depths than the other two species.

Bray's (1954) nutrient mobility concept seems to provide an equally plausible explanation, not only for the observations of Chang et al. (1969) with P and K but for those of Bhoj and Kapoor (1970) with nitrogen and water as well. Basically, Bray's concept suggests that the relatively mobile forms of a nutrient or compound (NO_3-N or water) can be extracted more or less quantitatively from what he calls the "root system sorption zone." On the other hand, the "root surface sorption zone," from which the relatively immobile nutrient forms (P and K) are extracted, represents only a small percentage of the total soil volume. Hence, the amounts of these immobile nutrients that must be present in the soil substrate are many times greater than the crop requirement. In interpreting the results of an experiment with corn planted in sod, Kurtz et al. (1952) concluded that higher amounts of mobile nutrients would be needed if the initial supply were just sufficient for the corn (or sod) alone. For the relatively immobile nutrients, on the contrary, these authors concluded that a soil supply sufficient for one species would likely be sufficient for the intercrop. Fertilization rates with mobile nutrients should therefore be based on actual plant use, whereas the rate of fertilization with the immobile nutrients would be based on estimates of the relative sufficiency of the soil supply. A simplistic approach for fertilizing intercropped species with immobile nutrients would thus be to aim at maintaining a certain level of "adequacy" in the soil system. From the research standpoint, it remains to be determined whether, and to what degree, this adequacy level changes under differing intercropping patterns.

Many of the fertility studies with intercropped species to date have been concentrated on nitrogen management with corn as one of the interplanted species, e.g., corn-rice (IRRI, 1974), corn-beans (Del Valle, 1975), and corn-pigeon peas (Dalal, 1974). In Costa Rica, differences in land equivalent ratio (LER, Table 4) were minor when beans were interplanted in "full" stands of corn if the nitrogen supply was relatively low. Although not consistently so, LER values tended to increase with high rates of nitrogen. A positive relationship between nitrogen supply and LER has also been observed in the Philippines (IRRI, 1974). By and large, however, the results in Table 4 suggest that proportionate yields of two interplanted species, each of which re-

Table 4. Relative yields and land equivalent ratios when corn and beans were interplanted
at differing full-stand percentages with varying levels of N fertilization
(Oelsligle & Pinchinat, unpublished)

	Full-stand percentage of corn (C) and beans (B)								
	100C – 50B			100C – 100B			50C – 100B		
Nitrogen rate	Relative yield*			Relative yield			Relative yield		
	C	B	LER†	C	B	LER	C	B	LER
0	0.78	0.41	1.19	0.59	0.58	1.17	0.38	0.89	1.27
100	0.83	0.37	1.20	0.55	0.63	1.18	0.31	0.74	1.05
200	0.77	0.37	1.14	0.61	0.63	1.24	0.32	0.69	1.01
300	1.00	0.40	1.40	0.78	0.64	1.42	0.40	0.80	1.20
Avg.	0.84	0.39	1.23	0.63	0.62	1.25	0.35	0.78	1.13

* Relative yield = Yield of interplanted species "X"/Yield of sole-cropped species "X".
† Land equivalent ratio (LER) = relative yield of interplanted species "X" plus relative
yield of interplanted species "Y". LER has been used by researchers in the Philippines (IRRI, 1974) to compare the productivity of various cropping combinations; it
must be greater than 1.00 for any advantage to accrue from intercropping.

spond similarly to nitrogen, would remain relatively constant as the nitrogen
regime was altered. They further suggest that the cropping combination as
well as the rate of fertilization with nitrogen may need altering to accom-
modate the farmer's objectives (maximum grain yield, maximum protein or
energy production, or highest economic return).

TIMING AND PLACEMENT

Intercropped species may differ in their rate of nutrient uptake and in
the period of peak nutrient demand. Furthermore, the pattern of nutrient
uptake for a particular crop may change when placed in direct competition
with another species. Most intercropping patterns still allow localized placement of a particular nutrient. When corn is grown with a legume, for example, nitrogen can be applied when and where the corn requires it, possibly
without affecting the N-fixing capabilities of the legume. For intercropping,
considerations concerning the placement of P should not differ greatly from
sole cropping; the important point is to make sure that the particular pattern
will permit P incorporation at a time to insure adequate availability. For
either long-term or short-term crops, late applications of P are seldom beneficial. For example, Ofori (1970) observed that cassava roots stopped absorbing P when they began their storage function.

SOURCES

The chemical reactions which nutrient carriers undergo in soil should
not be drastically different for intercropping than for sole cropping. Sulfur-
coated urea (Englestad et al., 1972) has been used for flooded rice and likely

has some applications for intercropping. A fertilizer which would release N at a rate comparable to the N demands of a particular crop would be ideal. Such a product would be especially attractive for crops which require 6 to 10 months to complete their growth cycle. Slow-release materials would also make it possible to reduce the frequency of N applications and avoid some of the practical problems inherent in fertilizing any intensive cropping pattern. Rock phosphate also merits consideration for intercropped systems. It would probably not suffice for quick-growing, high-demand crops, especially on high-pH soil; but this slowly-soluble, and usually less-expensive, form of P may be satisfactory for interplanted, long-season species such as cassava. Since some phosphorus fertilizer can usually be applied in bands at the initiation of a cropping sequence, an attractive practice would be to band apply small amounts of a relatively soluble P source for the quick-growing species and to broadcast a larger quantity of rock phosphate for the intercrop combination. Nutrient-source experiments on intercropped systems, especially with N and P,, seem particularly relevant because little quantitative information is available.

Intercropping leguminous green manure crops with cereals is another possible way to supply nitrogen. Agboola and Fayemi (1971) reported that yields of four successive corn crops, each of which was fertilized with nitrogen, were comparable with corn yields from a corn-legume intercrop without nitrogen fertilizer. When the corn was neither fertilized nor grown with a legume, however, grain yields from the fourth crop of corn were reduced to one-half that of the first.

Mixed Intercropping

Due to the somewhat "randomized" spatial arrangement of plants, fertilization practices appropriate for this system are probably the most complex of the various multiple cropping patterns. To date, little has been published concerning the fertilization of mixed-crop systems. Perhaps the most intensive studies on fertilization and management of mixed cropping has been with grass-legume mixtures for forage production (Baylor, 1974; Spain, 1975; Serrao & Neto, 1975). Work of this nature has demonstrated the competitive capacity of different grass and legume cultivars and also the importance of fertilizer management in maintaining balanced populations (Drolsom & Smith, 1976).

FERTILIZER RATES

From the viewpoint of fertility management, the ideal combination of species for mixed intercropping would seem to be those with similarly-shaped nutrient-absorption curves as well as comparable total nutrient requirements. If neither the accumulation pattern nor total nutrient demand coincide in some degree, applying fertilizer for two or more crops must be a compromise at best; and the rate appropriate for one crop may be either too high or too low for the other(s). A case in point is a recent observation with corn and sweet potatoes in North Carolina (R. E. McCollum, unpublished data). On Coastal Plain soils, corn requires some 150 to 175 kg N/ha for maximum yields; sweet potatoes require 75 to 90 kg. When the two species were planted in mixed culture (row intercropped) and fertilized appropriately for corn, the sweet potatoes remained vegetative until the corn matured. On zero-N plots, both corn and sweet potatoes were severely N-deficient, but potato plants had enlarged roots on them quite early in the production cycle.

Because the total population of plants in mixed cultures is usually higher than in monoculture (Willey & Osiru, 1972), the recovery percentage of nutrients applied as fertilizer should surely increase; but higher application rates, particularly of the mobile nutrients, will likely be needed. Santhirasegaram (1967) reported a 50% reduction in coconut (*Cocos nucifera*) yields (from 1,332 to 703 kg/ha per year) when the understory napiergrass (*Pennisetum purpureum*) was not fertilized, but coconut yields for the fertilized grass-coconut mixture were comparable with sole-cropped coconut.

Interspecific competition for nutrients in mixed intercrops is probably more direct (and more intense) than in row intercropping. Dalal's (1974) comparisons of nutrient uptake by mix- and row-intercropped corn and pigeon peas, particularly during early growth, support this view (Table 2). In this example, however, the mixed-crop system consisted of planting the two species in the same row; and it is likely that competition for water and light, as well as nutrients, was more intense.

PLACEMENT AND TIMING

All of the considerations relevant to the timing and placement of fertilizer applications for row intercropping seem equally applicable to mixed intercropping. Additional factors which may make the placement and timing of fertilizer application for mixed intercropping even more complex are differences among species in rooting patterns and the logistical problems of putting a given nutrient at the desired place at the appropriate time. Tracer studies by Kamath and Subbiah (1971) showed that the recovery of fertilizer-applied P from the surface 25 cm (10 inches) of soil by intercropped wheat and gram (*Phaseolus mungo*) was roughly comparable to monoculture (Table 5), but recovery from the second 25-cm (10-inch) layer by intercropped gram was considerably greater than gram in monoculture. Until more concrete data are generated, however, it would appear that the safest procedure for applying relatively immobile nutrients is to broadcast and incorporate them at the time most suitable, logistically, for the cropping pattern. Mobile nutrients can always be applied as top dressing when desired; the timing of these top dressings may of necessity be a compromise between the ideal for each crop and that which most nearly fits the total demand curve of the crop combination(s) involved.

Table 5. Effect of depth of placement and intercropping on uptake of fertilizer P by wheat and gram (Kamath & Subbiah, 1971)

Soil depth	P in the plant derived from tagged fertilizer (^{32}P)			
	Monoculture		Intercropped	
	Wheat	Gram	Wheat	Gram
cm	% of total			
0–10	29.2	22.1	36.2	15.1
10–20	14.7	3.1	12.7	8.1
20–30	1.4	0.3	1.3	0.4

Aside from nitrogen supply, soil acidity and P fixation are perhaps the next most serious fertility problems in tropical latitudes. One of the standard procedures to counter P fixation problems has been to place the fertilizer in bands under or near the crop row. Recent work in Brazil (North Carolina State University, 1974) has shown that a combination of broadcast and banded P produced corn yields comparable to higher broadcast rates. Where farmers are using mixed cropping practices, the fertilizer is usually applied in a small hole either beside or below the seed. Since this practice results in minimal contact between the fertilizer and the soil, it is essentially equivalent to row placement. An interesting area for research would be to determine what constitutes an adequate rate of P application under these circumstances. When P fixation is not a severe problem, its management is not nearly as critical. On a soil in India, which was considered medium in P and a relatively poor P fixer, there was little difference between banded and broadcast P when applied to a cowpea-sunn hemp (*Crotalaria juncea*) combination (Gautam et al., 1964).

SOURCES

The points made for row intercropping with regard to nutrient sources should also apply for mixed intercropping, the main difference being those nutrients which become less available with time. With mixed cropping, banding per se is not possible. If P fixation is known to be severe, for example, high applications of slightly-soluble P carriers and localized placement, insofar as the cropping pattern permits, should help overcome it.

CONCLUSIONS

Appropriate fertility management of soil for multiple cropping systems requires answers to the same basic questions as those posed for sole-crop agriculture. Once the characteristics of a soil and of the crops to be planted on it are known, management decisions on how to maintain adequate nutritional regimes in multicrop systems involve questions about rates, dates, sources, and placement of the various soil amendments. Our thesis is that solutions to each of these problems become more complex as cropping intensity is increased.

Bench-mark data on total nutrient demand, nutrient removal in harvested products, and rates of nutrient accumulation during ontogeny are needed for each species in a given multicrop system. Many such data from sole-crop research are available, but information on how and to what degree these data apply to the host of multicrop patterns, either extant or anticipated, is scarce. Particularly needed are performance data (both crop and nutrient) from well-planned experiments involving the more complex intercropped patterns. The generation of such data would provide information on the relative effectiveness of nutrients applied to multicropped soils and a better understanding of how a given plant species competes for nutrients when grown in close proximity with another. Neither commerical nor subsistence agriculture operates in an economic vacuum, and the economic and social environment within which multiple cropping is practiced is a perennial consideration. Where soil conditions are so adverse that their correction by chemical amendments is economically nonfeasible, adapting a species or a variety to the soil rather than the converse may be the more desirable alternative. In any event, researchers should not forget that their ultimate objective is to provide farmers (large and small) with the know-how for producing more food at economically-attractive costs.

LITERATURE CITED

Agboola, A. A., and A. A. Fayemi. 1971. Preliminary trials on the intercropping of maize with different tropical legumes in Western Nigeria. J. Agric. Sci. Camb. 77:219–225.

Andrews, D. J., and A. H. Kassam. 1976. The importance of multiple cropping in increasing world food supplies. p. 1–10. In R. I. Papendick, P. A. Sanchez, and G. B. Triplett (ed.) Multiple cropping. Spec. Pub. No. 27. Am. Soc. of Agron., Madison, Wis.

Baylor, J. E. 1974. Satisfying the nutritional requirements of grain-legume mixtures. p. 171–188. In D. A. Mays (ed.) Forage fertilization. Soil Sci. Soc. of Am., Madison, Wis.

Bhoj, R. L., and P. C. Kapoor. 1970. Intercropping of maize in spring planted sugarcane gives high profits with adequate nitrogen use. Indian J. Agron. 15(3):242–246.

Bradfield, R. 1970. Increasing food production in the tropics by multiple cropping. p. 229–242. In D. G. Aldrich (ed.) Research for the world food crisis. Pub. No. 92, Am. Assoc. Adv. Sci., Washington, D. C.

Bray, R. H. 1954. A nutrient mobility concept of soil-plant relationships. Soil Sci. 78:9–22.

Chang, W., C. H. Chang, and F. W. Ho. 1969. Competition between sugarcane and intercrops for fertilizer tagged with P^{32} and Rb^{86}. J. Agric. Assoc. China 67:43–49.

Cooke, G. W. 1969. Plant nutrient cycles. p. 75–95. In Transition from extensive to intensive agriculture with fertilization. Int. Potash Inst. Proc. VII Colloq. Berne, Switzerland.

Cordero, A., and G. S. Miner. 1974. Programa de calibración de análisis de suelos para la fertilización de arroz y maíz en Costa Rica. p. 533–548. In E. Bornemisza y A. Alvarado (ed.) manejo de suelos en la America Tropical. North Carolina State Univ., Raleigh.

Dalal, R. C. 1974. Effects of intercropping maize with pigeon peas on grain yield and nutrient uptake. Exp. Agric. 10:219–224.

Dalrymple, D. G. 1971. Survey of multiple cropping in less developed nations. FEDR-12. USDA, U. S. Government Printing Office, Washington, D. C.

DeDatta, S. K., and P. M. Zarate. 1970. Environmental conditions affecting the growth characteristics, nitrogen response and grain yield of tropical rice. Biometeorology 4(1):71–89.

Del Valle, R. 1975. Efecto de la fertilización con NPK en el sistema maíz frijol asociado, bajo las condiciones del Valle de Monjar. Tesis Ing. Agron., Universidad de San Carlos de Guatemala, Guatemala.

Drolsom, P. N., and Dale Smith. 1976. Adapting species for forage mixtures. p. 223–234. In R. I. Papendick, P. A. Sanchez, and G. B. Triplett (ed.) Multiple cropping. Spec. Pub. No. 27. Am. Soc. of Agron., Madison, Wis.

Englestad, O. P., J. G. Getsinger, and P. J. Stangel. 1972. Tailoring of nitrogen fertilizers for rice. Nat. Fert. Div. Center. Bull. Y-52. Muscle Shoals, Alabama.

Foy, C. D. 1974. Effects of aluminum on plant growth. p. 601–642. In E. W. Carson (ed.) The plant root and its environment. Univ. Press of Virginia, Charlottesville.

Gautam, O. P., V. H. Shah, and K. P. M. Nair. 1964. Agronomic investigations with hybrid maize. II: Study of intercropping, row spacing and method of phosphorus application with hybrid maize. Indian J. Agron. 9(4):247–254.

Hanway, J. S., and W. E. Thompson. 1971. How a soybean plant develops. Iowa State Univ. Coop. Ext. Ser. Spec. Report 53 (Rev.).

Ibrabim, M. E., and M. O. Kabesh. 1971. Effect of associated growth on the yield and nutrition of legume and grass plants I. Wheat and horsebeans mixed for grain production. UAR J. Soil Sci. 11(2):271–283.

Indian Agricultural Research Institute. 1972. Recent research on multiple cropping. IARI Res. Bull. (New Series No. 8). New Delhi, India.

International Rice Research Institute. 1972. Rice, science, and man. IRRI, Los Baños, Philippines.

International Rice Research Institute. 1974. Ann. Report for 1973. p. 11–34. IRRI, Los Baños, Philippines.

Jones, M. J. 1974. Effects of previous crop on yield and nitrogen response of maize at Samaru, Nigeria. Exp. Agric. 10:273–279.

Kamath, M. G., and B. V. Subbiah. 1971. Phosphorus uptake pattern by crops from different soil depths. Proc. Int. Symp. Soil Fert. Eval. (New Delhi) 1:281–291.

Kurtz, T., S. W. Melsted, and R. H. Bray. 1952. The importance of nitrogen and water in reducing competition between intercrops and corn. Agron. J. 44:13–17.

Lal, R., B. T. Kang, F. R. Moorman, A. S. R. Juo, y J. C. Moomaw. 1974. Problemas de manejo de suelos y posibles soluciones en Nigeria Occidental. p. 380–417. In E. Bornemisza y A. Alvarado (ed.) Manejo de Suelos en la America Tropical. North Carolina State Univ., Raleigh.

Mengel, K. 1969. Factors limiting maximum yield. p. 33. In Transition from extensive to intensive agriculture with fertilizers. Int. Potash Inst., Proc. VII Colloq. Berne, Switzerland.

North Carolina State University. 1973, 1974. Agronomic-economic research on tropical soils. Soil Sci. Dep., Raleigh, N. C.

Nye, P. H., and D. J. Greenland. 1960. The soil under shifting cultivation. Tech. Comm. No. 51. Commonwealth Bur. of Soils, CAB. Bucks, England.

Ofori, C. S. 1970. Absorption and translocation of phosphate through cassava tubers (Manihot esculenta Cranz). Ghana J. Agric. Sci. 3(2):203–205.

Plucknett, D. L., J. P. Evenson, and W. G. Sanford. 1970. Ratoon cropping. Adv. Agron. 22:205–326.

Ponnamperuma, F. N., and R. U. Castro. 1972. Varietal differences in resistance to adverse soil conditions. p. 677–684. In Rice breeding. IRRI, Los Baños, Philippines.

Salinas, J. G., and P. A. Sanchez. 1975. Soil-plant relationships affecting varietal and species differences in tolerance to low available soil phosphorus. Ciencia e cultura (Brazil). In press.

Santhirasegaram, K. 1967. Intercropping of coconuts with special reference to food production. Ceylon Coconut Plant. Rev. V(1):12–24.

Sarma, V., and R. V. Patil. 1971. Residual effects of sorghum and maize fertilization on succeeding crops of groundnuts. J. Indian Soc. Soil Sci. 19(3):313-316.

Serrão, E. A., and M. S. Neto. 1975. The adaptation of tropical forages in the Amazon region. p. 31-52. *In* E. C. Doll and G. O. Mott (ed.) Tropical forages in livestock production systems. Spec. Pub. No. 24. Am. Soc. of Agron., Madison, Wis.

Spain, J. M. 1975. The forage potential of allic soils of the humid lowland tropics of Latin America. p. 1-8. *In* E. C. Doll and G. O. Mott (ed.) Tropical forages in livestock production systems. Spec. Pub. No. 24. Am. Soc. of Agron., Madison, Wis.

Spain, J. M., C. A. Francis, R. H. Howles, y F. Calvo. 1974. Diferencias entre especies y variedades de cultivos y pastos tropicales en su tolerancia a la acidez del suelo. p. 313-335. *In* E. Bornemisza y A. Alvarado (ed.) Manejo de Suelos en la America Tropical. North Carolina State Univ., Raleigh.

Stanford, G. 1973. Rationale for optimum nitrogen fertilization in corn production. J. Environ. Qual. 2(2):159-166.

Vicente-Chandler, J., F. Abruña, R. Caro-Costar, J. Figarella, S. Silva, and R. W. Pearson. 1974. Intensive grassland management in the humid tropics of Puerto Rico. Univ. Puerto Rico. Agric. Exp. Stn. Bull. 223.

Webster, C. C., and P. N. Wilson. 1966. Agriculture in the tropics. Longmans, Green and Co., Ltd., London, England.

Willey, R. W., and D. S. O. Osiru. 1972. Studies on mixtures of maize and beans (*Phaseolus vulgaris*) with particular reference to plant population. J. Agric. Sci. Camb. 79:517-529.

Integrated Pest Management in Multiple Cropping Systems

J. A. Litsinger and Keith Moody[1]

Multiple cropping allows for crop intensification in two dimensions, vertical and horizontal (Fig. 1). We think of yield per crop as the vertical dimension and yield per year as the horizontal dimension. Yield per crop can be increased by planting high-yielding varieties, using fertilizers and pesticides, planting denser stands, irrigating, and intercropping. Sequential and relay cropping are means of intensifying yield in the horizontal dimension. The goal of research is to increase food production in both dimensions, even in existing multiple cropping patterns. It has been well documented (Rivnay, 1964, 1972; Smith, 1972; Nickel, 1973) that pests and their populations change in response to the inputs associated with the vertical dimension of intensive cropping.

DEVELOPMENT OF TECHNOLOGY

The challenge to pest management specialists is to assist in the development of technology to produce higher-yielding cropping patterns without creating conditions that favor equally higher potentials for pests. It is expected that pests and the technology used in dealing with them will change in kind and degree in conjunction with the adoption of new cropping patterns (Pradan, 1968; Paharia & Mehta, 1970). These changes in crop combinations will require more sophisticated management decisions on the part of the farmer (Harwood & Price, 1976).

A researcher concerned with pest problems will need to widen his research perspective in order to be effective (Harwood, 1974a). Research on pests has normally been done on a single crop basis. In multiple cropping, it

---

[1]Associate entomologist and associate agronomist, respectively, International Rice Research Institute, P. O. Box 933, Manila, Philippines.

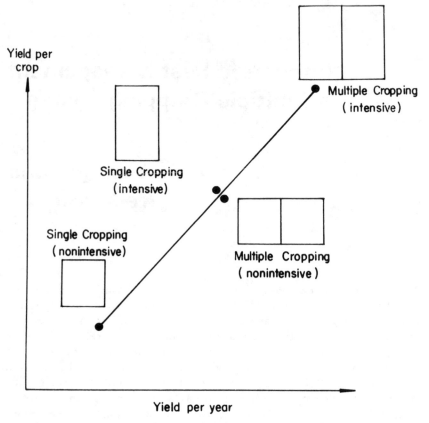

Figure 1. Crop intensification in two dimensions.

is necessary to study pests over the entire cropping period, because the pests of one crop might be influenced by the previous crop(s) as well as by companion crops in intercropping patterns.

New intercropping and sequential cropping patterns will require a more thorough awareness of crop-crop interactions. The use of pesticides will need to be reevaluated with respect to drift and phytotoxicity problems in new crop combinations and their residual effects on nontarget hosts in relay or sequential croppings.

If herbicides are used for weed control, the possibility of toxic residues carrying over from one crop to the rest has to be taken into consideration. This is less likely to be a problem in the tropics than in temperate regions. Paner (1975) reported that herbicides applied to rainfed lowland rice (*Oryza sativa* L.) were not toxic to watermelons (*Citrullus vulgaris* Schrad.) or muskmelons (*Cucumis melo* L.) planted immediately after rice. In Nigeria, Moody (unpubl.) succeeded in establishing a full stand of cowpeas [*Vigna unguiculata* (L.) Walp.] 2 months after application of atrazine [2-chloro-4-(ethylamino)-6-(isopropylamino)-s-triazine] (4 kg active ingredient/ha). However, herbicide residues could possibly build up to toxic proportions if one herbicide were applied repeatedly to the same land.

Residues from insecticide applications to the preceding crop may also linger in the soil and interact adversely with the relay or following crop either by contamination of edible plant parts or by possible phytotoxic action. The residual effect may, however, be beneficial in controlling pests. Raros (1973) demonstrated that a soil application of carbofuran (2,3-dihydro-2,2-dimethyl-7-benzofuranyl methylcarbamate) (2 kg active ingredient/ha) to corn seedlings for the corn borer (*Ostrinia furnacalis* Guenee) provided residual protection against the beanfly (*Ophiomyia(=Melanagromyza) phaseoli* (Tryon)) on a relay mung bean [*Vigna radiata* (L.) Willcyek.] crop in the Philippines.

New technology such as direct seeding, relay cropping, supplemental irrigation, minimum tillage, and shorter-maturing varieties is being developed to extend the cropping period, particularly in warmer climates, to enable more crops to be grown in a year. These innovations will allow for some juggling for crop sequences and planting times. A portion of pest management research in multiple cropping patterns will be predictive in nature. For the most part, accurate assessments of the status of pests will be difficult to extrapolate from small field trials to more extensive areas planted to new cropping patterns. Because of lack of basic information on changing technology, it is difficult to foresee the extent of pest problems that may emerge from large areas planted to new cropping sequences (Farnworth & Golley, 1974, p. 8). Predictions of the consequences of new technology have not yet been advanced. Predictions were not offered as to changes in pest status resulting from the adoption of no-till or minimum tillage in the Corn Belt of North America (Musick & Petty, 1973) or from the introduction of the new high-yielding, short-statured rice varieties in Asia (Smith, 1972; Nickel, 1973). The state of our knowledge is inadequate to make such predictions, and may always be, since pests are not static and can change to meet new stresses (Whitten, 1970; Farnworth & Golley, 1974, p. 6-7; Erlich et al., 1975). However, every effort should be made to predict changes in pest status and to advise on remedial action if necessary.

Since researchers in multiple cropping are concerned with change, there is a need to understand the base from which the change will be made. As Harwood (1974b) says, "We are oriented toward developing and putting into use new technology, making sure it fits our targeted environment." This environment includes the farmer and his ability to choose the most appropriate pest management technology. Therefore, a researcher must have an awareness of the farmers' knowledge and culture. If the farmers' culture offers no incentive for change, they will be slow in adopting new technologies. As has been noted repeatedly in the Green Revolution data (Brady, 1972; Crosson, 1975; Hopper, 1975), the rapidity of change will depend primarily on the ability of society's institutions (educational, political, social, economic, and religious) to encourage adoption of new cropping patterns and pest management practices, by providing material benefits to farmers. These benefits include land reform, credit availability, fertilizer, and pesticides.

We are also looking at agricultural systems and their potential for absorbing multiple cropping (Harwood & Price, 1976). These systems are generally divided into two basic types, broadly called traditional or small-scale agriculture and "modern" large-scale agriculture. Small-scale agriculture embodies its own set of qualities and generally connotes a farm size in the magnitude of several hectares, low energy subsidy in terms of power and agrochemicals, and a high labor input. Large-scale agriculture portrays the opposite set of circumstances, which combine large tillage area, high energy subsidy, and low labor requirements. The latter system is considered to be more fragile (Rivnay, 1964; Janzen, 1973; Nickel, 1973; van Emden & Williams, 1974). The wider use of agrochemicals has profoundly influenced pest populations, causing a few species to become abundant at the expense of others. The all-encompassing nature of multiple cropping, as we defined it, demands a comprehensive approach such as that embodied in the science of population ecology with its holistic tenets (Farnworth & Golley, 1974, p. 37–42).

Within the terms of this ecological framework, pests are defined as those organisms that have surpassed man's tolerance levels in their exploitation of temporary habitats (agroecosystems) created by him to cultivate his crops. The pest species dealt with in weed science, entomology, plant pathology, and zoology have the ability to flourish in disturbed habitats (Southwood & Way, 1970).

The complex nature of multiple cropping demands that cropping patterns and systems be modeled. The pest component will be incorporated into the overall model and act to influence decisions relating to the costs and returns of new cropping patterns. Models will be formulated to include each pest and once constructed could fulfill several goals to pest management. They can function to interpret cause and effect relations of modifiable variables; determine options for conflicting pest control strategies and tactics; form a basis from which to extrapolate data from one location to another; assist the scientist in knowing where to focus research efforts.

Models are only now being advanced for the ecology of pests (Southwood & Way, 1970; Conway, 1973) and determining pest management strategies (Barr et al., 1973; Watt, 1970) for single crops. It is our opinion that much more basic work needs to be done before models of pest ecologies and management systems can be formulated for multiple cropping patterns and systems. The research methodology for studying pests in multiple cropping patterns is only now being developed.

Many variables and their effects on pests need to be determined as a result of introducing new crop species, replacing varieties, and arranging crops in time and space.

CROPPING EFFECTS

The development and application of more intensive cropping technology could change pest problems by creating a more favorable environment for pests and by increasing disturbance of the ecosystem, which could also encourage the same pest species to flourish. Intensive agriculture or crop management could result in expansion of the temporal habitat of the community which could release the pest potential as man strives to extend the cropping period.

On the other hand, overall beneficial effects could result from planting shorter-maturing varieties and thereby, decreasing host exposure. Crop diversity through mixtures may also lead to greater pest stability and greater competitive effect with weeds, and extension of the cropping period may allow naturally-occurring biocontrol agents to sustain higher population levels.

The pest population will respond to the crops themselves as well as to the arrangement of crops in time and space (Fig. 2).

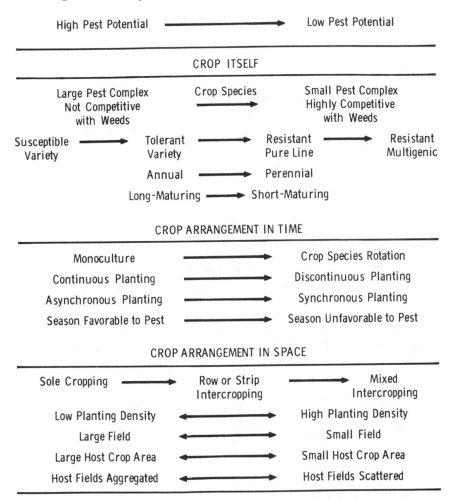

Figure 2. Kinds of crops and their arrangement in time and space evaluated as to the potential development of pest problems. Some effects are seen to be high in pest potential, some intermediate, and some low.

Crop Itself

CROP SPECIES

Plant species differ in attractiveness and suitability as hosts of arthropods, pathogens, and nematodes. Crops such as cassava (*Manihot esculenta* Crantz.) have few recorded pests (Lozano & Booth, 1974). Others, notably solanaceous crops, have large pest complexes, which are greater in the tropics than in temperate regions (Wellman, 1968).

When new crop species are introduced into an area, caution must be exercised to prevent the introduction of exotic pests along with the new plant material (Rawat, 1968). In addition, indigenous insects (Rao, 1970) and weeds (Salisbury, 1961) may change in status to become pests as new crops are introduced or planted at unprecedented times.

For a given region the growth habit of the crop species results ultimately in a certain array of weed species. Competition between crops and weeds is usually most severe when the competing plants are most alike in vegetative habits and demands upon resources (Agricultural Board, 1968b, p. 23). In the U. S., weeds that persist in small-grain fields vary in competition with geographic area and are different for spring and fall plantings (Agricultural Board, 1968b, p. 25-28). Such weeds are adapted to the vegetative cycle and habits of small-grain crops. Several annual weed species persist as residual infestations in corn (*Zea mays* L.) year after year.

CROP VARIETY

Within each species there is a range of pest susceptibility among varieties or cultivars.

Choosing a pest-susceptible, high-yielding variety could mean that the cost of protecting the crop from pest damage would be greater than the gain from the higher yield. Such a variety cannot be grown profitably until a more economical pest management technology has been developed.

Genetic resistance is a powerful defense against arthropods, pathogens, and nematodes (McNew, 1972; Janzen, 1973) and against parasitic weeds. Great strides have been made in incorporating pest resistance into new breeding lines of higher-yielding varieties (Pathak, 1970; Shafer, 1974). Since a crop is usually attacked by a complex of pest species, it often is not enough to have resistance against only one pest. It would be desirable to breed plants that are resistant to a wide variety of pests, as rice breeders have done (IRRI, 1974). Even where the objective is to obtain protection against only one pest species, it would be desirable to have several gene sources of resistance (Browning & Frey, 1969).

Many crop varieties are tolerant to pest attack and compensate for damage. Also the growth characteristics of some varieties are such as to reduce the growth of weed species by providing unusually good canopy cover.

ANNUAL OR PERENNIAL CROP

It is generally held that the natural enemies of pests sustain themselves better in perennial than in annual crops because the cultivation of perennial crops results in less disturbance of the soil, more stability, and more structural diversity (Rao, 1970; Southwood & Way, 1970; van Emden & Williams, 1974). More instances of success in biocontrol of insects have been reported for perennial crops than for annual crops.

The period of costly weeding is longer for perennial tree crops than for annuals (Wycherly, 1970). If weeding is neglected in tree crops, maturity would be delayed and a significant cumulative economic loss would result. Nevertheless, occasional neglect in these more robust crops does not lead to disaster. With annual crops, an unchecked invasion of weeds during a critical phase can lead to serious loss or crop failure.

SHORT-MATURING VERSUS LONG-MATURING CROP

A short-maturing crop is less exposed than a long-maturing crop and therefore tends to avoid the brunt of a pest attack. As a general rule, the most serious losses from weeds occur during the first third of the life cycle of a crop. Usually, therefore, a late-maturing crop or cultivar would have to be weeded longer than a short-maturing crop for optimum yields.

However, in the Philippines, 'IR 8,' a short-strawed, early-maturing rice variety, competed less effectively with barnyard grass [*Echinochloa crus-galli* (L.) Beauv.] than 'H 4,' a taller, later-maturing variety (De Datta et al., 1969). Smith (1974) observed that the ability of rice cultivars to compete with barnyard grass was in proportion to the period of maturity for the cultivars—the longer the period of maturity, the greater the ability to compete with the weed.

Tall, late-maturing soybean [*Glycine max* (L.) Merr.] cultivars frequently compete better with weeds than short, early-maturing varieties. With sorghum (*Sorghum bicolor* L.) hybrids, high competitive ability and resultant decrease in yield of weeds were related to rapid emergence and seedling development (Guneyli et al., 1969).

Crop Arrangement in Time

MONOCULTURE

In many parts of the world, certain areas are planted exclusively to one crop species, year after year. The same crop can be grown each season with fallow between unfavorable seasons.

Monoculture reduces diversity of species of pests. The few species tend to explode in numbers because they have a greater potential for building up under conditions of less interference or competition (Rivnay, 1964; Adams et al., 1971; Smith, 1972; Nickel, 1973).

CROP ROTATION

The alternation of crop species in time has long been known to lessen the incidence of pests (Nusbaum & Ferris, 1973). The success lies in choosing (usually by experience) sequences of crops having the fewest pests in common. The best results are usually achieved by combinations of botanically unrelated crops following one another.

For example, two possible rotations of equal growth duration could be (i) upland rice intercropped with green corn followed by mung beans-cowpeas-fallow and (ii) upland rice intercropped with green corn followed by glutinous corn-cowpeas-fallow (Fig. 3). In the first rotation, enhanced pest problems would be expected from cowpeas following mung beans; both are legumes, and they attract similar pests and have similar growth habits. But in the second rotation, glutinous corn and cowpeas are not related and have different growth habits and attract different pests. The green corn in the second rotation would be expected to transfer more pests to glutinous corn than to mung beans. Polyphagous insects, such as cutworms (*Noctuidae*), grasshoppers (*Acrididae*), and *Heliothis* spp. have the capacity to build up across crops with time and attack both corn and legumes.

Rotation is particularly effective in lowering populations of soil-borne diseases (Chohan, 1968; Agricultural Board, 1968a) and nematodes (Agricultural Board, 1968c; Nusbaum & Ferris, 1973; Brodie & Murphy, 1975). These organisms, however, usually have resistant stages, such as spores or cysts, that can persist and allow the population to survive for several years under host-free conditions. Not all crop combinations are equally effective (Johnson et al., 1975). Soil insects such as wireworms (*Elateridae*) and white grubs (*Melolonthinae*), usually have a wide range of hosts, which restricts the

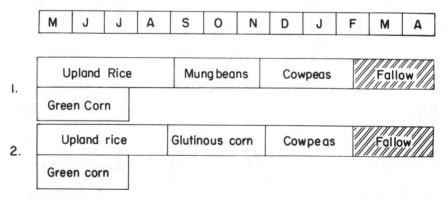

Figure 3. Two possible cropping patterns contrasting botanically related and unrelated crops in rotation.

choice of crops in rotation on the same land (Paharia & Mehta, 1970). Rotations of about 4-year's duration under host-free conditions are usually necessary to reduce the pest population to a tolerable level (Gibson et al., 1958).

Crop rotation is also of value in controlling insect and disease organsims that possess great powers of dispersal. As one crop species replaces another, the onset of attack is delayed, and with this head start, the crop may outgrow the damage.

The effect of rotation is even greater if unrelated crops with different pest complexes are planted in neighboring fields. Ideally there would be an absence of alternate noncrop hosts, such as weeds within and between fields.

Crops having different life cycles, and for which different weed control practices are followed, should be chosen in order to reduce the buildup of certain weed species. The rotation should be planned so that no group of weeds has the possibility of undisturbed·development. In addition, correct sequences of crops may cause more vigorous crop growth and thus increase competition with weeds. However, Paharia and Mehta (1970) warn that intensive cropping may deplete soil nutrients. If crops are not properly fertilized, weeds may have an edge in competition.

Pest populations may be surpressed by rotating two varieties of the same crop species—one variety resistant to soil-borne diseases but low-yielding, the other high-yielding but disease-susceptible (Chohan, 1968). In principle, the procedure is the same as rotating two crop species.

CONTINUOUS VERSUS DISCONTINUOUS CROPPING IN TIME

Presumably a pest species would build up with each successive planting of crop hosts until crop growth has been impaired. At this point, the crop stand and food source would be reduced causing intraspecific pest competition for scarce host plants.

Rice is a plant that can be cropped one to four times a year, the number of times depending on climate, water availability, and variety (Fig. 4). One would expect increasingly greater pest problems as the number of plantings increased. The recent outbreaks of the brown planthopper [*Nilaparvata lugens* (Stal)] in Asia have been fostered by continuous cultivation of flooded lowland rice (Pathak, 1968). Because of pest buildup in time, crops could not be grown continuously on the same land. One would be hesitant to plant continuous vegetables, for example, unless there were varieties resistant to a multitude of pests (Rawat, 1968).

Ratoon cropping has fostered major pest problems with diseases as well as with insects, especially in cotton (*Gossypium* sp.) (Plucknett et al., 1970) and rice (Ou & Ling, 1966). Ratooning crops such as sugarcane (*Saccharum officinarum*) and sorghum is still a common practice in regions where insects, diseases, and nematodes are not restricting. Use of the same weed-control practices in ratooned crops as in plant crops could lead to increased weed problems. In addition, the ability of a crop to compete with weeds may be

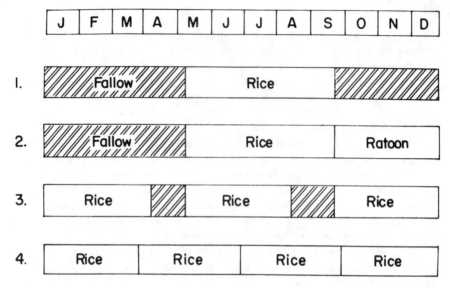

Figure 4. Four possible cropping patterns for lowland rice grown in puddled soil one to four times a year.

lower because of reduced plant population and reduced growth. Weed control in ratooned crops deserves further research because weed control may be the key to successful ratooning of some crops (Plucknett et al., 1970).

Even if one rotates crop species, certain polyphagous pests that carry over and flourish from crop to crop, are bound to appear. These tend to become severe as the cropping period is extended. Likewise, the rate of increase of grasses in the weed flora will be accelerated with a longer cropping period (Anderson & Whan, 1974).

Continuous cropping, which means closing the seasons (no crop-free periods) can be disastrous (Janzen, 1970). Serious pest problems have erupted in desert areas newly opened to irrigation where continuous cropping became possible (Rivnay, 1972; Smith, 1972).

In spite of factors which can lead to severe pest problems, it is also possible (with insects) that given the presence of effective parasites or predators, continuous cropping may lead to reduced pest problems. If only a few pest species exist, continuous cropping may create the stability needed for entomophagous insects to persist and continuously act in pest suppression. This stability is usually lacking in agroecosystems in which frequent disruptions are caused by plowing under a crop after harvest (Huffaker, 1974).

ASYNCHRONOUS VERSUS SYNCHRONOUS PLANTING

The appearance of many insects and diseases is synchronized with a certain stage in the life cycle of the host plant. Therefore, relatively few generations are possible per crop. When that stage passes, the pests must disperse to find a new host in the right growth stage. If there are no host fields at the receptive stage within the range of pest dispersal, the pest population suffers unless the pests can find an alternate host, such as weeds, or has evolved mechanisms to survive over the host-free period. Monophagous pests, such as the pink bollworm [*Pectinophora gossypiella* (Saunders)] on cotton, have been held in check by maintaining a crop-free season uniformly over a region (M. J. Way, 1970, unpublished report).

Asynchronous plantings between adjacent or nearby fields tend to favor pest buildup, whereas synchronous plantings reduce the exposure time of the host to the pest. This effect becomes important in the context of multiple cropping when two different cropping patterns exist side by side.

SEASONAL EFFECT

The effect of season on pest abundance is well known, and adjustment of planting or harvesting times has proved to be an inexpensive means of preventing some pest problems (Singh, 1968). During the formulation of new cropping patterns the specialist should be aware of this. For example, a short-maturing rice variety can be seeded early in May instead of mid-June, and the following crop, mung beans, can be planted in August instead of November (Fig. 5). A farmer can plant three crops in a year instead of two. However, pest problems on mung beans may be worse in August than in November; consequently, green corn may be a better crop than mung beans in the second pattern.

Crop Arrangement in Space

MIXED AND ROW INTERCROPPING

It may be hypothesized that the pest-reducing effects would be maximal in mixed intercropping. This is because plants of the same crop species are more randomly distributed and hence more isolated from their own kind under mixed than under row intercropping.

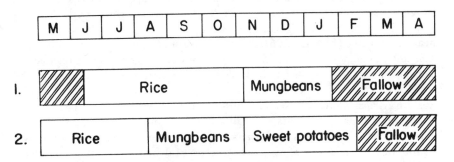

Figure 5. Two possible cropping patterns contrasting planting date and growth duration of the first rice crop and multiple cropping potential.

Mixed intercropping, typical of more traditional, less productive systems (such as shifting agriculture and related bush-fallow), usually involves the use of many crop species planted in a scattered or staggered pattern by hand (Moody, 1975). Pest problems in mixtures are reported to be less than in sole cropping (Aiyer, 1949; Pimentel, 1961a; Batra, 1962; Nickel, 1973; Trenbath, 1974). Other interacting factors associated with this type of agriculture have a direct bearing on pest numbers. They include low soil fertility, a brief cropping period, traditional varieties, and use of agrochemicals.

Intercropping of corn and peanuts (*Arachis hypogaea* L.) decreases the incidence of the corn borer [*Ostrinia furnacalis* (Guenee)] (R. S. Raros, 1973, unpublished; IRRI, 1974) in the Philippines. Because of severe insect damage, cowpeas are seldom planted as a sole crop in northern Nigeria. In that region, cowpeas are planted into a sorghum-millet (*Setaria* sp.) intercrop during the weeding operation, a month after seeding the cereals (Baker & Norman, 1975). The spreading canopy of the cowpeas smothers weeds and makes further weeding unnecessary (Summerfield et al., 1974). In the Congo basin, the reason given for growing cucurbits with corn is that the companion crop shades out the weeds and thus helps to conserve moisture (Miracle, 1967, p. 54).

In the Philippines, when mung beans were used as an intercrop in corn, corn yield was greater than when corn was grown alone, and the weights of weeds decreased. Results were far less encouraging when peanuts were used as the intercrop. The difference between mung beans and peanuts in this respect appears to be due to more rapid early growth of mung beans, and to differences in leaf canopy (Bantilan et al., 1974).

With intercropping the following physical and biological factors affect pest populations:

Physical interference—Within mixtures, nonhost crops for a pest may physically interfere with the pest's ability to find a host. The nonhost crop may act so as to entrap fungal or bacterial spores, either rain-splashed or wind-borne (Leonard, 1969), reducing the quantity of available inoculum.

Rows of densely-planted thorny plants have been used to exclude vertebrate pests and foraging animals from fields in India (Aiyer, 1949).

Tall plants may obscure and thus protect the adjacent host in mixtures. However, an erect barrier, such as a tall row crop, interferes with the horizontal air currents, causing wind-dispersed pests, such as aphids, to settle out near the barrier (Lewis, 1965). In a cowpea-sorghum row intercropping in Tanzania, a chrysomelid (*Ootheca* sp.) pest of cowpeas became aggregated because of the tall sorghum (R. C. Finlay, H. Y. Kayumbo, J. H. Monyo, and A. N. Moruru, 1974. The Morogoro intercropping research project. Fifth Eastern African Cereals Research Conference, Malawi, 10–16 March).

Where a mixture consists of tall and short components, the short ones may be visible to insects or birds sensing the plants from directly above. In Indonesia, a mixture of two rice varieties of different heights is broadcast into fields. The grain of the short, early-maturing variety is hidden, thus preventing birds from devastating the crop. The birds also attack the late crop, but the effect is diluted on a per-field basis because most of the rice in the region matures at the same time (A. Sjarifuddin, 1975, personal communication, Central Research Institute of Agriculture, Bogor, Indonesia).

One of the advantages of mixtures, compared with single cropping is the increased utilization of solar energy through better distribution of canopy (Trenbath, 1974). The more complete cover provided by a mixture of crop species reduces light penetration to the soil, which reduces weed growth. Cleave (1974) argued that mixed intercropping patterns may have evolved specifically to minimize the labor cost of weed control.

The indirect effect of shading by the taller companion crop has been found beneficial in at least one instance. Northern Nigeria, where sesame (*Sesamum indicum* L.) is row intercropped with taller corn or sorghum, a pyralid webworm (*Antigostra* sp.) caused less damage to sesame in the intercropping than in the sole crop (A. H. Kassam, 1973, personal communication, Institute for Agricultural Research, Zaria, Nigeria). The effect was believed to be a combination of shade and physical obstruction.

A closed canopy has negative effects as the microclimate becomes more humid and is a favorable condition for growth of fungal diseases (Trenbath, 1974).

The crop background of a mixture may affect insects that respond to visual cues in locating a host (Southwood & Way, 1970). The color or shape of nonhost plants may attract or repulse a flying pest. A beneficial effect for corn is implied in the peanut background in a corn-peanut row intercropping in the Philippines. Fewer corn borers (*Ostrinia furnacalis* Guenee) were found in corn intercropped with peanuts, even when the peanut crop was replaced by rows of green burlap sacks between the corn rows (R. S. Raros, 1973, unpublished; IRRI, 1974). Smith (1969) noted a positive attraction of aphids to brussels sprouts (*Brassica oleracea* L. var. *gemmifera*) as a result of a crop silhouetted against a bare soil background. This effect may also be operating with the beanfly [*Ophiomyia phaseoli* (Tryon)] on mung beans as reported from Indonesia, where weedy mung beans had a lower infestation than weed-free mung beans (J. McIntosh, 1975, personal communication, Central Research Institute of Agriculture, Bogor, Indonesia). However, Moody and Whitney (1974) observed that sucking insects did more damage to developing cowpea and soybean seeds when weeds are present. They suggested that the weeds provided a more favorable environment for the insects or stood in the way of some of the insecticide, preventing it from reaching the target.

Because of their greater structural diversity, mixtures create more ecological niches for harboring fauna (Pimentel, 1961a; van Emden & Williams, 1974). Conditions are therefore favorable for more herbivore and carnivore species. If the richer species diversity favors the beneficial carnivores, pest management will gain. Thus, in the previously cited sample of corn-peanut intercropping, predatory spiders (*Lycosa* spp.) were more effective against the corn borer in the intercropping than they were in corn grown as a sole crop (R. S. Raros, 1973, unpublished; IRRI, 1974).

Biological interference—Nonhost plants in mixtures may emit chemicals that adversely affect pests, thereby protecting the host plants. By sensing chemicals given off by some plants, some insects are aided in finding a suitable host. Contrariwise, nonhosts may emit repulsive chemicals that mask the presence of a nearby host. Gardeners know that strong-smelling plants, such as onion (*Allium cepa* L.), garlic (*A. sativum* L.), coriander (*Coriandrum sativum* L.), and tomato (*Lycopersicon* sp.) can prevent insect buildup.

Tomatoes row-intercropped with cabbage (*Brassica oleracea* L. var. *capitata*) lessened but no means prevented damage by the diamondback moth [*Plutella xylostella* (L.)] to cabbage (IRRI, 1974; Buranday & Raros, 1975). Tahvanainen and Root (1972) have postulated that this effect may be more widespread, especially in natural ecosystems, than has been thought.

Visser and Vythelingham (1959) and Wallace (1963) reported that the intercropping of marigold (*Tagetes* sp.) adversely affected nematodes (*Pratylenchus, Tylenchorhynchus, Rotylenchulus,* and *Meliodogyne*) that would have severely damaged the susceptible hosts in the mixtures. It was suggested that marigold acted as an antagonistic crop in that its roots released chemicals that repelled or killed nematodes.

Birchfield and Bistline (1956) found that when *Crotolaria* was row intercropped, the nematode [*Radopholus similis* (Cobb) Thorne] was killed. *Crotolaria* has also been successfully used to reduce populations of root-knot nematodes (Agricultural Board, 1968c). It was presumed that *Crotolaria* acted as a trap crop since it is susceptible to nematode infestation but interferes with the completion of the nematode's life cycle inside the roots where they remain throughout their lives.

The presence of the nonhost may have an indirect effect on inducing resistance to disease organisms. The examples pertain to cereal rusts. Obtaining multiline resistance by blending several varieties or genotypes, each possessing resistance to different disease races, is an established practice (Adams et al., 1971). Each genotype possesses a similar phenotype, of the most desirable agronomic traits. The seeds to be sown in one field are mixed in proportions that match the extent of the more common pathogenic races. The results have shown that where several virulent strains are present in a mixture of resistant and susceptible varieties, competitive inhibition occurs between the strains, and the virulent strains therefore develop more slowly on the susceptible genotypes (Leonard, 1969). Johnson and Allen (1975) postulated that nonvirulent spores landing on nonhosts induced resistance to future attack by virulent spores, even those of other disease species.

STRIP CROPPING

Strip cropping is the growing of diverse crops side by side on many small fields. This patchwork of fields can be an important effect on pest populations. The pest management implications of this diversity of crop species, varieties, and age structures were noted in a small coastal valley in Peru and has been well documented (Hambleton, 1944; Smith & Reynolds, 1972).

The valley is composed of many small farms which before the 1920's were planted to sugarcane, cotton, corn, and several minor crops. Between 1920 and 1940 the area planted to cotton was expanded and the valley became a virtual monoculture. The bollworm [*Heliothis virescens* (F.)] changed in status from an occasional pest to a major problem requiring application of insecticides in ever-increasing dosages and with ever-increasing frequency which changed minor pests into major ones as their natural enemies were killed off. Eventually cotton growing became too expensive and the people reverted to their traditional agriculture. As the number of crops increased, *Heliothis* returned to the status of an occasional pest. The diverse fields still provided the bollworm with hosts but they also created habitats for the bollworm's natural enemies.

Corn and cotton planted in adjacent fields have been found to decrease *Heliothis* attack on cotton in Australia, Malawi, South Africa, and North America (Pearson, 1958). The corn acts as a trap or diversionary crop. Usually only one larva survives per ear, although many eggs are deposited. This reduces the population and the cotton is protected. Corn also harbors many predators of the bollworm (M. J. Way, 1970, unpublished report).

However, in other parts of the world (the Sudan, Rhodesia, and Colombia) having similar diversity of crops, *Heliothis* has remained a serious pest (M. J. Way, 1970, unpublished report; Smith & Reynolds, 1972).

In the U. S., alfalfa (*Medicago sativa* L.) and sorghum have been grown as diversionary crops adjacent to cotton in an effort to reduce the amount of insecticide necessary to control cotton pests (Stern, 1969; Fye, 1972).

Because of the genetic diversity achieved, planting of small fields to different varieties of the same crop is a way to buffer the explosive buildup of pests and diseases that have been recorded in the past—for example, an outbreak of late blight (*Phytophthora infestans* Mont de Bory) in potatoes (*Solanum tuberosum* L.) in Ireland, and the southern corn leaf blight (*Helminthosporium maydis* Nis. *et* Miy.) epidemic in North America (Adams et al., 1971). The built-in genetic protection inherent in the small farms typical of developing countries should not be overridden by the widespread adoption of one crop with a narrow germplasm base (Suneson, 1960).

LOW VERSUS HIGH PLANT DENSITY

Plant density affects the incidence of pests. With wind- or soil-borne disease spores, the wider the separation between individual host plants, the less likely it becomes that organisms will infect new plants (Wilson & Baker, 1946; Chilvers & Brittain, 1972). However, the spread of wind-borne diseases depends more on the number of dispersals than on the distance between hosts (Leonard, 1969). Virus diseases spread more easily to adjacent than to distant plants. Thus, in mixed intercropping where plants of the same species are widely separated, one would expect a slower rate of disease transmission.

Pimentel (1961b) has studied the effect of plant density on insect infestations. Widely spaced plants initially attracted fewer insects and tended to be less damaged than dense stands of the same species. This advantage gave way with time as the insect pests build up rapidly on a per-plant basis. The opposite effect was reported by Way and Heathcote (1966), who cited many examples of less damage per plant in densely planted stands. A'Brook (1968) noted a background response on widely spaced, well-weeded peanuts which attracted more of the aphid vector of rosette virus disease. The disease was reduced by planting dense stands of continuous ground cover.

In the Philippines, it was found that when corn plants in a corn-peanut intercrop were widely spaced, there were fewer corn borer egg masses per plant than when the plants were more closely spaced (IRRI, 1973). Low plant densities favor weeds; generally, the weed growth decreases as density of planting increases.

LARGE VERSUS SMALL FIELDS

The structure created by many small adjoining fields in one in which there is a large amount of field border in the proportional relation between border and cropped areas. This fact is significant for three reasons. First, the uncultivated borders provide shelter or alternate hosts for insects, diseases, and rodents (De Bach, 1964, p. 471-473; van Emden, 1965; Dempster & Coaker, 1974). Second, weeds can spread from border areas into cropped areas. Third, some pests are more damaging in borders than in a cropped area. Grasshoppers lay more eggs along borders than inside. Leafhoppers [*Empoasca fabae* (Harris)] concentrate their feeding along the alfalfa perimeter when populations are low. Rodents are more damaging along the edges of fields than in the center. The reverse is apparently true under population pressure.

HOST CROP AREA

A pest's distribution is a function of its ability to disperse. Mountains, deserts, and oceans are physiographic barriers to pests. Wind-borne spores, seeds, and insects can be carried over great distances to infest new fields. For a pest to successfully colonize a newly-planted crop there must be a sufficient pest population generated from a previous crop source—the greater the area planted to the previous host crops within a physiographic zone, the greater will be the pest buildup to invade a newly-planted field. These buildups and migrations have been well documented from temperate zones where a particular pest cannot overwinter in an area and must reinvade each spring.

We argue that the extent of land area devoted to host crops is a contributing factor for pest buildup. Turnipseed (1973) reported that soybean insect pests became more severe as the area devoted to soybeans increased in the U. S.

However, as a corollary, for a given level of invading pest population from a previous source—the larger the present host crop area, the more diluted the effect will be, especially if the pest was capable of only one generation per crop. The potential for pest build up within a large area planted to host crops is therefore negative. This argument would break down, however, in situations where the pest is short-lived and produces several generations per crop.

To summarize, it is beneficial in the short run to plant a large area to one crop, but if the following crops are also hosts of the pest, then the large planting creates greater pest build-up on subsequent crops.

DISTRIBUTION OF HOST FIELDS

Within a physiographic zone and for a given area planted to host crops, the pest potential for any one field is a function of the distribution of fields— the more aggregated the host fields from the previous crop, the greater is the pest potential on a nearby, newly-planted field. If the fields of the previous crop were scattered, then the potential pest build up on the present crop becomes less.

Again, this is a two-sided coin as we argue that it is beneficial for fields to be aggregated for the sake of the present crop because this would dilute the pest population migrating into the area. The argument becomes stronger if the pest has only one generation per crop.

PEST MANAGEMENT TACTICS

Development of pest management technology for multiple cropping systems must take into account the resources of the farmer. Pest control tactics differ for large-scale and small-scale farmers as each has a different resource base of capital, labor, power, land, and, management capability.

Capital

The large-scale farmer's ability to put money into intensive pest management technology is greater than that of the small-scale farmer. Calendar spray schedules are developed with the large-scale farmer in mind. The problems inherent in relying on this approach have been amply discussed (Smith, 1973; Newsom, 1974). For the most part the large-scale farmer demands more pest protection as his plant injury threshold in much lower than is the case with small-scale farmer.

Pesticides are powerful tools in pest management, and there seems to be great potential for increased pesticide usage by small-scale farmers who, because of little capital and little knowledge of proper techniques, do not benefit from them. Whether a small-scale farmer should first invest in pesticides or in fertilizers is debatable. One report (Indian Council of Agricultural Research, 1968) states that fertilizers should have priority. But Haswell (1973, p. 144) states the opposite, contending that herbicides are more valuable than fertilizers in subsistance farming. The reasoning is that elimination of weeds means less labor and more produce, whereas the use of fertilizers means more labor—and more produce only where conditions for response to fertilizers are optimal.

The small-scale farmer would probably prefer an economical, broad-spectrum type of pesticide that could be used on several crops against a wide variety of pests. The use of insecticides in this category could well be self-defeating if it meant foregoing the use of biocontrol agents. In this light, granular systemic insecticides, although more expensive initially, would be preferable to sprays, which are generally effective as contact pesticides and hence reach many nontarget hosts. In addition, sprays wash off in tropical rains, and they require the use of relatively expensive sprayers. Sprayers could be shared by farmers in cooperatives and could be put to other uses, for example, spraying plant growth substances.

Research should emphasize the development of the optimal use of pesticides to find the lowest dosages and application frequency. Proper pesticide timing is important. Treating seeds with pesticide provides early-season protection and is an economical use of pesticide. Since seeds are frequently used as foods, storage protection should emphasize the container, not the seeds if stored.

Pesticides in storage degrade rapidly under hot, humid conditions. Since small-scale farmers use pesticides in small amounts, pesticides should be available in small containers and should have good resealing ability.

Labels in the local language should explain the proper use of each pesticide. Farmers in the tropics wear little protective clothing and they should be informed as to which pesticides they can handle safely. In some developing countries, pesticide legislation should be enacted; in others, the pesticide laws should be strengthened.

If herbicides are used, they should be safe in several unrelated crops. Phytotoxicity problems stemming from residual activity of herbicides on succeeding crops will restrict the usage of many herbicides currently recommended for monoculture use. Less effective herbicides which do not pose phytotoxicity problems would be advantageous on balance if they controlled most of the weeds (J. L. Hammerton, 1974. Problems of herbicide use in peasant farming. Paper presented at the annual meeting of the Weed Science Society of America, Las Vegas, Nevada). The remaining weeds can be controlled by hand or hand-tool weeding or by closed crop canopies.

Where small-scale farmers lack capital to purchase pesticides, other control methods such as plant resistance will be favored. Care must be taken when introducing new crops or replacing established varieties with new, high-yielding ones, as they may be pest susceptible. Pest resistance in plants is a cheap weapon and many traditional varieties infer either resistance or tolerance to a wide spectrum of pests, including weeds. Multiline pest resistance should be sought for the most number of pests in each variety. At least several varieties with different sources of resistance should be planted in a region. Planting of small heterogeneous fields insures diversity of germplasm and thus reduces the stress of pest resistance to new varieties. Introduced varieties must compete with weeds as well as the traditional varieties that the farmer has been growing. If they do not, the farmer will have to spend even more of his time in weeding.

Labor—Power

The labor that goes into pest management should be integrated with other labor such as that required in planting and harvesting. The pest control operation that requires the most labor is hand weeding, which is the weed control method usually practiced by small-scale farmers. These farmers can substitute tractor power with manual labor to increase the efficiency of pesticide application by hand placement of granular soil insecticides at the base of each plant, which allows for longer residual activity and hence reduces the total amount required. Spot treatments on only a part of the field may be all that is necessary to stop an infestation. Individual diseased plants can be rogued to remove the inoculum source. Trellises and stakes can be erected to suspend vegetables above ground level for better aeration and less contact with soil-borne organisms. Bags can be placed over fruit to exclude tephritid fruit flies. Hand-picking of insects may be helpful.

Land

Small landholders may have different options for pest management than their large-scale counterparts. The large amount of border area in small fields can be a refuge for biocontrol agents and therefore be an asset in insect control. Border areas, however, also harbor alternate hosts for pests (Dempster & Coaker, 1974). Management of the border area is a part of pest management. The farmer can remove or foster certain plant species within the border area depending on the detrimental or beneficial effects.

Management Capability

The large-scale farmer has more ready access to information on new pest control technology and is better educated to understand its proper use, however, the small-scale farmer is likely to be receptive to new management ideas if they are practical and within his budget (Harwood, 1975). The large-scale farmer tends to make management decisions on a quantitative rather than qualitative basis. He is more concerned with the price of pesticides and fertilizers than with choosing methods of pest control. He has fewer options in pest management technology than the small-scale farmer.

Many traditional cropping patterns have built-in pest protection mechanisms and flexibility that lessen the gross effects of pest damage (Norton,

1976). By planting crops that can be harvested either green or mature, for example, corn and beans (*Phaseolus* sp.), the small-scale farmer can adjust to pest attack. In tropical countries the greens of many tuber and vegetable crops, for example, sweet potatoes [*Ipomoea batatas* (L.) Poir.] and squash (*Cucurbita* sp.) are also edible.

General Pest Management Strategy

Research on pest management in multiple cropping systems should take into consideration crop-crop interactions, be they intercrop, relay, or sequential, and the performance of individual crops. Extension of the cropping period is of great importance in multiple cropping. Research must be concerned with the entire cropping period. What happens to the first crop may affect succeeding crops. This might mean fostering entomorphagous insects or suppressing weeds from season to season. The task is to control pests remembering that they exist the year round. Pests perhaps can be suppressed by actions taken several generations or crops removed from the present crop.

What has emerged is a belief that there cannot be one type of pest control technology, such as pesticides, resistant varieties, biocontrol, or cultural control. This would be particularly true if several crops were grown in a year. Pesticides or resistant varieties alone result in spectacular benefits in the short run, but in the long run, they are likely to break down because the pests do not remain static. The build-up of tolerant weeds to unacceptable levels can rapidly occur with continued use of the same herbicide. Where several methods of pest control are used, crops continue to have protection; if one method fails, the others act as a buffer.

If there is a key factor in pest management in multiple cropping systems, it is diversity of control methods. But diversity per se is not to be encouraged, because some combinations of control methods exacerbate the problems. The combinations must be planned, and they must be applied at the right time. Smallman (1955) stated that the pest is constantly changing in response to selection pressures, and the more diverse the selection pressures (pesticides, resistant varieties, natural enemies, and cultural practices), the greater the resilience against pests. The validity of this approach has been well documented (Peterson, 1974).

Disciplines also need to be integrated (Farnworth & Golley, 1974). What is good for the entomologist may not be so for the agronomist or economist. Technology for multiple cropping by small-scale or large-scale farmers will be developed best by a close liason between the farmer and a multidisciplinary team of scientists at the local level. In the past, direct transfer of pest control technology from the developed to developing countries has involved mainly pesticides (Glass et al., 1971). Reliance on pesticides suits the resources of the large-scale farmer in temperate regions but not necessarily those of the small-scale farmer in the tropics.

LITERATURE CITED

A'Brook, J. 1968. The effect of plant spacing on the numbers of aphids trapped over the groundnut crop. Ann. Appl. Biol. 61:289-294.

Adams, M. W., A. H. Ellingboe, and E. C. Rossman. 1971. Biological uniformity and disease epidemics. BioScience 21(21):1067-1070.

Agricultural Board, National Research Council. 1968a. Principles of plant and animal pest control. Vol. 1: Plant-disease development and control. National Academy of Sciences, Washington, D. C. 205 p.

Agricultural Board, National Research Council. 1968b. Principles of plant and animal pest control. Vol. 2: Weed control. National Academy of Sciences, Washington, D. C. 476 p.

Agricultural Board, National Research Council. 1968c. Principles of plant and animal pest control. Vol. 4: Control of plant-parasitic nematodes. National Academy of Sciences, Washington, D. C. 166 p.

Agricultural Board, National Research Council. 1969. Principles of plant and animal pest control. Vol. 3: Insect-pest management and control. National Academy of Sciences, Washington, D. C. 508 p.

Aiyer, A. K. Y. N. 1949. Mixed cropping in India. Indian J. Agric. Sci. 19:439-543.

Anderson, W. K., and I. F. Whan. 1974. Multiple cropping in Australia. J. Aust. Inst. Agric. Sci. 40:29-35.

Baker, E. F. I., and D. W. Norman. 1975. Cropping systems in northern Nigeria. p. 334-361. In Proceedings of Cropping Systems Workshop, IRRI, Los Baños, Philippines. 396 p.

Bantilan, R. T., M. C. Palada, and R. R. Harwood. 1974. Integrated weed management. I. Key factors affecting crop and weed balance. Philippine Weed Sci. Bull. 1(2):14-36.

Barr, R. O., P. C. Cota, S. H. Gage, D. L. Haynes, A. N. Kharkar, H. E. Koenig, K. Y. Lee, W. O. Ruesink, and R. L. Tummala. 1973. Ecologically and economically compatible pest control. p. 241-264. In Insects: studies in population management. Ecological Society of Australia, Memoirs No. 1. Canberra. 295 p.

Batra, H. N. 1962. Mixed cropping and pest attack. Indian Farming 11(11):17-19, 25:11(12):23, 40.

Birchfield, W., and F. Bistline. 1956. Cover crops in relation to the burrowing nematode, Radopholus similis. Plant Dis. Rep. 40:398-399.

Brady, N. C. 1972. Challenge to public agencies. p. 362-373. In Pest control strategies for the future. National Academy of Sciences, Washington, D. C. 376 p.

Brodie, B. B., and W. S. Murphy. 1975. Population dynamics of plant nematodes as affected by combinations of fallow and cropping sequence. J. Nematology 7(1):91-92.

Browning, J. A., and K. J. Frey. 1969. Multiline cultivars as a means of disease control. Annu. Rev. Phytopathol. 7:355-382.

Buranday, R. P., and R. S. Raros. 1975. Effects of cabbage-tomato intercropping on the incidence and oviposition of the diamondback moth, Plutella xylostella (L.). Philippine Entomologist 2(5):369-374.

Chilvers, G. A., and E. G. Brittain. 1972. Plant competition mediated by host specific parasites—a simple model. Aust. J. Biol. Sci. 25(4):749-756.

Chohan, J. S. 1968. Disease problems in new cropping patterns and rotations in the erstwhile Punjab state. p. 562-564. In Proceedings of Symposium on Cropping Systems in India. Indian Council of Agricultural Research, New Delhi.

Cleave, J. H. 1974. African farmers: labor use in the development of small-holder agriculture. Prager, N. Y. 253 p.

Conway, G. R. 1973. Experience in insect pest modelling: a review of models, uses and future directions. p. 103-130. In Insects: studies in population management. Ecological Society of Australia, Memoirs No. 1. Canberra. 295 p.

Crosson, P. R. 1975. Institutional obstacles to expansion of world food production. Science 118:519-524.

De Bach, P. 1964. Biological control of insect pests and weeds. Reinhold, N. Y. 844 p.

De Datta, S. K., J. C. Moomaw, and R. T. Bantilan. 1969. Effects of varietal type, method of planting, and nitrogen level on competition between rice and weeds. Proceedings of Asian-Pacific Weed Control Interchange 2:152-163.

Dempster, J. P., and T. H. Coaker. 1974. Diversification of crop ecosystems as a means of controlling pests. p. 106-114. In D. P. Jones and M. E. Solomon (ed.) Biology in pest and disease control. 13th Symposium of British Ecological Society, Oxford. Blackwell, Oxford. 398 p.

Emden, H. F., van. 1965. The effect of uncultivated land on the distribution of cabbage aphid (Brevicoryne brassicae) on an adjacent crop. J. Appl. Ecol. 2(1):171-196.

Emden, H. F., van, and G. F. Williams. 1974. Insect stability and diversity of agroecosystems. Annu. Rev. Entomol. 19:455-475.

Erlich, P. R., R. R. White, M. C. Singer, S. W. McKechnie, and L. E. Gilbert. 1975. Checkerspot butterflies: a historical perspective. Science 188:221-228.

Farnworth, E. G., and F. B. Golley. 1974. Fragile ecosystems: evaluation of research and application in the neotropics. A report of the Institute of Ecology, Athens, Ga. Springer-Verlag, N. Y. 258 p.

Fye, R. E. 1972. The interchange of insect parasites and predators between crops. PANS 18(2):143-146.

Gibson, K. E., M. C. Lane, W. C. Cook, and E. W. Jones. 1958. Effect of some crop rotations on wireworm populations in irrigated lands. USDA Tech. Bull. 1172. 19 p.

Glass, E. H., R. J. Smith, Jr., J. I. Thomason, and H. D. Thurston. 1971. Plant protection problems in Asia. Report by the East Asian Pest Management Study Team. Cornell University, Ithaca, N. Y. 66 p.

Guneyli, E., O. C. Burnside, and P. T. Nordquist. 1969. Influence of seedling characteristics on weed competitive ability of sorghum hybrids and inbred lines. Crop Sci. 9: 713-716.

Hambleton, E. J. 1944. Heliothis virescens as a pest of cotton, with notes on host plants in Peru. J. Econ. Entomol. 37:660-666.

Harwood, R. R. 1974a. The resource utilization approach to cropping systems improvement. p. 249-260. In Proceedings of Farming Systems Workshop. ICRISAT, Hyderabad, India. 548 p.

Harwood, R. R. 1974b. Farmer-oriented research aimed at crop intensification. p. 12-32. In Proceedings of Cropping Systems Workshop. IRRI, Los Baños, Philippines. 396 p.

Harwood, R. R., and E. C. Price. 1976. Multiple cropping in tropical Asia. p. 11-40. In R. I. Papendick, P. A. Sanchez, and G. B. Triplett (ed.) Multiple cropping. Spec. Pub. No. 27. Am. Soc. of Agron., Madison, Wis.

Haswell, M. R. 1973. Tropical farming economics. Longman, London. 174 p.

Hopper, W. D. 1975. To conquer hunger: opportunity and potential will. John A. Hanna International Development Lecture Series, Michigan State University, East Lansing.

Huffaker, C. B. 1974. Some implications of plant-arthropod and higher level, arthropod-arthropod food links. Environ. Entomol. 3(1):1-9.

Indian Council of Agricultural Research. 1968. Pests and disease problems in new cropping patterns of Andra Pradesh. p. 557-559. In Proceedings of Symposium on Cropping Patterns in India. Indian Council of Agricultural Research, New Delhi.

International Rice Research Institute. 1973. IRRI annual report for 1972. Los Baños, Philippines. 246 p.

International Rice Research Institute. 1974. IRRI annual report for 1973. Los Baños, Philippines. 266 p.

Janzen, D. H. 1970. The unexploited tropics. Bull. Ecol. Soc. Am. 51(3):4-7.

Janzen, D. H. 1973. Tropical agroecosystems. Science 182:1212-1219.

Johnson, A. W., C. C. Dowler, and E. W. Hauser. 1975. Crop rotation and herbicide effects on population densities of plant parasitic nematodes. J. Nematol. 7(2):158-168.

Johnson, R., and D. J. Allen. 1975. Induced resistance to rust diseases and its possible role in the resistance of multiline varieties. Ann. Appl. Biol. 80(3):359-363.

Leonard, K. J. 1969. Factors affecting rates of stem rust increase in mixed plantings of susceptible and resistant oat varieties. Phytopathology 59(12):1845-1850.

Lewis, T. 1965. The effect of an artificial windbreak on the distribution of aphids in a lettuce crop. Ann. Appl. Biol. 55:513-518.

Lozano, J. C., and R. H. Booth. 1974. Diseases of cassava (*Manihot esculenta* Crantz.). PANS 20(1):30–54.

McNew, L. 1972. Concept of pest management. p. 119–133. *In* Pest control strategies for the future. National Academy of Sciences, Washington, D. C. 376 p.

Miracle, M. P. 1967. Agriculture in Congo basin. Univ. of Wisconsin Press, Madison. 355 p.

Moody, K. 1975. Weeds and shifting cultivation. PANS 21(2):188–194.

Moody, K., and W. K. Whitney. 1974. The effect of weeds on insect damage and developing cowpea and soybean seeds. p. 16–26. *In* Proceedings of Fourth Nigerian Weed Science Group Meeting. Univ. of Nigeria, Nsukka.

Musick, G. J., and H. B. Petty. 1973. Insect control in conservation tillage systems. p. 120–125. *In* Proceedings of Conservation Tillage Symposium. Soil Conserv. Soc. of Am., Ankeny, Iowa. 241 p.

Newsom, L. D. 1974. Pest management: history, current status and future progress. p. 1–18. *In* G. Maxwell and F. A. Harris (ed.) Proceedings of Summer Institute on Biological Control of Plant Insects and Diseases. Univ. Press of Mississippi, Jackson. 647 p.

Nickel, J. L. 1973. Pest situation in changing agricultural systems—a review. Bull. Entomol. Soc. Am. 19(3):136–142.

Norton, G. A. 1976. Multiple cropping and pest control: an economic perspective. Meded. Fac. Landbouwwet. Rijkuniv. Gent.

Nusbaum, C. J., and H. Ferris. 1973. The role of cropping systems in nematode population management. Annu. Rev. Phytopathol. 11:423–440.

Ou, S. H., and K. C. Ling. 1966. Virus disease of rice in the South Pacific. FAO Plant Prot. Bull. 14(5):113–121.

Paharia, K. D., and P. R. Mehta. 1970. Plant protection in the context of multiple cropping. p. 137–143. *In* Report of National Seminar on Multiple Cropping, New Delhi, Indian Council of Agricultural Research, New Delhi.

Paner, V. E., Jr. 1975. Multiple cropping researches in the Philippines. p. 188–202. *In* Proceedings of Cropping Systems Workshop. IRRI, Los Baños, Philippines. 396 p.

Pathak, M. D. 1968. Ecology of rice pests. Annu. Rev. Entomol. 13:257–294.

Pathak, M. D. 1970. Genetics of plants in pest management. p. 138–152. *In* R. L. Rabb, and F. E. Guthrie (ed.) Concepts of pest management. Proceedings of a conference held at North Carolina State Univ., Raleigh, March 24–27, 1970. 272 p.

Pearson, E. O. 1958. The insect pests of cotton in tropical Africa. Commonwealth Institute of Entomology, London. 355 p.

Peterson, G. D., Jr. 1974. Pest management: concepts, objectives and problems. Paper of the East-West Food Institute No. 2, East-West Center, Honolulu, Hawaii. 157 p.

Pimentel, D. 1961a. Species diversity and insect population outbreaks. Ann. Entomol. Soc. Am. 54:76–86.

Pimentel, D. 1961b. The influence of plant spatial patterns on insect populations. Ann. Entomol. Soc. Am. 54:61–69.

Plucknett, D. L., J. P. Evenson, and W. G. Sanford. 1970. Ratoon cropping. Adv. Agron. 22:285–330.

Pradan, S. 1968. New pest control patterns for new cropping patterns. p. 572–577. *In* Proceedings of Symposium on Cropping Patterns in India. Indian Council of Agricultural Research, New Delhi.

Rao, B. S. 1970. Pest problems of intercropping in plantations. p. 245–252. *In* E. K. and J. W. Blencowe (ed.) Crop diversification in Malaysia. Yau Seng Press, Kuala Lumpur. 300 p.

Raros, R. S. 1973. Crop protection with carbofuran and its effect on soil—and litter-associated mites and collembola. p. 12. *In* Proceedings of 5th National Pest Control Council Conference of the Philippines. Pest Control Council of the Philippines, Los Baños.

Rawat, R. R. 1968. Pest problems in cropping systems. p. 565–571. *In* Proceedings of Symposium on Cropping Patterns in India. Indian Council of Agricultural Research, New Delhi.

Rivnay, E. 1964. The influence of man on insect ecology in arid zones. Annu. Rev. Entomol. 9:41–62.

Rivnay, E. 1972. On irrigation—induced changes in insect populations in Israel. p. 349–367. *In* M. T. Farvar and J. P. Milton (ed.) The careless technology, Natural History Press, N. Y. 1030 p.

Salisbury, E. 1961. Weeds and aliens. Collins, London. 384 p.

Shafer, J. F. 1974. Host plant resistance to plant pathogens and insects: history, current status, and future outlook. p. 238–247. *In* F. G. Maxwell, and F. A. Harris (ed.) Proceedings of Summer Institute of Biological Control of Plant Insects and Diseases. Univ. Press of Mississippi, Jackson. 647 p.

Singh, S. 1968. Plant protection problems of cropping patterns. p. 153–161. *In* Proceedings of Symposium on Cropping Patterns in India. Indian Council of Agricultural Research, New Delhi.

Smallman, B. N. 1955. Integrated insect control. Aust. J. Sci. 28(6):23.

Smith, J. G. 1969. Some effects of crop background on populations of aphids and their natural enemies on brussels sprouts. Ann. Appl. Biol. 63:326–330.

Smith, R. F. 1972. The impact of the green revolution on plant protection in tropical and subtropical areas. Bull. Entomol. Soc. Am. 18(1):7–14.

Smith, R. F. 1973. Management of the environment and insect pest control. p. 3–17. *In* Proceedings of FAO Conference on Ecology in Relation to Plant Pest Control. FAO, Rome. 326 p.

Smith, R. F., and H. T. Reynolds. 1972. Effects of manipulation of cotton agro-ecosystems on insect pest populations. p. 373–406. *In* M. T. Farvar and J. P. Milton (ed.) The careless technology. Natural History Press, N. Y. 1030 p.

Smith, R. J., Jr. 1974. Competition of barnyard grass with rice cultivars. Weed Sci. 22:423–426.

Southwood, T. R. E., and M. J. Way. 1970. Ecological background to pest management. p. 6–29. *In* R. L. and R. E. Guthrie (ed.) Concepts of pest management. Proceedings of a conference held at North Carolina State University, Raleigh, March 25–27, 1970. 272 p.

Stern, V. M. 1969. Interplanting alfalfa on cotton to control lygus bugs and other insect pests. p. 55–69. *In* Proceedings of Tall Timbers Conference on Ecological Animal Control by Habitat Management. No. 1. Tall Timbers Research Station, Tallahassee, Fla.

Summerfield, R. J., P. A. Huxley, and W. Steele. 1974. Cowpea (*Vigna unguiculata* (L.) Walp.). Field Crop Abstr. 27:301–312.

Suneson, C. A. 1960. Genetic diversity—a protection against diseases and insects. Agron. J. 52:319–321.

Tahvanainen, J. O., and R. B. Root. 1972. The influence of vegetational diversity of the population ecology of a specialized herbivore *Phyllotreta cruciferae* (Coleoptera: Chrysomelidae). Oecolgia (Berlin). 10:321–346.

Trenbath, B. R. 1974. Biomass productivity of mixtures. Adv. Agron. 26:177–210.

Turnipseed, S. G. 1973. Insects. *In* B. E. Coldwell (ed.) Soybeans: improvement, production, and uses. Agronomy 16:545–572. Am. Soc. of Agron., Madison, Wis.

Visser, T., and M. K. Vythilingham. 1959. The effect of marigolds and some other crops on the *Prathylenchus, Meliodogyne* populations in the soil. Tea Q. 30:30–38.

Wallace, H. R. 1963. Control. p. 231–266. *In* The biology of plant parasitic nematodes. Edward Arnold Ltd., London.

Watt, E. F. 1970. The systems point of view in pest management. p. 71–83. *In* R. L. Rabb, and F. E. Guthrie (ed.) Concepts of pest management. Proceedings of a conference held at North Carolina State University, Raleigh, March 25–27, 1970. 272 p.

Way, M. J., and G. D. Heathcote. 1966. Interactions of crop density of field beans, abundance of *Aphis fabae* Scop. virus incidence and aphid control of chemicals. Ann. Appl. Biol. 57:409–423.

Wellman, F. L. 1968. More diseases on crops in the tropics than in the temperate zones. CEIBA 1:17–28.

Whitten, M. J. 1970. Genetics of pests in their management. p. 119–137. *In* R. L. Rabb, and F. E. Guthrie (ed.) Concepts of pest management. Proceedings of a conference held at North Carolina State University, Raleigh, March 25–27, 1970. 272 p.

Wilson, E. E., and G. A. Baker. 1946. Some features of the spread of plant diseases by air-borne and insect-borne inoculum. Phytopathology 36:418–432.

Wycherley, P. R. 1970. Discussions on weed control. p. 235–236. *In* E. K. and J. W. Blencowe (ed.) Crop diversification in Malaysia. Yau Seng Press, Kuala Lumpur. 300 p.

Water and Wind Erosion Control Aspects of Multiple Cropping[1]

F. H. Siddoway and A. P. Barnett[2]

The ever increasing need for food will require bringing more land into crop production and more intensified farming of present cropland. Both can contribute to increased water and wind erosion. However, cropping management options embodied in multiple cropping concepts can enhance soil protection through increased vegetative cover during critical erosion periods as compared with conventional cropping systems.

This paper discusses the impact of selected multiple cropping systems and management methods within the systems for controlling erosion. Vegetative cover is the most important factor in erosion control and is intimately related to cropping systems. Although the methods and practices used for wind and water erosion control are by no means mutually exclusive, they will be discussed separately. With few exceptions, practices applied for the control of one form of erosion aid in controlling the other.

WATER EROSION

The world's crop and pasturelands cover some 6 billion hectares and nearly all of it needs some degree of protection from soil erosion by water (Stout, 1965). Particularly serious problems exist in most of Africa, certain areas of South America, Central America, the Philippines, India, China, the Near East countries, and the U. S. Overuse of land, loss of cover from peri-

[1] Contribution from Northern Plains Soil and Water Research Center, Western Region, USDA-ARS, Sidney, Montana; and Southern Piedmont Conservation Research Center, Southern Region, USDA-ARS, Watkinsville, Georgia; in cooperation with Montana Agric. Exp. Stn., Montana State Univ. and Univ. of Georgia Agric. Exp. Stn., respectively. Montana State Univ. Journal Number 668.
[2] Supervisory soil scientist, USDA, Sidney, Montana and agricultural engineer, USDA, Watkinsville, Georgia.

odic droughts, and the lack of capitol to apply conservation measures have contributed to the problem. In the U. S., approximately 7 metric tons/ha per year of soil are removed from the 400 million hectares of field and pasturelands (Schwab et al., 1966). These losses vary from 4 to 225 metric tons/ha per year from open-tilled crops to less than 2 metric tons/ha per year from well-established pastures (Kohnke & Bertrand, 1959). A more recent report showed that 35 million hectares of U. S. cropland were averaging more than 17 metric tons/ha per year; 53 million hectares, less than 7 metric tons/ha per year; and 88 million hectares, between 7 and 17 metric tons/ha per year (USDA, 1967).

Water erosion is a major force sculpturing the face of the earth (Leopold et al., 1964) and the process is normally accelerated by cultivation. The two principle eroding agents are raindrop impact which detaches soil particles and overland flow which transports the particles away from the source (Smith & Wischmeier, 1957).

Over 40 years of research by the U. S. Department of Agriculture in cooperation with the state agricultural experiment stations has identified the major erosion factors and determined the major numerical relationships of these factors to soil loss rate in the Universal Soil Loss Equation (USDA, 1975; Wischmeier & Smith, 1965). This equation is:

$$A = RKLSCP$$

where A is the estimated average annual soil loss in metric tons per hectare. R is a rainfall factor which reflects the combined potential of raindrop impact and turbulence of runoff to transport dislodged particles from a field. It is directly proportional to total kinetic energy of a storm times its maximum 30-minute rainfall intensity (Wischmeier & Smith, 1958) and varies from about 20 to over 350 in the conterminous U. S. K is an inherent soil-erodibility factor determined experimentally and related to soil texture, structure, organic matter, and permeability and ranges from about 0.02 to 0.60. LS is a topographic factor that combines the effects of slope length and steepness. The factor varies from 0.07 for an 8-m, 0.5% slope to 31.0 for a 180-m, 40% slope. C is a cover management factor ranging in value from 0.001 for a well-managed woodland to 1.0 for tilled, continuous fallow. P is for supporting erosion control practices which reduces the fractional erodibility from 1 in the absence of practices to about 0.2 depending upon land slope and the specific practices of contouring, contour strip cropping and the type of crops, contour listing, and contour terracing. The factors R, K, and LS are the climatic, soil, and topographic resource factors that the farm manager works with, and the C and P factors the erosion control management options at his disposal. Within the framework of multiple cropping, many effective options are available as will be discussed.

The objectives of water erosion control systems are to: (i) mitigate the effects of raindrop impact and (ii) reduce the erosive capacity of overland flow. The first objective is achieved by providing cover to protect the land from raindrop impact and the second by slowing the rate of runoff by soil surface roughness and vegetative cover, reducing grades and length of travel, and conveying runoff to noneroding waterways. Methods for achieving water erosion control include land-forming measures, cropping systems, and long-term soil structure benefits accrued from continued use of conservation methods. Systems of furrows, terraces, and diversion ditches are used on cultivated areas to deliver excess water to protected waterways.

Regardless of the system of terraces or other topographic modifications applied in controlling water erosion, the overriding principle of control is the duration and intensity of vegetative cover. This principle applies whether farming is on the extensive mechanized scale of the western world or on a subsistance, small-land-parcel scale of the developing nations.

Work from southern Rhodesia illustrates the effective protection afforded by complete cover (Hudson, 1957; Hudson & Jackson, 1962). Over a 6-year period, unprotected bare soil on a 4.5%, 27-m long slope, lost soil at the rate of 180 metric tons/ha per year while an identical adjacent plot protected by screen wire (mosquito gauze) suspended 15 cm above the surface eroded at less than 2 metric tons/ha per year. Without the particle detachment and surface puddling of raindrop impact, infiltration remained high and overland flow was minimized. Similarly, an evaluation of range cover in Texas and Oklahoma showed that for 90% effectiveness, 2,800 kg of close-growing crops per ha or 4,500 kg of tall, coarse crops per ha were required for adequate protection (Stallings, 1953). For 85% effectiveness, 1,100 kg of either close-growing or tall crops were equal. Effectiveness is referenced to 100% for zero erosion. A straw mulch applied immediately after cultivation at 4.5 metric tons/ha on Houston clay effectively controlled both runoff and erosion (Woodburn, 1944). During a 6-month period, erosion from the straw mulch was only 0.2 metric ton/ha and runoff 6% of the precipitation. Losses from plots without straw mulch were 47 metric tons/ha and runoff 44%.

As far back as the early 1930's (USDA, 1940), data from Statesville, North Carolina and Temple and Tyler, Texas, on three distinct soil types, illustrate the effectiveness of multiple cropping in controlling runoff and erosion by interposing a close-growing crop in sequence with row crops. For example, erosion losses in metric tons/ha per year from the Tyler study for the following treatments were: fallow, 140; monoculture cotton (*Gossypium* sp.), 50; a 2-year rotation of corn (*Zea mays* L.) with cover crops, 25; a rotation of corn, cotton, wheat (*Triticum aestivum* L.) and 2 years of lespedeza [*Lespedeza cuneata* (Dumont) G. Don], 20; grass, 0.02; and virgin woods, 0.004 metric tons/ha per year. In the relatively short production period of 43 years, monoculture cottonland would have lost 15 cm of topsoil. Although erosion control was not considered adequate at Statesville and Tyler on moderately steep slopes, the trend in cropping systems that followed for a number of years was winter cover crops and summer legumes in sequence with row crops for moderately steep land. While on the land the nonrow crops provided cover and increased organic matter and improved tilth for further protection of the subsequent row crop.

Table 1. Average annual runoff and erosion from 3% and 7% slopes cropped to a 2-year rotation of row crops with cover crops and to monoculture cotton, 1944–52 (Hendrickson et al., 1963)

Cropping	Class II land 3% slope, length 32 m		Class III land 7% slope, length 21 m	
	Runoff*	Erosion	Runoff*	Erosion
	cm	metric tons/ha	cm	metric tons/ha
Monoculture cotton	23	10.0	31	46.8
2-year rotation:				
Cotton-vetch	16	5.7	24	20.2
Corn-crotalaria	12	6.3	21	15.1
Rotation Average	14	6.0	22	17.6

* Annual rainfall averaged 126 cm.

Much of the erosion research during the 1940's and 50's and into the 60's was devoted to testing cropping systems based on row crops, relay-cropping, or double cropping with small grains and legumes in which only the row crop was harvested, and rotations of row crops 1 year and legumes or grasses for 1, 2, or more years before planting another row crop.

At Watkinsville, Georgia (Hendrickson et al., 1963), cotton-vetch (*Vicia* sp.) and corn-Crotalaria (*Crotalaria spectabilis*) were grown in a 2-year sequential row cover-crop rotation (Table 1). Erosion control was adequate[3] on Class II land, 6.0 metric tons/ha per year, but inadequate on Class III land which lost 17.6 metric tons/ha per year, indicating the need for improved management on the steeper land. In comparison, monoculture cottonland lost 46.8 metric tons/ha per year from Class III land.

From a 3-year cropping system of oats (*Avena sativa* L.)-Kobe lespedeza [*Lespedeza striata* (Thunb.) Hoak. & Am.], volunteer lespedeza, and cotton; runoff of only 14.5 cm/year and erosion of 7.2 metric tons/ha per year occurred on Class III land compared with 3.3 cm/year and 60.3 metric tons/ha per year erosion for monoculture cotton (Hendrickson et al., 1963). On steeper Class IV land, a 3-year cropping system of oats-kudzu [*Pueraria lobata* (Willd.) Ohwi], kudzu, and corn-kudzu provided excellent protection with only 7.3 cm/year of runoff and 1.2 metric tons/ha per year of erosion. Although this kudzu system provided excellent conservation, management was difficult. After 5 years, the kudzu began to thin out indicating that 2 years was not enough time for kudzu to recover from complete conventional tillage every third year.

Following the introduction of 'Coastal' bermudagrass (*Cynodon dactylon*) and tall fescue (*Festuca arundinacea* Schreb.) into the southeastern U. S. and combined with the availability of cheap fertilizer, grass sods in rota-

---

[3]Adequate refers to average annual erosion losses of 6.7 metric ton/ha. Acceptable erosion limits, ranging from 4.5 to 11.2 metric ton/ha per year, have been established by the Soil Conservation Service for different soils and conditions. Acceptable erosion limits are for the general case. For extremely shallow soils over slowly weatherable parent material, the limits may approach zero.

Table 2. Three-year cropping systems at Watkinsville, Georgia, with Coastal bermudagrass
or fescue and corn on 7% slope Cecil soil with a slope length of 21 m, conventional
contour tillage, 1961–67 (J. R. Carreker, unpublished data)

Crops	Runoff*	Erosion
	cm	metric tons/ha
Monoculture corn	17.8	27.1
First Coastal recovery after corn	5.7	5.1
Second Coastal	7.0	0.4
Corn	7.6	2.4
Rotation Average	6.8	2.6
Oats and first fescue after corn	13.8	2.0
Second fescue	7.1	0.2
Corn	11.6	4.4
Rotation Average	10.8	2.2

* 141.6 cm rainfall.

tion systems became practical. A typical 3-year rotation was 2 years of grass
for hay production followed by a year of row crop (Table 2) (J. R. Carreker,
personal communication). Compared with monoculture corn, Coastal
bermudagrass in rotation reduced erosion from cornland 11-fold and runoff
2-fold; oats-fescue and fescue in rotation reduced erosion from cornland 6-
fold and runoff 1.5-fold. Because of their extensive root systems and resistance to decomposition, these grasses are ideally suited for use on steeper
lands where it is economically necessary to grow row crops occasionally or
where row crops are used in conjunction with sod renovation.

One benefit of good management that is sometimes overlooked has been
termed "progressive conservation" (Hendrickson et al., 1963). Runoff and
erosion progressively decreased as the conservation practice continued with
time. Continuation of a 3-year rotation of oats-Kobe lespedeza, volunteer
lespedeza, and cotton reduced runoff and erosion during the years cotton was
on the land to 30 and 20%, respectively, below that of monoculture cotton
grown on similar Class III land (Fig. 1). The major reductions came during
the first two cycles of the rotation but benefits accrued with longevity.

Relay intercropping was one of several cropping patterns developed in
the mid-1940's at Watkinsville, Georgia. Small grain was intercropped by
drilling in cotton middles in mid-September before cotton harvest (Carreker,
1947). Table 3 shows results using this system of intercropping (Hendrickson et al., 1963). Each crop in the rotation reduced runoff and erosion when
it occupied the land as compared with monoculture cotton for the same
period. Over a 6-year period in Wisconsin, interplanting of alfalfa (*Medicago
sativa* L.) within 1.5-m corn rows lost only one-half as much soil as corn
planted alone in 1-m rows (Hays, 1961). When compared on a rotation basis,
the rotation corn, hay, and hay (corn interplanted) allowed only one-fourth
as much soil loss and one-third as much runoff as a corn, oats, and hay rotation.

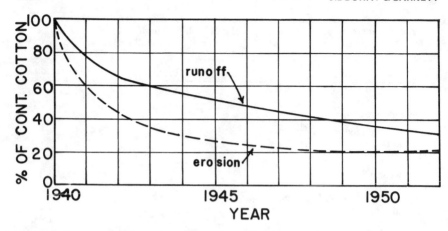

Figure 1. Progressive effect of erosion and runoff reduction of a 3-year rotation of oats-Kobe lespedeza, volunteer lespedeza, and cotton relative to monoculture cotton on Class III land (Hendrickson et al., 1963).

Many researchers (Carreker et al., 1972; Lewis, 1972; Triplett et al., 1972; Triplett et al., 1971; S. R. Wilkinson and G. A. Hillsman, 1968. Wheat seeded for grain or silage in bermudagrass sods. Agron. Abstra. 68:52) have studied various aspects of relay intercropping and double cropping, but few have related runoff and erosion control to these systems. Studies from Illinois (G. E. McKibben, personal communication) showed that no-tilled double cropping reduced soil losses by 93 and 80% on slopes of 9 and 5%, respectively, relative to conventionally-tilled, double cropping systems (Table 4). The introduction of no-till can significantly reduce erosion risks associated with double cropping relative to the conventional case where the land is exposed to rainfall during the seedbed-preparation and plant-establishment periods.

Table 3. Average runoff and soil losses by cropping periods from each of the crops in a 3-year rotation of oats relay-intercropped in cotton and Kobe lespedeza, volunteer lespedeza, and cotton compared with similar losses from monoculture cotton during the different periods when the crops in the rotation were on the land. Class III land; 7% slope (Hendrickson et al., 1963)

Rotation crop	Period	Months	Rainfall	Runoff Continuous cotton	Runoff Rotation crop	Soil loss Continuous cotton	Soil loss Rotation crop
	months	no.	cm	cm	cm	metric tons/ha	metric tons/ha
Oats Sown	Oct–May	8	92.1	19.3	13.2	26.5	6.9
lespedeza Volunteer	Jun–Mar	10	112.9	27.3	12.6	49.7	2.9
lespedeza	Apr–Feb	11	111.2	25.1	5.2	49.7	0.3
Cotton	Mar–Sept	7	82.4	16.9	11.0	46.3	13.3

Table 4. Double cropping soil and water losses in corn, wheat, and soybean cropping systems (G. E. McKibben, unpublished data)

Year	Crop	Conventional tillage Slope %		No-tillage Slope %	
		9	5	9	5
		Soil loss—metric tons/ha			
1969	Wheat after beans	25.9	5.4	2.6	1.8
1969	Corn after wheat	5.0	0.4	0.1	0.1
1970	Wheat after corn	13.8	4.7	0.5	0.4
1970	Corn after wheat	1.7	1.2	0.1	T
2-year average		23.2	5.9	1.7	1.2
		Runoff—%			
1969	Wheat after beans	38.0	17.1	38.0	26.9
1969	Corn after wheat	10.4	3.5	16.7	10.2
1970	Wheat after corn	40.4	23.4	29.2	24.2
1970	Corn after wheat	6.2	10.0	7.5	1.0
2-year average		23.8	13.2	22.8	15.6

A computation of the cropping and management factor C used in the Universal Soil Loss Equation (Wischmeier & Smith, 1965) was made to compare estimated soil loss combinations of no-till and conventional-till double cropped and 2-year crop rotations of wheat and soybeans [*Glycine max* (L.) Merr.] in southern Illinois (Hayes, 1973). Relative erodibilities for the systems were as follows: 2-year rotation, conventional-till, 100%; double cropped, conventional-till, 119%; 2-year rotation, no-till, 49%; and double cropped, no-till, 57%. The major reductions resulted from the introduction of no-till into both cropping systems. Similarly, in northern Mississippi, 3 years of conventionally-tilled continuous soybeans averaged 17.5 metric tons/ha per year soil loss compared with 2.5 metric tons/ha per year for no-till continuous soybeans and 1.8 metric tons/ha per year for no-till soybeans-wheat (McGregor et al., 1975). Differences among four no-till cropping systems studied were nonsignificant.

Data from Nigeria (Greenland, 1975) illustrate that erosion is minimized where no-till or minimum tillage is used with the maintenance of crop and weed mulches (Table 5). A further factor cited for reducing the erosion hazard was the use of mixed and relay-cropping techniques to keep a plant cover for most or all of the year, especially when combined with no-till methods.

The significance of cover and management, factor C in the Universal Soil Loss Equation (Wischmeier & Smith, 1965), within cropping systems is illustrated in Table 6 (USDA, 1975). Erosion is directly proportional to the C value when all independent factors (R, K, LS, and P) are held constant. The management program followed in the production of any of the crops has a great effect on erosion, perhaps more so than cropping systems per se.

Table 5. No-tillage effects on soil and water loss under maize [IITA, Ibadan (first season, 1973; rainfall, 780 mm; plots 25 × 4 m)] (R. Lal, IITA, unpublished data)

Slope	Soil loss		Runoff	
	No tillage	Plowed	No tillage	Plowed
%	——— metric ton/ha ———		——— mm ———	
1	0.03	1.2	11.4	55.0
10	0.08	4.4	20.3	52.4
15	0.14	23.6	21.0	89.9

Table 6. Generalized values of the cover and management factor, C, for a high level of productivity in the 37 states east of the Rocky Mountains (USDA, 1975)

Crop, rotation, and management†	C value
Base value: continuous fallow, tilled up and down slope	1.00
Corn	
1　　C, RdR, fall TP, conv (1)	0.54
2　　C, RdR, wc seeding, spring TP, conv (1)	0.40
3　　C (silage), W wc seeding, no-till pl in c–k W (1)	0.20
4　　C–C–C–W–M, RdL, no-till pl 2d & 3rd C (5)	0.076
5　　C, no-till pl in c–k wheat, 90% rc (1)	0.062
6　　C, no-till pl in c–k sod, 95% rc (1)	0.017
Meadow	
7　　Grass & Legume mix	0.004
Sorghum, Grain (Western Plains)	
8　　RdL, spring TP, conv (1)	0.43
9　　No-till pl in shredded 70% rc	0.11
Soybeans	
10　　B, RdL, spring TP, conv (1)	0.48
11　　B, no-till pl	0.22
Wheat	
12　　W–F, fall TP after W (2)	0.38
13　　Winter W, RdL, Aug TP, conv (Kans) (1)	0.19
14　　W–M, conv (2)	0.054

* Numbers in parentheses indicate number of years in the rotation cycle. No. (1) designates a continuous one-crop system.
† Abbreviations defined:

B　　-soybeans
C　　-corn　　　　　　　　　　　　　　　M -grass & legume hay
c–k　-chemical killed　　　　　　　　　　pl -plant
conv -conventional　　　　　　　　　　　W -wheat
F　　-fallow　　　　　　　　　　　　　　wc-winter cover
% rc -percent of soil surface covered by residue mulch after new crop seeding
RdR -residues (corn stover, straw, etc.) removed or burned
RdL -all residues left on field (on surface or incorporated)
TP　-turn plowed (upper 5 or more inches of soil inverted, covering residues)

WIND EROSION

Although considered most serious on agricultural lands of arid and semi-arid climates, wind erosion can occur whenever soil, vegetation, and climatic conditions are conducive. For example, damage to vegetable crops is often experienced in sandy-soil areas of the U. S. where rainfall exceeds 76 cm/year. Certain organic soils require special attention because of their inherent erodibility even though rainfall is adequate for crop production.

The most wide-spread erosion occurs where precipitation is inadequate or highly variable and vegetative cover must be continuously maintained. Agricultural areas most susceptible to wind erosion are North Africa and the Near East, parts of southern and eastern Asia, Australia, southern South America, arid and semiarid North America, and extensive areas in the USSR (FAO, 1960). Recurring moisture deficiency which limits crop-growth, moderate to strong winds when crops are absent or in early growth stages, and soils which contain appreciable sand-sized fractions are all common attributes of these areas. The 15 million hectares of fallow areas (Haas et al., 1974) in the Great Plains and western U. S. is the country's primary wind erosion problem (Fig. 2). Damage results from dry winter and early spring seasons which coincide with high winds and sparse vegetative cover (USDA, unpublished report). Although progress has been made in applying erosion control practices since the severe erosion of the 1930's (Chepil et al., 1963), the recurrence of drought in the mid-1950's, 1971, and early 1975 point out the vulnerability of contemporary dryland farming to climatic extremes. Wind erosion in the productive cornbelt states has accelerated in recent years (USDA, unpublished report) because of: (i) increased hectarage of row crops (namely soybeans); (ii) fall plowing of soybean land in preparation of next year's corn crop; (iii) decreased hectarage of meadowland; and (iv) increased field size to accomodate large mechanized equipment and in some localities, sprinkler irrigation systems. Even the humid South, where sandy soils of the Coastal Plains require special treatment for control, is susceptible (Carreker,

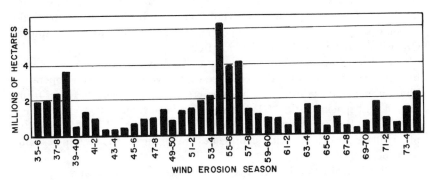

Figure 2. Hectares of land damaged annually by wind erosion in the Great Plains for seasons 1935–36 through 1974–75 (Soil Conservation Service, USDA, unpublished report).

1966). Many row crops and especially vegetables in the seedling stage are sensitive to wind erosion damage and require stringent control measures (Fryrear et al., 1975; Hayes, 1966; Cary et al., 1975).

While irrigation has improved the wind erosion situation in the Texas High Plains and other areas that were formerly dryland cropped under a crop-fallow system, thereby permitting longer cropland occupancy and higher production of crop residues, there are other instances where irrigation has definitely contributed to the problem. A large proportion of land broken out for irrigation development in the west was rangeland which was either too coarse-textured or the climate too arid for dry farming, and wind erosion, especially under low residue-row crop culture has been a problem. For example, one-half to two-thirds of the 243,000 ha scheduled for irrigation in the Columbia Basin Project in northwestern U. S. had soils susceptible to severe wind erosion (Mech, 1955). There are currently about 1 million hectares of sandy, irrigated land in the Columbia Basin that pose a major wind erosion problem (R. R. Allmaras, personal communication).

The primary factors that affect wind erosion and the methods applied for control can be examined within the framework of a wind erosion equation (Woodruff & Siddoway, 1965): $E = f(I, K, C, L, V)$, where E is potential average annual soil loss; I, soil and knoll erodibility; K, soil roughness; C, a climatic index based on wind speed and surface soil moisture; L, field size; and V, equivalent quantity of vegetation which takes into account kind and orientation of plant material.

The soil factor, I, is an inherent property that integrates all the variables of a soil's capacity to form clods greater than a minimum diameter that resists movement by wind. The dominant property is soil texture which has been used as an index to delineate wind erodibility groups (Hayes, 1972). Sandy soils because of their fragile dry aggregate structure and the clays because of their tendency to granulate under weathering are the most erodible and require careful management.

Direct soil tillage treatments are employed to create clods and increase surface roughness, K, (Anderson, 1966; Woodruff & Chepil, 1956; Woodruff et al., 1957). Deep plowing of sandy lands to bring finer-textured, clod-forming soil to the surface has been employed in the central and southern Great Plains (Chepil & Moldenhauer, 1962).

Soil roughness, K, other than that created by clods, can be manipulated by tillage or is a natural consequence of cultivation or seeding operations. Wind tunnel studies show that the most effective roughness for ridges formed on a height-spacing ratio of 1:4, ranged between 5 and 10 cm (Armbrust et al., 1964). Roughness magnitudes of this level can be achieved by most pre-plant tillage and can provide significant control during the seedling-establishment period.

The annual climatic factor, C, (Chepil et al., 1962) was developed from the relationship stating that rate of soil movement varies directly as the cube of wind velocity, V, (Bagnold, 1941) and inversely as the square of effective moisture (Chepil, 1956), which is assumed to be proportional to Thornthwaites P-E ratio. The factor ranges from about 5 to 150 from humid to arid climates.

Rate of soil movement by wind increases with distance leeward of the windward edge of a field until, if the field is large enough, the rate reaches a maximum that a given wind can carry (Chepil, 1957). The distance downwind where the maximum rate of flow is reached is a function of textural class (Fig. 3). The sheltered distance, L, in the equation is the distance along the prevailing wind erosion direction minus the distance (10 × barrier height) sheltered. Design criteria for shelterbelts and strip cropping patterns and orientations has been established to reduce field size for erosion control (Chepil, 1957; Skidmore, 1965).

Although wind erosion control practices of inducing soil cloddiness and roughening the soil by tillage, ameliorating aridity by irrigation, and reducing field size are all important, vegetative cover is the most important factor and the most relevant to the concept of all cropping systems, including multiple cropping. The variable, V, in the wind erosion equation (Skidmore & Woodruff, 1968) combines the primary variables: quantity, kind, and orientation of vegetative cover. Obviously, the wind erodibility of a field decreases with quantity of vegetation cover. For a given weight of cover, the more finely textured the material and the more uniform the distribution, the more effective is the control. Up to the quantity that completely covers the soil surface, vegetation that is oriented between horizontal and vertical is more ef-

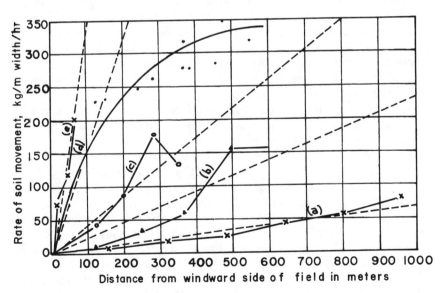

Figure 3. Rate of soil movement across wind-eroded fields: (a) silty clay loam of below-average erodibility for this soil class, (b) and (c) silt loam of below-average and average erodibility for this soil class, and (d) and (e) loamy sand of below average and near-average erodibility for this soil class. Straight, dashed lines indicate the approximate average rate of increase in soil flow with distance across the actual or extended fields (Chepil, 1957).

fective than flattened vegetation. In terms of erosion control, 560 kg/ha of growing small grain in 30-cm rows, 500 kg/ha of standing small grain stubble, 1,000 kg/ha of flattened small grain stubble, 2,000 kg/ha of standing sorghum (*Sorghum* sp.) stubble, and 2,900 kg/ha of flattened sorghum stubble are all equal in reducing erosion to a tolerable quantity for silt soils (Woodruff et al., 1972). Rows perpendicular to wind direction control wind erosion more effectively than rows parallel to wind direction (Siddoway, 1965; Skidmore et al., 1966).

Historically, the greatest advance in wind erosion control relative to the management of vegetative cover has been the application of stubble mulch on the extensive hectarage of summer-fallowed land. A shift from the moldboard plow to sweep, chisel, and rod implements provided a degree of protection over the fallow period. Cover cropping, a mild form of increased cropping intensity, has met with little success on semiarid drylands because soil water used by the cover crop was often at the expense of the subsequent cash crop. Tree shelterbelts may be considered a form of vegetation control but, with the exception of North Dakota, their broadscale application over extensive wind erosion problem areas has been minimal. A definite advantage of shelterbelts is the protection extended throughout the entire year in contrast to most vegetative control systems which are transitory.

The concept of multiple cropping systems is herein broadly interpreted in relation to wind erosion to include any intensification of traditional sole-crop systems. The intensification may or may not involve the growing of additional crops for direct production purposes but may involve additional crops for the express purpose of controlling wind erosion. Conversely, there is a potential for wind erosion control incidental to some forms of multiple cropping designed for the single purpose of increasing production. The incidental benefits could accrue from a longer period of crop occupancy on the land and the increased production of crop residues.

In moisture-deficient areas, even though the growing season is adequate, the opportunities for multiple cropping are limited. There are, however, several control techniques involving cropping that have been used and which involve principles of both increased cover and reduced field size.

North Dakota, because of the traditional system of summer fallow cropping and a high percentage of the state under cultivation, experiences wind erosion on summer fallow during the high wind intensity winter and spring seasons. One approach to control wind erosion and hold drifting snow on unprotected fallow has been to strip plant double rows of corn (Geiszler, 1961) and more recently double rows of sunflower (*Helianthus annus* L.) at intervals of 21, 11, and 5 m apart in late May or early June (Hoag & Geiszler, 1971). The crops are harvested the fall of the fallow year to leave tall stalks for winter protection. Durum spring wheat (*Triticum durum* Desf.) was seeded the following spring. The authors concluded after 3-years experience with this system that double rows of sunflower controlled wind erosion and also increased net returns by 20% over straight summer fallow cropping with spring wheat. Various other crops, notably flax (*Linum usitatissiumum* L.) and mustard (*Brassica* sp.), are row planted in late summer (Dodds, 1972) in strip intervals across summer fallow to control erosion. This strategy of controlling wind erosion applies the principle of using an additional crop in the cropping sequence to reduce field size. Strip planting of this nature has the advantage over solid cover cropping in semiarid areas, of not depleting nutrients and soil water over the entire field at the expense of the primary crop grown the following year.

Another strategy in the semiarid Great Plains uses level-bench terraces to impound snowfall or intense rainfall to increase storage of soil water to produce a crop more often than every other year (Wittmuss, 1968). Although designed primarily for water conservation, water and wind erosion are controlled because a forage or cereal crop occupy the land continuously. In North Dakota, alfalfa yielded 8,500 kg/ha per year on level benches compared to 3,400 kg/ha per year on natural topography. The improved water conservation attributed to the system was also adequate for annual cropping of small grains (Haas & Willis, 1971).

Research in the dryland area of Montana, with a tall wheatgrass (*Agropyron elongatum*) barrier system and cropping more often than every other year, has demonstrated a potential of practically eliminating wind erosion, even on sandy lands (Black & Siddoway, 1975). The double-row barriers which reach a mature height of about 120 cm on dryland are spaced about 15 m apart at approximately normal to prevailing winds. The height-spacing ratio of 1 to 12 followed established design procedure for wind erosion control and snow deposition to recharge soil water over the winter period. Over a 7-year period, trapped snow has recharged the soil profile over the first winter (9 months) to the same extent as 21 months of summer fallow. The increased soil water storage efficiency has supplied sufficient water for annual rather than biennial cropping. The perennial barriers provide year-round protection that is especially critical during the crop-establishment period by reducing wind speed over the land surface of the crop interval by about 50%. The system combines control measures implicit in size of field, L, and vegetative cover protection, V. Another approach being studied (R. R. Allmaras, P. L. Brown, and A. L. Black, personal communications) on drylands utilizes the no-till concept of seeding a small grain crop directly into stubble thereby eliminating the vulnerable summer fallow period and fully utilizing crop residues during the critical crop establishment period.

The cotton producing area of western Texas embodies a large hectarage of coarse-textured soils where wind erosion is a constant hazard because residues are meager and strong spring winds make establishment a problem. Various intercropping schemes with combinations of cotton rows and rows of a protective crop have been wind tunnel evaluated with results shown in Figure 4 (Fryrear, 1969). Blank rows (referenced to 1-m spacing) can be cotton stubble during the off-growing season with cropping rows as sorghum residue. A common implementation of this practice involves two 1-m rows of spring planted cotton, a blank row, and two rows of late-June planted sorghum, a blank row, and a repeat of this sequence (a 2 × 4 system). The

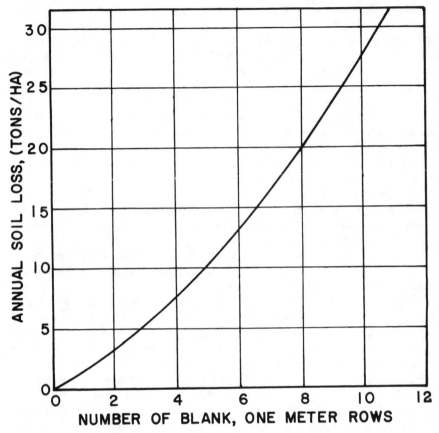

Figure 4. Relation between the number of blank rows (fallow or cotton) and the annual soil loss (Fryrear, 1969).

sorghum protects the soil during winter and spring. Provided two rows are protectively vegetated out of a total of six, erosion can be kept within a tolerance level of 11.2 metric tons/ha per year.

Another cropping strategem suggested for this extensive, erodible area (D. W. Fryrear, personal communication) is to grow a crop whenever time and soil water are adequate. For example, after wheat harvest, if moisture is favorable for seeding, cotton or soybeans could be no-till seeded in the stubble. This double cropping approach has been termed "opportunity cropping" (Anderson & Whan, 1974) in Australia. The system, as used there, involves either a winter or summer crop in lieu of summer fallow whenever sufficient rain falls for autumn seeding.

A similar system has been under study in the dryland cropping area of Alberta, Canada (D. T. Anderson, personal communication). Of eight rotations or cropping stratagems under study since 1951, the highest production, in terms of total digestible nutrients, resulted from spring wheat recropping contingent upon moist soil to a depth of 70 cm at seeding time. Only in 2 years since 1951 was the soil too dry to seed using this criterion. Using this system, the soil would be continuously protected against wind erosion, except for the occasional fallow, provided that seedbed preparation utilized residues on the surface. In worldwide cultivated drylands, this stratagem, based on a logical decision to seed based on soil water content at seeding time and rainfall probabilities during the crop-growth period, could improve cover and thereby reduce wind erosion relative to a fixed fallow-cropping system.

Double cropping systems, in spite of providing a longer period of land occupancy by viable cover, do not necessarily ensure a reduced incidence of wind erosion, but depend upon the soil condition, climate, and the fate of residues in seedbed preparation. Exposure of unprotected soil by seedbed preparation to establish two crops in a single year can increase the hazard. The hazard can be reduced with minimum or no-till seedbed preparation and in fact can best utilize the growing season if time is critical by planting one crop immediately following harvest rather than experiencing the delay of traditional seedbed preparation. An example derived from the wind erosion equation shows the advantage of using no-till in a sorghum-wheat rotation in the Texas High Plains under dryland and the further advantage of double cropping which is possible with irrigation (Hayes, 1973). In a sorghum-winter wheat sequence (year 1) and a winter wheat-sorghum sequence (year 2) using traditional tillage, calculated potential soil loss was 2.7 and 56.0 metric tons/ha per year, respectively. In a corresponding situation with the sorghum no-till planted in year 2, the respective potential losses were 2.7 and 0.0 metric ton/ha per year. Under irrigation with a wheat-sorghum double cropping sequence, wind erosion losses would be reduced to less than 2 metric tons/ha per year.

In contrast to field crops, most vegetables and specialty crops are damaged by extremely minor incidences of wind erosion during the critical early seedling stage and may not recover to produce economic returns (Fryrear et al., 1975). Many variations of row intercropping have been devised and are used to protect the sensitive crop, Table 7 (Woodruff et al., 1972). These combinations of protector and protected plants suffice for control under prevailing soil and climatic conditions in the given locations. Farmers in the southern Coastal Plains and Atlantic Coast-Flatwoods areas have established narrow (30–60 cm) strips of annuals such as small grains or sunflower and wider strips of perennials like sericea lespedeza, hedges of perennial shrubs or pines (Pinus spp.) to protect high value vegetable and other crops (Carreker, 1966). More recently, design criteria have been formulated for use with the wind erosion equation to achieve a selected degree of erosion control by various barrier spacings and heights (Hagen et al., 1972).

Cover crops, established after harvest of the row cash crops under irrigated agriculture of sandy soils, have been deemed a necessity for protection of otherwise bare soil (Mech & Woodruff, 1967). Where adequate growing season remains after potato (Solanum tuberosum L.) harvest, corn for silage and sudangrass [Sorghum sudenense (Piper) Stapf] for hay have been

Table 7. Buffer or row interplantings of cereal crops found to provide protection for various crops sensitive to wind erosion damage (Woodruff et al., 1972)

Kind of Buffer	Width of strip	Crop protected	Location
Rye*	1 drill row	2 rows of beets, carrots†	Michigan
Rye	1.2 m	6 m of melons‡	Michigan
Rye or Wheat	2.1 to 2.4 m	21 to 24 m of potatoes, beets	Michigan
Barley or Spring Rye	1 drill row	3 rows of onions§	Michigan (mucks)
Grain Sorghum	4 rows	8 to 10 rows of peanuts¶	Texas
Corn	4 rows	16 rows of tomatoes#	Texas
Rye	3.0 m	4 rows of peanuts	Florida
Rye	30 to 60 cm	9 m of tomatoes	S. Carolina
Rye	1.8 m	18 m of melons	New Jersey

* Secale cereale L.
† Daucus carota L.
‡ Citrullus lanatus
§ Allium cepal
¶ Arachis hypogaea L.
# Lycopersicon esculentum (Mill.)

successfully grown (Oregon Agric. Exp. Stn., 1974) followed by a fall planting of barley (Hordeum sp.) or oats for winter cover. In southern Idaho where the growing season after potato or sugarbeet (Beta vulgaris L.) harvest is extremely short, preharvest broadcast seeding of winter wheat for winter and spring cover has been tested (Cary et al., 1975). Potatoes or other row crops are then planted directly in the cover followed by hilling for potatoes or, for other crops, preemergence herbicides to kill the cover crop. The very existence of cultivated agriculture on some of these newly broken-out irrigated lands depends on either the successful development of multiple cropping techniques including cover crops combined with no- or minimum-tillage or a permanent wind barrier system, because the vulnerable minimum plant-cover period coincides with the high winter and spring winds.

CONCLUSIONS

The relatively recent accelerated effort to increase the world's capacity to feed an expanding population has placed increased stress on land resources in both developed and developing countries. Availability of large tractors and the introduction of mechanization into some developing countries have increased field size to more efficiently utilize the equipment. The larger fields and the capacity for more tillage can intensify erosion. Lands marginal for cultivated crop production because of associated erosion hazards or climatic limitations are being plowed out. Land is being used more intensively, particularly by row crops, and there has been a shift from soil conserving crops. Although continuous single cropping, a rotation of two row crops, or two row crops double cropped may be efficient and profitable, unless managed properly, the erosion potential may be increased.

Application of proven principles of erosion control within the concept of multiple cropping provide a built-in mechanism for erosion control. Relay cropping, strip cropping, intercropping, and ratoon cropping incroporate methods for additional and continuous protective cover. An essential element of the total management system is no- or minimum-tillage to utilize the residues of one crop while the other is being established. Satisfactory erosion control can be achieved by including reduced tillage in the total multiple cropping management system. Reduced tillage techniques also apply to developing countries and small holdings (Greenland, 1975). Multiple cropping concepts and reduced tillage should be integrated into all management systems where soil erosion is a hazard.

LITERATURE CITED

Anderson, D. T. (Chairman). 1966. Soil erosion by wind. Canadian Dep. of Agric. Pub. 1266. 26 p.

Anderson, W. K., and I. F. Whan. 1974. Multiple cropping in Australia? J. Aust. Inst. Agric. Sci. p. 29-35.

Armbrust, D. V., W. S. Chepil, and F. H. Siddoway. 1964. Effects of ridges on erosion of soil by wind. Soil Sci. Soc. Am. Proc. 28:557-560.

Bagnold, R. A. 1941. The physics of blown sand and desert dunes. Methuen & Co. LTD. London. 256 p.

Black, A. L., and F. H. Siddoway. 1975. Snow trapping and crop management with tall wheatgrass barriers in Montana. Great Plains Agric. Council Pub. 73, p. 128-137.

Carreker, J. R. 1947. A tractor-operated furrow seeder. Agric. Engr. 28(12):553-555.

Carreker, J. R. 1966. Wind erosion in the southeast. J. Soil Water Conserv. 2:86-88.

Carreker, J. R., J. E. Box, Jr., R. N. Dawson, E. R. Beaty, and H. D. Morris. 1972. No-till corn in fescuegrass. Agron. J. 64:500-503.

Cary, J. W., R. S. Kohl, D. T. Westerman, and R. W. Richman. 1975. Row cropping sandy soils under sprinklers using a winter grain cover to control wind erosion. Idaho Agric. Exp. Stn. Bull. No. 549, 14 p.

Chepil, W. S. 1956. Influence of moisture on erodibility of soil by wind. Soil Sci. Soc. Am. Proc. 20:288-292.

Chepil, W. S. 1957. Width of field strips to control wind erosion. Kansas Agric. Exp. Stn. Tech. Bull. 92, 16 p.

Chepil, W. S., and W. C. Moldenhauer. 1962. Deep plowing of sandy land. USDA Production Research Report No. 64, 14 p.

Chepil, W. S., F. H. Siddoway, and D. V. Armbrust. 1962. Climatic factor for estimating wind erodibility of farm fields. J. Soil Water Conserv. 17:162-165.

Chepil, W. S., F. H. Siddoway, and D. V. Armbrust. 1963. Climatic index of wind erosion conditions in the Great Plains. Soil Sci. Soc. Am. Proc. 27:449-451.

Dodds, D. L. 1972. Wind erosion control on summer fallow and continuous cropland. North Dakota Ext. Cir. SC-572, 8 p.

Food and Agriculture Organization. 1960. Soil erosion by wind and measures for its control on agricultural lands. FAO Agric. Dev. Paper No. 71. FAO, Rome. 88 p.

Fryrear, D. W. 1969. Reducing wind erosion in the Southern Great Plains. Texas Agric. Exp. Stn. MP-929, 10 p.

Fryrear, D. W., D. V. Armbrust, and J. D. Downes. 1975. Plant response to wind erosion damage. p. 144-146. In 30th Annual Proceedings of the Soil Conserv. Soc. Am. 10-13 Aug. San Antonio, Texas.

Geiszler, G. N. 1961. Corn rows control wind erosion. N. D. Farm Res. 21(11):13-14.

Greenland, D. J. 1975. Bringing the green revolution to the shifting cultivator. Science 190(4217):841-844.

Haas, H. J., and W. O. Willis. 1971. Water storage and alfalfa production on level benches in the Northern Plains. J. Soil Water Conserv. 26:151-154.

Haas, H. J., W. O. Willis, and J. J. Bond. 1974. Summer fallow in the western United States. USDA Conservation Research Report No. 17, Chapter 1.

Hagen, L. J., E. L. Skidmore, and J. D. Dickerson. 1972. Designing narrow strip barrier systems to control wind erosion. J. Soil Water Conserv. 27:269–272.

Hayes, W. A. 1966. Guide for wind erosion control in the northeastern states. USDA, Soil Conservation Service, 27 p.

Hayes, W. A. 1972. Designing wind erosion control systems in the Midwest Region. USDA, SCS, Lincoln, Nebraska, RT SC-Agron. Tech. Note LI9.

Hayes, W. A. 1973. Double cropping. p. 207–212. In Proceedings National Conference Conservation Tillage, Soil Conserv. Soc. of Am., Ankeny, Iowa.

Hays, O. F. 1961. New tillage methods reduce erosion. J. Soil Water Conserv. 16:172–175.

Hendrickson, B. H., A. P. Barnett, J. R. Carreker, and W. E. Adams. 1963. Runoff and erosion control studies on Cecil soil in the southern Piedmont. USDA, ARS, Tech. Bull. No. 1281, 33 p.

Hoag, B. K., and G. N. Geiszler. 1971. Sunflower rows to protect fallow from wind erosion. N. D. Farm Res. 28:7–12.

Hudson, N. W. 1957. Erosion control research. Progress report on experiments at Henderson Research Station 1953–55. Bull. 1927, reprinted from Rhodesia Agric. J. 54(5):297–323. Salisbury, Rhodesia.

Hudson, N. W., and D. C. Jackson. 1962. Results achieved in the measurement of erosion and runoff in southern Rhodesia. Fed. Dep. of Conserv. and Ext. Tech. Memo. No. 4, Salisbury, Rhodesia.

Kohnke, Helmut, and A. R. Bertrand. 1959. Soil Conservation. McGraw Hill, New York. 298 p.

Leopold, L. B., M. G. Wolman, and J. P. Miller. 1964. Fluvial process in geomorphology. W. H. Freeman and Co., San Francisco.

Lewis, W. M. 1972. No-tillage production systems for double cropping and for cotton and other crops. p. 146–152. In Proceedings No-Tillage Systems Symposium, Ohio State Univ., Ohio Agric. Res. and Dev. Center, and Chevron Chemical Co.

McGregor, K. C., J. D. Greer, and G. E. Burley. 1975. Erosion control with no-till cropping practices. Trans. of ASAE 18(5):918–920.

Mech, S. J. 1955. Wind erosion control in the Columbia Basin. Washington Agric. Exp. Stn. Cir. 268, 5 p.

Mech, S. J., and N. P. Woodruff. 1967. Wind erosion on irrigated lands. In R. M. Hagan, H. R. Haise, and T. W. Edminster (ed.) Irrigation of agricultural lands. Agronomy 11:964–973. Am. Soc. of Agron., Madison, Wis.

Oregon Agricultural Experiment Station. 1974. Covercrop eyed for potatoes. Oregon Agric. Prog. 20(4):6.

Schwab, G. O., R. K. Frevert, T. W. Edminster, and K. K. Barnes. 1966. Soil and water conservation engineering. John Wiley & Sons, Inc., New York. 683 p.

Siddoway, F. H. 1965. Effect of kind, amount, and placement of residue on wind erosion control. Ph.D. Thesis. Kansas State University, Manhattan, Kansas. Library Number LD-2668D5-1965-S568. 108 p.

Skidmore, E. L. 1965. Assessing wind erosion forces: Direction and relative magnitudes. Soil Sci. Soc. Am. Proc. 29:587–590.

Skidmore, E. L., N. L. Nossaman, and N. P. Woodruff. 1966. Wind erosion as influenced by row spacing, row direction, and grain sorghum population. Soil Sci. Soc. Am. Proc. 30:505–509.

Skidmore, E. L., and N. P. Woodruff. 1968. Wind erosion forces in the United States and their use in predicting soil loss. USDA Agric. Handbook No. 346, 42 p.

Smith, D. D., and W. H. Wischmeier. 1957. Factors affecting sheet and rill erosion. Trans. Am. Geophysical Union 38(6):889–896.

Stallings, J. H. 1953. Continuous plant cover—the key to soil and water conservation. Better Crops Plant Food 37(10):13–20, 40–44.

Stout, B. A. 1965. Soil erosion by water, some measures for its control on cultivated lands. FAO Agric. Dev. Paper No. 81. FAO, Rome, 284 p.

Triplett, G. B., Jr., D. L. Jeffers, D. M. Van Doren, Jr., and C. R. Weaver. 1971. Double cropping wheat and soybeans. Ohio Rep. 56(2):24–26.

U. S. Department of Agriculture. 1940. Influences of vegetation and watershed treatments on runoff, silting, and stream flow. USDA, Misc. Publ. No. 397, 80 p.

U. S. Department of Agriculture. 1967. National inventory of soil and water conservation needs. USDA Statistical Bull. 461, 211 p.

U. S. Department of Agriculture. 1975. Control of water pollution from cropland, Volume 1. U. S. Government Printing Office. Rep. No. ARS-H-5-1, 111 p.

Wischmeier, W. H., and D. D. Smith. 1958. Rainfall energy and its relationship to soil loss. Trans. Am. Geophysical Union 39(2):285-291.

Wischmeier, W. H., and D. D. Smith. 1965. Predicting rainfall-erosion losses from cropland east of the Rocky Mountains. USDA, ARS Agric. Handbook 292, 47 p.

Wittmuss, H. D. 1968. Topographic modification of land for moisture entrapment. Trans. of ASAE 11:384.

Woodburn, Russel. 1944. Reduced loss of soil, less runoff when mulch used. Mississippi Agric. Exp. Stn., State College, Mississippi. Farm Research 6(8):7.

Woodruff, N. P., and W. S. Chepil. 1956. Implements for wind erosion control. Agric. Engr. 37:751-754, 758.

Woodruff, N. P., W. S. Chepil, and R. D. Lynch. 1957. Emergency chiseling to control wind erosion. Kansas Agric. Exp. Stn. Tech. Bull. 90, 24 p.

Woodruff, N. P., Leon Lyles, F. H. Siddoway, and D. W. Fryrear. 1972. How to control wind erosion. USDA Agric. Infor. Bull. No. 354, 22 p.

Woodruff, N. P., and F. H. Siddoway. 1965. A wind erosion equation. Soil Sci. Soc. Am. Proc. 29:602-608.

Machinery Adaptations for Multiple Cropping[1]

D. C. Erbach and W. G. Lovely[2]

Multiple cropping patterns may impose design and operational restrictions on the implements used for mechanizing crop production. However, the machinery requirements for growing a crop in many multiple cropping patterns are no different than for growing the same crop as a sole crop.

Mechanization of crop production is most easily accomplished when operations, such as tillage, spraying, or harvesting, can be performed uniformly over the entire field area. When two or more crops are grown on the same land area at the same time, mechanization becomes more complex because the operation performed on, or for, one crop must be done in a manner that will not damage the other crop or crops.

Most machinery has been developed for sole crop production. The adaptations needed to make this equipment acceptable for multiple cropping depend on the multiple cropping pattern to be used. The adaptations needed are also influenced by the level of mechanization involved, the crop species to be grown, and the edaphic and climatic conditions in which the crops will be grown.

The objectives of this paper are to review the limited literature that discusses machinery adaptations for multiple cropping, to discuss problems associated with mechanizing multiple cropping, and to suggest modifications that may be made to equipment that will make it more acceptable for use in multiple cropping systems.

MECHANIZATION OF CROP PRODUCTION

All crop production operations can be performed by hand or with the use of simple tools. However, the work is often difficult and the production

[1]Journal Paper No. J-8266 of the Iowa Agric. and Home Econ. Exp. Stn., Ames, Iowa. Project 1815.
[2]Agricultural engineer, ARS, USDA, Ames, Iowa and staff scientist, National Program Staff, ARS, USDA, Beltsville, Maryland.

per farmer is low. Therefore, whenever possible, crop production is mechanized to increase production per farmer and to reduce drudgery for the farmer.

Mechanizing a crop production operation is easiest when the operation can be done over the entire area of the field and when precise equipment operation is not essential. An example is tillage for small grain production. The entire area is tilled and the exact location, depth, and speed of the tillage tool as it passes over the field are not critical.

It is difficult and expensive to mechanize an operation requiring exact positioning of a tool at irregularly spaced locations. Selecting and harvesting ripe fruit without damage to the plant or immature fruit is an example.

ADAPTATIONS IN MACHINERY NEEDED FOR MECHANIZATION OF MULTIPLE CROPPING

The presence of a crop other than the one that an operation is being performed on, or for, is the greatest factor influencing machinery adaptations needed for mechanization of multiple cropping. This effect is greatest with inter-, relay and mixed cropping patterns. Restrictions imposed by growing season and moisture supply limitations affect modifications needed for mechanizing double and triple cropping patterns.

Equipment useable with more than one crop is desirable to avoid the expense of multiple sets of machinery. Compromise is necessary between hav-

Figure 1. Double cropping soybeans after wheat. To save time and moisture, planting is done immediately after wheat harvest. Note combine in the background. (Photo courtesy of Allis-Chalmers, Farm Equipment Division.)

ing equipment to do the job right and keeping expenses low enough to make the cropping system profitable. Determination of the number and size of machines needed must be based on an economic analysis of the conditions of each farm (Camper et al., 1972).

Strip Cropping

No machinery adaptations are necessary when each crop is planted in a strip wide enough for independent tillage, planting, cultivation, and harvesting. If herbicides are used, application must be precise so that adjacent crops will not be damaged by chemical drift.

Double Cropping

There are no special machinery needs when there is sufficient time for seedbed preparation between harvest of the first crop and planting of the second. This is, in effect a sequential pattern of sole crops.

Often the second crop will not mature unless it is planted as early as possible. An example of this is double cropping of soybeans [*Glycine max* (L.) Merr.] or sorghum [*Sorghum bicolor* (L.) Moench] after wheat (*Triticum aestivum* L.). Also, the moisture available for growth of the second crop may be limited. For these conditions, successful double cropping depends on efficient use of the available growing season and moisture supply (Anderson & Whan, 1974; Camper et al., 1972; Hamilton, 1974). The equipment must be suitable for quickly harvesting a crop and planting the succeeding crop. If moisture is limited, tillage for seedbed preparation must be minimized to prevent moisture loss that could delay crop emergence and early growth. If time is limited, field operations for seedbed preparation must be minimized (Streeter, 1973). A few days' delay in planting or emergence can significantly reduce yields and may cause an otherwise successful cropping system to fail (Sanford et al., 1973; Unger & Stewart, 1976).

In a no-tillage system, the planter can follow immediately behind the harvesting machine (Fig. 1). Because no seedbed preparation is needed, soil moisture is not lost by preplanting tillage. Plant residue from the previous crop left on the soil surface reduces runoff and erosion, increases infiltration, reduces evaporation, and protects crop seedlings from wind damage (Fig. 2). Also, reducing tillage tends to prevent deterioration of soil properties (Anderson & Whan, 1974; Hayes, 1973).

If seedbed preparation is eliminated, the planter should have a furrow opener that will operate in plant residue, penetrate hard soil, and place the seed in a uniformly favorable environment for germination and emergence. Conventional planters, designed for clean-tilled, well-worked soil, are seldom satisfactory in a no-tillage system. Plant residue, hard soil, or sod usually prevent furrow openers from functioning properly. Seed placement and

Figure 2.   Soybeans, planted without tillage, are emerged in wheat stubble.   (Photo courtesy of Chevron Chemical Company, Ortho Division.)

Figure 3.   Six row, no tillage planter with fluted coulters in front, followed by single disk openers for fertilizer placement and double disk openers for seed furrow.   (Photo courtesy of Chevron Chemical Company, Ortho Division.)

emergence are then erratic, resulting in nonuniform growth and maturity, harvesting delays, and yield reductions (Anderson & Whan, 1974).

Many modified conventional planters have been used successfully in untilled soil. Often a coulter is mounted ahead of the planter furrow opener (Sanford et al., 1973) to cut the surface plant residue and till a narrow strip of soil, thereby enabling the furrow opener to penetrate to the desired seed depth. Straight, rippled or fluted coulters have been used (Fig. 3). A shovel running in front of the furrow opener gives good soil penetration but is easily clogged by plant residue. In untilled soil, double-disk furrow openers clog less than runners because they cut residue and roll.

Soil and residue conditions in which a planter must operate can be quite variable. Methods and planter settings that work well under some conditions may work poorly under others. For example, when plant residue is dry and the soil surface is dry and firm but not hard, double-disk openers work well without a coulter. But if the residue is difficult to cut or the soil is hard, planting without a coulter is unsatisfactory. Additional weight may be needed to increase penetration in hard soil. A tank filled with water often is mounted on the coulter tool bar to provide the additional weight.

Powered rotary cutting devices for tilling narrow strips ahead of the planter furrow opener and for opening seed furrows work well for planting into sod that has been killed with a contact herbicide.

Conventional planters rely on the free-flowing characteristics of the surface layer of soil in a well-tilled field for covering the seed. But, when planting in untilled soil, especially when hard or wet, a positive furrow closing mechanism is needed; a covering disk is most satisfactory. Under certain conditions a press wheel will close the seed furrow. If the seed is placed in contact with untilled moist soil, little compaction above the seed is needed or desirable. If the soil is fairly dry and loose, compaction may improve germination.

A till-planter has given uniform seed placement and stand establishment without preplanting tillage (Wittmuss et al., 1971) (Fig. 4). This planter has a straight coulter to cut the residue, and a sweep set at a shallow pitch to remove plant residue and dry soil from the seed zone. The depth of operation depends on plant residue, soil, and climate. A runner furrow opener operates in a clean band behind the sweep. The seed is firmed against untilled soil with a press wheel and covered with covering disks.

Grain drills do not work well in no-tillage systems. They do not penetrate residue well, and seed placement is not uniform. They also disturb the soil considerably, and moisture loss may be excessive.

Preplanting tillage and planting may be combined in one pass over the field. A chisel plow, usually with coulters mounted in front of each shank, a power rotary cultivator, or a tandem disk may be used to till ahead of the planter. These approaches allow some mechanical weed control and fertilizer incorporation. Their disadvantages, as compared with no-tillage systems, are greater power requirement, slower planting, increased loss of moisture, and a narrower range of acceptable operating conditions.

Figure 4. Till-planter with straight coulter, slot opener, seed press wheel, and covering disks. A sweep, to remove plant residue and dry soil from the seed row can be used in place of the slot opener. (Photo courtesy of Fleischer Manufacturing Company.)

If soil is dry, addition of water to the seed zone at planting may speed germination and emergence and extend the growing season of the crop. Planter attachments are available for injecting water into the seed furrow at planting.

With no-tillage planting, dry or liquid fertilizer can be applied with the planter or broadcast on the soil surface. If applied with the planter, a furrow opener similar to that needed for seed placement is necessary to cut the surface plant residue and penetrate hard soil or sod. Nitrogen applied as anhydrous ammonia must be injected. A coulter may be needed in front of each injection knife to cut the plant residue so that it will not wrap around applicator shanks and clog the machine.

Time between harvest of the first crop and planting of the second can be reduced if the anhydrous ammonia is applied after the crop has emerged. Enough phosphorus, potassium and other nutrients for the entire crop sequence should be applied when the soil is tilled so that the nutrients will be better distributed in the soil profile. In a double crop pattern, enough fertilizer should be applied when the seedbed for the first crop is prepared to meet the needs of both crops.

For effective weed control, selection of herbicide and application technique must be made based on consideration of tillage system, crop weed infestation, and other cropping system factors. Postemergence contact herbicides must be applied with greater volumes of water and at higher pressures to nontilled fields to insure that the spray penetrates heavy plant residue and contacts the weeds. Plant residue may hinder cultivation with sweep cultivators. Rolling, disk, and power rotary cultivators with crop shields work well in heavy crop residue. They can be adjusted to work for a wide range of crops, weeds, and residues (Erbach & Lovely, 1974). Mulch cultivators with wide sweeps, alone or in combination with rod weeders, work well under dryland conditions.

Minimizing soil disturbance may reduce infestation of some weeds and increase infestation of others. The inability to control some troublesome weeds may prevent use of no-tillage cropping.

Harvesting the first crop before it is fully mature can allow earlier planting of the second crop and maximize use of the available growing season, but specialized facilities are required to store, dry, or process the crop. The equipment required for harvesting a crop in a double cropping pattern is basically the same as for harvesting the crop as a sole crop. However, it is important that after the first crop is harvested the field should be left in good condition for seedbed preparation or planting.

In general, for successful double cropping, machinery must be available to quickly harvest and plant. The equipment must be free of unnecessary appendages, shanks, chains, and other components that can catch residue. It also must have adequate clearance to allow residue and soil to pass freely so that blockage is minimized.

Because crops in a double-cropping pattern often have a limited moisture supply and a short growing season, they may not grow as tall or branch as much as the same crops grown under normal conditions. For these conditions, narrower rows and higher plant populations may increase shading of weeds and increase yields. Therefore, equipment may be needed to plant, cultivate, and harvest narrow rows.

Intercropping

When crops are grown side by side in alternate rows, equipment must be operated more precisely to prevent damage to the adjacent crop. The rows must be spaced properly to allow traffic paths for passage of the equipment needed for production of each of the crops. An example is planting sugarcane (*Saccharium* sp.) in 1 m rows to allow cultivation with bullock labor for intercropping potatoes (*Solanum tuberosum*) (Akhade et al., 1975). The equipment must be small enough to pass between the rows of the crops or must be able to straddle one or both crops. Small, manually operated, engine powered equipment or hand tools will allow closer spacing of the crop rows than will animal powered equipment or equipment with large wheels. When small grains or vegetables are intercropped with a perennial crop—such as in an orchard when the young trees are developing, or in a coconut (*Cocos nucifera*) plantation (Nair et al., 1974)—the equipment must be maneuverable enough to pass between the perennial plants.

Relay Cropping

To make more efficient use of the growing season and of the available moisture, the second crop can be planted before the first crop is harvested. The planting and seedbed preparation equipment for the second crop must be able to pass between, or must have sufficient clearance to straddle, the rows of the first crop.

If the first crop is broadcast, then it may be difficult to plant without damaging the first crop. Aerial seeding may be used for relay planting of

grasses and grains in broadcast or row crops (Sanford et al., 1974; Streeter, 1973). A broadcast spreader may also be used for planting and will distribute the seed more uniformly. With these planting techniques it is not possible to cover the seeds, so soil conditions at the time of seeding and rainfall, temperature, and humidity conditions after seeding must be favorable for germination and establishment of the crop seedling. The soil surface should be moist when the crop is planted, a light rain should occur after planting, and weather conditions after planting should limit evaporation from the soil until the crop is established. If the second crop is planted just before leaves drop from the first crop, the leaves can serve as protection for the seeds until germination.

When harvesting the first crop, traffic should be limited so damage to the interseeded crop is minimized.

Mixed Cropping

Machinery for production of two crops that are planted and harvested simultaneously and with the same machines, as is done with mixtures of forage crops, require no special adaptations. When, as is usually the case, planting dates, harvesting dates, and plant species characteristics are different, mechanization is difficult. A machine designed to select the proper plant, or area, and to perform the desired operation without damaging other crop plants would be complex and expensive. Therefore, few machines have been developed for mechanization of mixed cropping. Production with this type of planting pattern is usually done with hand tools or with hand carried, mechanically powered devices.

Pesticides must be applied accurately to prevent damage to susceptible crops. Equipment for directional application, shielding, and drift reduction are needed.

ADAPTATIONS THAT WILL AID MECHANIZATION OF MULTIPLE CROPPING

Changes that will make the planting pattern more regular will aid mechanization, as will increasing the uniformity of plant size and maturity. Planting in rows or strips sufficiently wide to allow passage of all equipment used will eliminate the need for equipment adaptations.

Because multiple cropping involves a fairly steady cycle of planting and harvesting, it may be necessary to maintain traffic paths to aid mechanization of the system. These paths can be spaced to match the wheel spacing of a wide span tool and personnel carrier. The carriers would straddle the crops and would carry laborers and, depending on the operation being performed, seed, fertilizer, or the harvested crop. The carriers could also supply power for manually operated tools for planting, mechanical weed control, pesticide application, and harvesting. This technique would allow for the flexibility and precision required for mixed cropping, increase production, and reduce drudgery.

The traction paths could be designed so that little land would be removed from production and so that the carrier could operate independent of weather conditions.

DISCUSSION

Multiple cropping can increase financial returns per unit area of land per year and because the system is labor intensive, it also can generate employment for many people (Singh & Mohan, 1973; Nair et al., 1974; Wang & Liang, 1973; Singh, 1973). Mechanization of a farming system can greatly increase the production per farmer. The production per unit area of land, however, may not be increased and the requirements and limitations of machines may even reduce the production per unit area. Mechanization may also force unemployment. Therefore, the desirability for mechanization of many multiple cropping systems must be considered.

If the labor needs of the production system are not uniform with time, there is need for equipment to aid at times of peak demand, commonly planting and harvesting (Khanna, 1973).

Machinery adaptations needed for mechanization of multiple cropping depend on the cropping pattern and on the level of mechanization. Specification of equipment needs is difficult because they are dependent on specific soil conditions and cropping patterns.

Except for double cropping in highly mechanized production systems, little information is available on machinery adaptations for multiple cropping.

The level of mechanization for most multiple cropping is low. The major equipment need for multiple cropping seems to be not that it must be adapted, but that equipment for production at this level of technology must be developed.

LITERATURE CITED

Akhade, M. N., M. Singh, and B. S. Bhambani. 1975. Grow potato as intercrop in sugarcane. Indian Farming 25(1):3-4, 28.

Anderson, W. K., and I. F. Whan. 1974. Multiple cropping in Australia? J. Aust. Inst. Agric. Sci. 40:29-35.

Camper, H. M., Jr., C. F. Genter, and K. E. Loope. 1972. Double cropping following winter barley harvest in eastern Virginia. Agron. J. 64:1-3.

Erbach, D. C., and W. G. Lovely. 1974. Weed control with conservation tillage production of corn and soybeans. J. Soil Water Conserv. 29:44-45.

Hamilton, R. E. 1974. One plus one-double cropping grows in Corn Belt. Soil Conserv. 39:14-15.

Hayes, W. A. 1973. Double cropping. p. 207-212. In Proceedings National Conference Conservation Tillage. Soil Conserv. Soc. of Am., Ankeny, Iowa.

Khanna, S. K. 1973. Design considerations of harvesting equipment in multiple cropping. Agric. Mech. Asia 4(2):31-34.

Nair, P. K. R., R. Varma, and E. V. Nelliat. 1974. Intercropping for enhanced profits from coconut plantation. Indian Farming 24(4):11-13.

Sanford, J. O., D. L. Myhre, and N. C. Merwine. 1973. Double cropping systems involving no-tillage and conventional tillage. Agron. J. 65:978-982.

Sanford, J. O., D. L. Myhre, and N. C. Merwine. 1974. Double cropping: aerial seeding of wheat before soybean harvest. Miss. Agric. For. Exp. Stn. Res. Highlights 27(10).

Singh, K. 1973. Farm size, mechanization and labour employment. Agric. Mech. Asia 4(2):47-56.

Singh, K., and S. Mohan. 1973. A case study of the economics of multiple cropping in Delhi State. Agric. Mech. Asia 4(2):35-40.

Streeter, Carroll P. 1973. VII. Multiple cropping—Centuries-old technique gets new results. p. 63-68. In Reaching the developing world's small farmers, A Special Report from the Rockefeller Foundation, N. Y.

Unger, P. W., and B. A. Stewart. 1976. Land preparation and seeding establishment practices in multiple cropping systems. p. 255-273. In R. I. Papendick, P. A. Sanchez, and G. B. Triplett (ed.) Multiple cropping. Spec. Pub. No. 27. Am. Soc. of Agron., Madison, Wis.

Wittmuss, H. D., D. E. Lane, and B. R. Somerhalder. 1971. Strip till-planting of row crops through surface residue. Trans. ASAE 14:60-63, 68.

Wang, J., and T. Liang. 1973. A multiphase strategy for agricultural mechanization. Agric. Mech. Asia 4(2):57-63.

Multiple Cropping Systems are Dollars and "Sense" Agronomy

P. E. Hildebrand[1]

A Salvadorean farmer trying to feed his family on a hectare of irrigated land. A Guatemalan farmer planting beans (*Phaseolus* sp.) between rocks in powder-dry soil while keeping a hopeful eye out for rain which will signal the start of the rainy season. Two men, neighbors but on different sides of an international boundary, planting different crops. What do they have in common? Multiple cropping systems. The systems are different even though located near each other where climatic conditions are similar. Yet, each of these men has developed a multiple cropping system which simultaneously fulfills a complex blend of agronomic, cultural, and economic conditions peculiar to his own area and his farm and family situation. This is the promise and the challenge of multiple cropping systems.

This paper[2] defines terms which are essential to economic considerations in cropping systems, and then describes the more relevant bio-economic relationships. Later, with the use of examples, it illustrates how economics affects and must be incorporated into cropping systems. Finally, a model for research in multiple cropping systems will be presented which utilizes the capabilities of broadly oriented scientists to provide improved systems tailored to specific farm conditions and of more specialized scientists to refine the systems over time.

PRODUCTIVITY OF MULTIPLE CROPPING SYSTEMS

Productivity is a term widely used but seldom well defined. In monoculture it is often considered simply as production per unit of land area. Here the term yield is used for that concept and the term *production* to refer to yield times area. In this way, productivity can be reserved for its more technical use which is output (or yield) of any product per unit (either total

---

[1]Agricultural economist, The Rockefeller Foundation, assigned as coordinador de Socioeconomía Rural, Instituto de Ciencia y Tecnología Agrícolas (ICTA), Guatemala.
[2]The following persons made useful comments on earlier drafts: Chris O. Andrew, Edwin C. French, T. M. Fullerton, and James L. Walker.

or additional units) of any particular input or factor of production. In other words, to describe productivity one must define the product and the input to which he is referring. Productivity could refer, for instance, to yield per unit of seed, labor, or water as well as per unit of land. It can also refer to energy or protein produced per unit of one of the inputs used in the production process.

Inputs

The habit of using yield per unit of land area as the primary measure of productivity in agriculture stemmed from our traditional concentration on monoculture, and a basic assumption that land was the most limiting factor for a farmer. Historically in the U. S. advances in monoculture technology proceeded hand in hand with the development of the infrastructure required to support it. This infrastructure provided markets, credit, chemicals, seed, and machinery in quantities and qualities usually sufficient so that in most cases the farmer's basic limitation really was land.

In lesser developed countries today, however, infrastructure is not always capable of supplying sufficient quantities of inputs so factors other than land are often more limiting to farmers (Hildebrand & Luna, 1973). For farmers in this situation, measures of productivity other than yield per unit of area become more important. In the Punjab region of West Pakistan, for example, yield per unit of water has historically been much more important to the farmer than yield per unit of land even though the average farm size is only about 3 ha (West Pakistan, 1967). Under certain conditions in Colombia (Andrew, 1969) and Guatemala (Reiche et al., 1976), one finds that for some crops farmers refer to their production in terms of yield per unit of seed planted because to them seed, which they can eat or sell and which often is ruined before planting time, is a much more scarce resource than land.

In the U. S. where farm labor is relatively scarce and high priced, it is common to refer to labor productivity or output per man hour of labor. This concept is also important to farmers in areas even where rural labor is generally considered abundant. In Central America large areas are affected by a 6 month dry season and a 6 month rainy season. When the rains begin everyone plants at the same time over large areas and labor becomes scarce. Hence, even though there is frequent under employment in these areas, at a critical time in the production process labor is one of the most limiting factors of production and the productivity of labor for planting is an important consideration.

Products

Problems of measuring output are relatively few when dealing only with single-crop monoculture. A field of corn (*Zea mays* L.) produces corn, a field of beans produces beans and a field of beets (*Beta vulgaris* L.) produces beets. Occasionally refinements are added and a field of corn could produce silage or grain, the output of a field of beets could be measured in metric tons of sugar as well as metric tons of beets, and sometimes the production of protein from a field of beans or from a field of alfalfa (*Medicago sativa* L.) is considered. But the measurement of production from a multiple cropping system is much more complicated. A field might yield both beans and corn and a measure must be devised which helps determine when a farmer is better off raising the production of corn and decreasing the production of beans or vice versa or raising the production of beans proportionately more or less than corn.

The unit for measuring production from a multiple cropping system must satisfy several criteria. First, it must be common to all the products. Protein, energy, or dry matter, for instance, could have this attribute. Second, it should be relatively easy to measure. Third, it must be capable of reflecting quality differences between the products. Fourth, it must provide a means of comparing different cropping systems.

Energy is a candidate for measuring product that is currently on everyone's mind. This meets the four criteria cited above, but it falls short in a fifth, and this may be the most important of all. *The manner of measuring product from a multiple cropping system must be meaningful to a farmer* in such a way that it helps him to allocate his resources between competing uses on the farm. While any unit which fails to meet this criterion may be interesting from a purely scientific point of view, it will not be useful as an aid in designing systems for farmers.

The *market value of the products* may be the only unit available which meets all five criteria. Its major weakness, the fact that prices change over time and differ between regions, is at the same time one of its major strengths. This attribute allows it to adjust to changing conditions. As an example, different forms of energy have a different value in the market place. If at some point this value is out of adjustment with reality then price will change to reflect the new supply and demand situation (unless artificial controls are operating in the economy). Bio-climatic conditions in Guatemala are appropriate for the production of sweet potatoes (*Ipomoea batatas* Lam.), but few farmers produce this source of energy because the Guatemalan market puts too low a value on it. Instead, they produce beans and corn which provide energy in a form desired by the buyers and this is reflected back to the farmer in the market value of the product. The author considers market value as the best unit available for measuring products in a multiple cropping system.

BIO-ECONOMIC RELATIONSHIPS RELEVANT TO MULTIPLE CROPPING SYSTEMS[3]

There are three bio-economic relationships which form the basis for design and analysis of multiple cropping systems. One deals with the relation-

---

[3]In this paper these concepts receive only cursory treatment. For a complete yet readable presentation see Bradford and Johnson (1953).

ship between input and output, a second treats the interaction of two or more inputs to produce a given product, and the third concerns the effects between two or more crops.

Factor—Product

The most basic bio-economic relationship relevant to cropping systems is that between quantity and value of inputs (factors) and quantity and value of production (product). It is based on the biological response of plants to a factor of production. The growth curve of plants over time (as an input) or the response to fertilizer are examples with which all are familiar.

The rational range of input use can be defined biologically as being between the amounts of input (X) which are equal to or greater than the quantity which maximizes average physical production (APP) and equal to or less than the quantity which maximizes total physical production (TPP) (Fig. 1). Economically, this range is narrowed by considering the price of the input and the price of the product. The curve which results from multiplying the total physical product by its price is total value product (TVP) and from it are derived average value product or AVP (total value product divided by number of units of input) and marginal value product or MVP (the value added to production by the last unit of input) (Fig. 2). The minimum rational limit of input use is the same as that determined trom a strictly biological consideration, or the amount which maximizes average value product. This is also the amount which minimizes unit cost of production with respect to the same input, a concept important to a small farmer with few resources. The maximum rational limit is the amount at which marginal value product is equal to the price per unit of the input (Px). This is the amount which maximizes profit (total value product minus cost of the input) and always represents fewer units of input than that which maximizes total physical product unless the input is free.

Any recommendation to a farmer regarding the use of one or more inputs in a single crop or in a cropping system must fall within these economic limits. If it pays to use the input at all, one should use no less than the minimum as defined above because efficiency (average physical or average value product) increases up to that point and unit cost of production declines. Even farmers who are short of capital, if they apply any of the input, should be encouraged to use no less than this amount. The small irrigation farmer in the Punjab distributes his precious water so as to apply this quantity and the small farmer in the south of Colombia does the same with his potato (*Solanum tuberosum*) seed. In both cases, the farmer leaves some of his land idle (or in another crop) in order to increase the average productivity of the scarcest input.

The maximum economic limit on input use is more meaningful to the farmer with abundant capital or credit. At this level, the farmer makes more net income even though the efficiency with which he is using his capital and

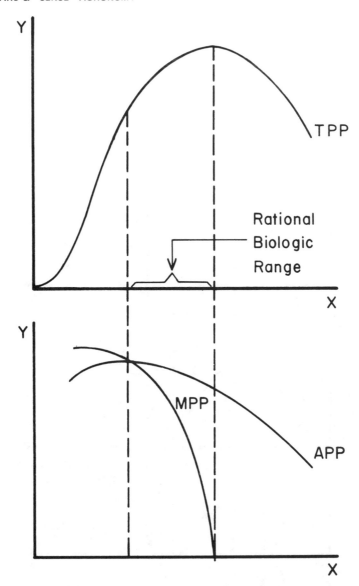

Figure 1. Rational biologic range of input use.

inputs is less than the maximum possible. In view of his favorable economic situation, however, it is not critical for him to be so concerned with this measure of efficiency. Also, because of his higher economic status, he is better able to cope with the risks associated with using more and more inputs at ever decreasing levels of productivity and increasing unit costs of production.

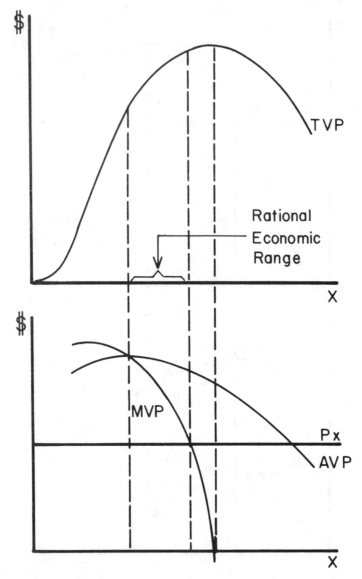

Figure 2. Rational economic range of input use.

Factor—Factor

The second basic bio-economic relationship relevant to the design of cropping systems is that dealing with how to combine two or more factors of production, or inputs, to produce a given product. This relationship is

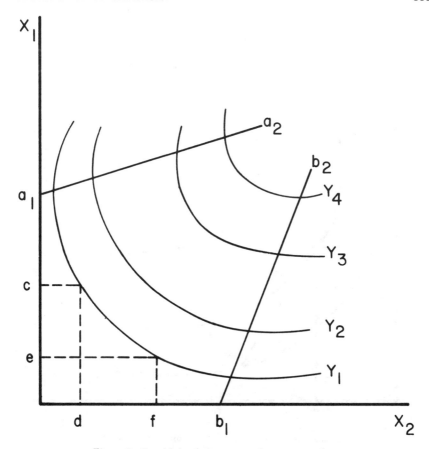

Figure 3. Combining inputs to produce one product.

presented graphically in Figure 3. In this figure, the quantity of two inputs, X_1 and X_2 are measured on the two axes. Topographically, the amount of product, which would be measured on a third axis, is presented by contours or iso-product lines (Y_1, Y_2, etc.) shown in the figure. Contour Y_4 represents more of the product than contour Y_3 which represents more than Y_2 etc. Along any one iso-product contour, any combination of X_1 and X_2 represented will produce the same amount of product (based on the biological relationship between the factors and the product). On contour Y_1, for example, c units of X_1 and d units of X_2 produce the same amount of product as e units of X_1 and f units of X_2.

Once again, without regard to economics, a rational range of combination of factors X_1 and X_2 can be defined. This range is that between the scale lines $a_1 a_2$ and $b_1 b_2$ because outside this range, the use of more of one input, without changing the use of the other input, decreases the total amount of product forthcoming.

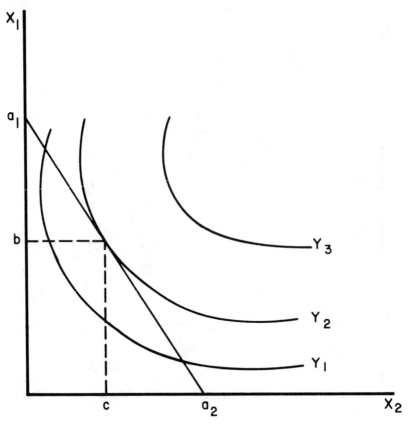

Figure 4. Best economic combination of inputs to use.

Economically, the best combination of the two factors to use to produce *a given amount of product* depends on the prices of the two inputs. If factor X_1 in Figure 3 is inexpensive relative to X_2, one would suppose the combination of c of X_1 and d of X_2 to be a better (lower cost) means of producing Y_1 of the product than e of X_1 and f of X_2. Figure 4 represents this case. The iso-cost line $a_1 a_2$ represents all combinations of the two inputs which can be purchased for a given cost, and more X_1 can be purchased for this amount than X_2. For the amount of cost represented by $a_1 a_2$ the best combination is b units of X_1 and c units of X_2 because more of Y can be produced for the given cost with this combination than with any other. Mathematically, the best combination of inputs is the amount which satisfies the relationship $MPPx_2/MPPx_1 = Px_2/Px_1$ where the biological factor-product relationship is $Y = f(X_1, X_2)$ and the given cost $C = Px_1 X_1 + Px_2 X_2$ and Px_1 and Px_2 are prices of the inputs X_1 and X_2 respectively.

If the amount of capital available to a farmer is not limited, then he must consider how much to produce by purchasing more X_1 and X_2. In its simplest form this procedure reduces to a factor-product relationship in

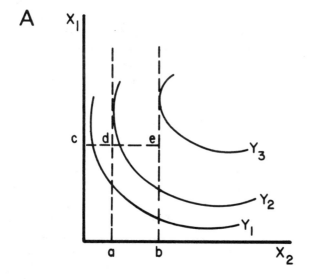

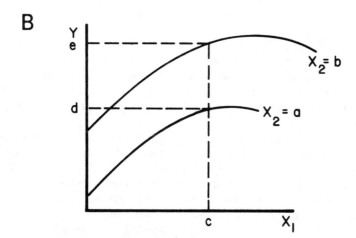

Figure 5. Interaction effect of one input on productivity of another.

which the factor becomes a combination of X_1 and X_2 in some fixed proportion. A premixed fertilizer such as 16–20–0 is a common example where the
use of this particular formula is based on the assumption that 16 units of N
and 20 units of P_2O_5 satisfy the least cost factor-factor relationship over all
levels of application.

The factor-factor relationship can also help to visualize the effect on
factor productivity caused by the interaction of inputs. Figure 5B is derived
from 5A and shows the effect on the amount of product Y produced by a
given amount of X_1 (= c) as the amount of X_2 is raised from a units to b

units. The lower curve in 5B shows the factor-product relationship between X_1 and Y when X_2 is fixed at a units, or $Y = f(X_1|X_2 = a)$. The upper curve is $Y = f(X_1|X_2 = b)$. The relationship can readily be interpreted if one considers X_1 to be nitrogen and X_2 to be water availability, and quantity a of X_2 is insufficient for proper plant growth while quantity b is adequate.

Product—Product

The most important bio-economic relationship relevant to multiple cropping systems is that between two or more crops or products. Historically, in making recommendations to farmers, each crop has generally been considered independently even if more than one crop was being produced on the farm. This is a valid procedure from the farmer's point of view only if he has no limit to the capital he can spend on each of the crops and uses the amount of each input required in each crop to maximize profit (equate marginal value product with price of the input). On most farms, in most areas of the world, this is not the case. When funds are scarce, a farmer must decide upon the quantity of an input to use on one product based not only on its profitability in producing that product but also in the profitability of competing uses of that input in other products.

In Figure 6, AVP_A and MVP_A are the average value product and marginal value product of X in producing A while AVP_B and MVP_B are the same functions for product B. The Y axis of the graph in this case is in terms of market value because we are measuring the response of two different crops, and the X axis measures physical units of input X to produce either product A or product B.

If a farmer is going to apply any of input X he should use no less than amount c for crop B because this is the lower rational limit as defined previously in the discussion of the factor-product relationship. If he is exceedingly limited on funds he could apply only c units of X in the production of B without using any in the production of A because the marginal productivity of X in A is too low to warrant its use for that crop.

After deciding to use c units to produce B, if funds are still available, a units of X could be purchased to produce A and $d-c$ additional units could be invested in X to produce B. If after investing in a units for A and d units for B, additional funds are still available for investment in this input, the amount destined for A and the amount allocated to B should be proportioned such that the MVP of X in A is always equal to the MVP of X in B. The use of b units in A and e units in B, resulting in an MVP in both crops equal to f, would be an example. The upper limit in the use of X is the quantity for which the MVP in each crop drops to the price of the input, g, and the maximum profit level of investment has been achieved for both products.[4]

---

[4] Admittedly, this is a rather loose description and presents a slight error in allocation between the investment in c total units and $d + a$ total units, but to clarify this would unduly complicate an already complex concept and figure. The reader is referred again to Bradford and Johnson (1953), or Heady and Dillon (1961, p. 48–50).

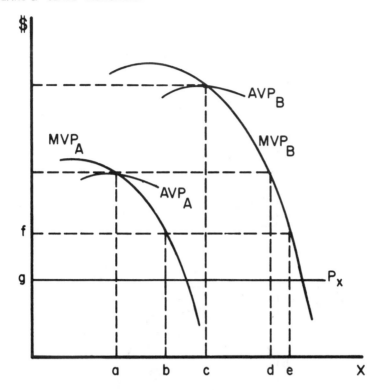

Figure 6. Allocation of an input between two products.

The important concept to be gleaned from these last few paragraphs is that as one is considering investing in more and more of an input to be used in two (or more) crops, the amount allocated to each crop should always be such that the MVP of the input is equal in each alternative use. For farmers with limited capital to invest, this concept has important implications and means that no one crop can be considered independently from any other. The critical importance of this principle to a multiple cropping system should be obvious and will be illustrated with an example in a later section of this paper.

The product-product relationship also has important implications in another aspect of multiple cropping systems. In Figure 7A are shown two independent production functions for crop A and crop B as they respond biologically to an input (or package of inputs) X. In Figure 7B the quantities of crops A and B produced are measured on the two axes. The curve *bcde* in Figure 7B shows all possible combinations of A and B which the farmer can produce by using his inputs, X, in one or in both crops and is known as the *production possibilities curve*. This curve manifests some important characteristics. As some of the inputs are shifted from producing all A (*b* units of Y_A) to producing mostly A but some B, the output of both crops increases (portion of the production possibilities curve between *b* and *c*). Obviously, *c* is a better combination of crops for the farmer than *b* because he produces

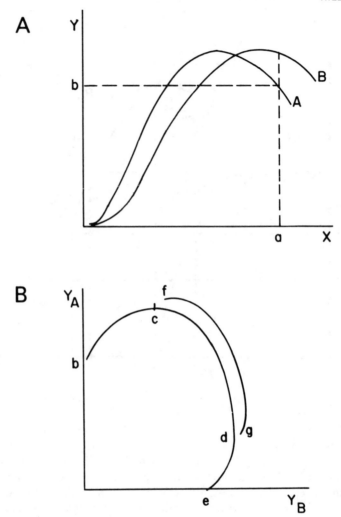

Figure 7. Combination of crops with a fixed set of resources.

more of both for the same cost (using the same set of inputs). Economists call this phenomenon complementarity between two products. To differentiate it from a similar biologic effect it can be called *economic complementarity.*

The best combination of crops A and B to produce with a given set of resources depends on the price of the two products and will always fall between *c* and *d* on the production possibilities curve, the area in which the crops are competitive. In this area, more of one crop can be produced only at the expense of the other. Some of the most interesting work in cropping systems deals with the effects of competitive crops. Shifting the relative populations of corn and beans is a common example (IRRI, 1973).

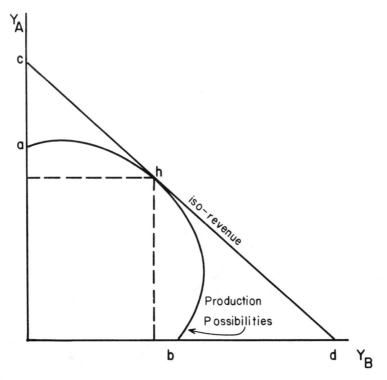

Figure 8. Best economic combination of crops to produce for a farmer with abundant resources.

The production possibilities curve *fg* in Figure 7B demonstrates *biologic complementarity* between the two products. This kind of complementarity is caused by the relationship which exists between a legume and a grain in a rotation or in a multiple cropping system. This phenomenon differs from economic complementarity in that it causes a shift upward of the whole production possibilities curve without any increase in inputs on the farm. The result is the same, however, in that more of both products are produced for the same investment. All who have worked with multiple cropping systems have seen the effect of this cause of complementarity.

A third concept important to the study of cropping systems is derived from the product-product relationship and is shown in Figures 8 and 9. Production possibilities curve *ahb* in Figure 8 is the same as in Figure 7B and represents a farm which has abundant resources. The production possibilities curve *ef* in Figure 9 represents a farmer so short of resources that he barely achieves the minimum rational level of input use in either crop A or crop B. When he uses his resources in both crops, the amount in each is less than that required to reach the minimum rational level. This situation gives rise to the inverted production possibilities curve in Figure 9.

The line *chd* in Figure 8 is an iso-revenue line representing all combinations of A and B which would result in the same income to the farmer. At *h*,

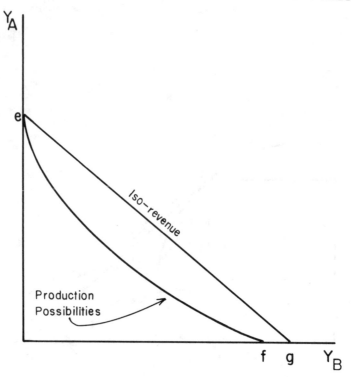

Figure 9. Best economic combination of crops to produce for a farmer with inadequate
    resources.

the point of tangency, the production possibilities curve reaches the highest
possible iso-revenue curve and hence this represents the best combination to
produce. The equating of the two slopes at the point of tangency is the same
as equating the MVP's of the input (or inputs) in each of the crops, as discussed previously.

The form of the production possibilities curve is fixed biologically and
by the amount of resources the farmer has. The slope of the iso-revenue
curve is determined by the prices of A and B. As a result, the best combination of A and B shifts as prices of the crops change. For a farmer with
abundant resources, his best alternative will nearly always be a combination
of the two crops, which means he should have a diversified farm.

The iso-revenue curve in Figure 9 represents a farmer with few resources. In this situation it is apparent that specialization in one crop or the
other should yield more income. Yet in the case of subsistence farms the
most common type with inadequate resources, they are nearly always diversified. In this regard, a multiple cropping system, which could be considered
and can be managed as a single enterprise, can have important economic implications. It allows a farmer to concentrate in one basic economic activity—
his multiple cropping system—but at the same time produce several crops
for subsistence and his need or desire to reduce risks. Yet because he is

specializing, he moves to a higher iso-revenue curve and increases his meager earnings.

SOCIO-ECONOMIC CONSIDERATIONS IN DESIGN OF MULTIPLE CROPPING SYSTEMS

Three of the most important bio-economic relationships affecting multiple cropping systems have been presented. In this section three examples of how bio-economic and socio-economic considerations have been incorporated into work on multiple cropping systems will be described. The first two are examples of systems for different conditions in Central America. The third illustrates the use of the product-product relationship in fertilizer experiments and recommendations.

A Salvadorean Multiple Cropping System

El Salvador, the smallest Central America Republic has, along with Haiti, the highest population density in the western hemisphere, numbering nearly 225 people/km^2 (500/mile^2). Although the country is more industrialized than the average in Central America, it still depends heavily on agriculture to generate income, feed its people, and employ the still predominantly rural population.

In 1973, in the face of worsening rural conditions and a declining food supply, the country placed urgent priority on the production of basic grains and vegetables, generating productive sources of rural employment and increasing rural income, with special emphasis given to irrigated areas. It was in response to these conditions that the Salvadorean system of multiple cropping was designed (Hildebrand & French, 1974).

Some of the most important considerations in designing the system were the following:

1. The system could utilize mechanization for land preparation but should not depend on it because the majority of farmers do not have access to tractors.
2. It should create additional, remunerative employment per unit of land area as well as increase family income potential.
3. The system could include vegetables but must be based on corn and beans, the staple diet of the country, without which the system would be unacceptable to the farmer.

As developed, the most interesting characteristic of the system is the use of double or twin rows of corn which allow more open space between them for other crops without reducing the corn population.[5] The double

---

[5] For information on how and why the double row concept was developed as well as a history of the development of the system see E. C. French, 1975. Development of multiple cropping systems for small farmers in El Salvador. Unpublished M.S. thesis. Dep. of Horticulture, New Mexico State University, Las Cruces, New Mexico.

rows are planted 30 cm apart and the present recommendation is 1.5 m between the centers of twin rows (Fig. 10). In practice, this distance varies because the rows are usually made by bullocks and a wooden plow which provides poor control on row width.

In the basic system (Hildebrand et al., 1975), radishes (*Raphanus sativus* L.) and beans are planted in the space between the twin corn rows simultaneously with, or a few days before the corn is planted. Radish harvest (about 30 days) occurs just as they are beginning to compete with the beans for solar energy. The beans reach a mature green pod stage before being shaded excessively by the corn and when mature are pulled, providing working space once again between the double rows of maturing corn.

Before the corn is "doubled"[6] cucumbers (*Cucumis sativus* L.) are planted between the twin rows after applying fertilizer, soil insecticides, and/ or nematocides. This preplanting process also includes bed formation and weeding. After the cucumbers germinate the corn is harvested or doubled and the leaves are stripped off so that full sunlight is available for the cucumber plants. The cucumbers are staked with twine to a tripod formed from corn stalks in the double rows providing important advantages at low cost.

Before the last cucumber harvest, cabbage (*Brassica oleracea* var. *capitata*) [broccoli or cauliflower (*B. oleracea* var. *botrytis*)] is transplanted on the outer edges of the bed and following the last cucumber harvest the corn stalks and cucumber plants are cut and placed in the rows between the cabbage. Three to 4 weeks following the transplant of the cabbage, corn is planted, once again in double rows, in the space where formerly there were beans. Three to 4 weeks after tasseling of the corn and shortly after the harvest of the cabbage, pole beans can be planted at the edges of the corn to use the stalks as soon as they are doubled.

The pole beans are the seventh crop; the complete system being easily terminated within a year's time. With irrigation, the system produces two full corn crops, more than the equivalent of one full bean crop, heavy cucumber and cabbage crops and a partial crop of radishes. The system is so labor intensive that a family can manage only up to a half hectare, yet income for the family is considerably more than they could make on several times that amount of land in traditional production methods. In one year, on 900 m^2, this system produced U. S. $772 in net family income or net income plus value of family labor (Chacon & Barahona, 1975).

The system is not complicated for farmers accustomed to multiple cropping systems although highest productivity does depend on closely adhering to a calendar of events. No tools beyond simple hand tools and wooden plows are required except for sprayers, which most have because of a recent increase in vegetable production in the irrigated areas. In general, the farmers use the varieties they know and the system is sufficiently flexible that they are encouraged to, and do, modify it on their own.

---

[6]A process common to the area in which the stalks are bent over just below the ears after reaching physiological maturity, so they can be left inverted in the field to dry and await harvest in the dry season.

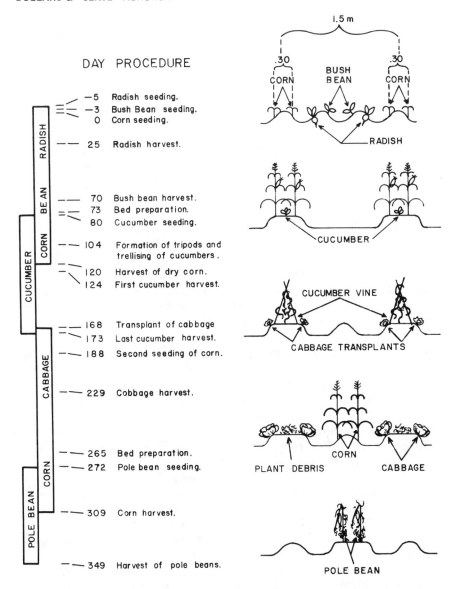

DAY PROCEDURE

1.5 m

.30 CORN   BUSH BEAN   .30 CORN

−5   Radish seeding.
−3   Bush Bean seeding.
0   Corn seeding.

25   Radish harvest.

RADISH

70   Bush bean harvest.
73   Bed preparation.
80   Cucumber seeding.

104 Formation of tripods and trellising of cucumbers.

CUCUMBER

120 Harvest of dry corn.
124 First cucumber harvest.

168 Transplant of cabbage
173 Last cucumber harvest.

188 Second seeding of corn.

CUCUMBER VINE

CABBAGE TRANSPLANTS

229 Cabbage harvest.

265 Bed preparation.
272 Pole bean seeding.

PLANT DEBRIS   CORN   CABBAGE

309 Corn harvest.

349 Harvest of pole beans.

POLE BEAN

Figure 10. Basic multiple cropping system developed for El Salvador.

Because of the interest of farmers in the system and in the way it satisfies the urgent priorities of the country, a program to introduce it on a pilot basis over a large part of the country was initiated by the extension service less than 2 years after design of the system was originated. If results are as expected, this will be a national program in 1976. At the same time, the system as designed is serving as the basis for several new research projects which will refine the basic system and provide increasingly better recommendations, varieties and ideas to farmers.

A Multiple Cropping System for Grain Production in a Dry Area

In southeastern Guatemala, the government has initiated an intensive program to increase grain production [corn, sorghum (*Sorghum* sp.) and beans] and increase the income of the small and medium farmers in the area. The majority of small farmers till rolling to steep land, much of it rocky (some almost pure rock), highly susceptible to the drought conditions which characterize the region. The most common traditional system is corn, sorghum, and beans all planted together. Yields for small farmers (fewer than 3.5 ha) in the area in 1974 were 536 kg/ha for corn, 412 kg/ha for beans and 631 kg/ha for sorghum (Reiche et al., 1976). Under employment is common among the small farmers in this area during most of the year, but there is a severe shortage of labor for planting in May and June when the rains start. This is created by the strong seasonality of the rains, their uncertainty even in the rainy season and a short critical period for planting. To cope with these conditions the farmers have devised a unique system. As the rains are approaching, but before they start, they plant their scarce and valuable bean seed in powder-dry soil. As soon as the rains start, and they hopefully, but not always, begin with heavy downpours, the corn and sorghum are planted on top of the beans without knowing where these were sown.

With the local varieties and in this system, if the beans germinate before the corn and sorghum are planted, they tend to dominate the taller species, while these will dominate if they germinate before the beans. Hence, timing is critical and is aggravated by the fact that planting is done by hand, using a metal-tipped pole. As a result, there is feverish activity to plant corn and sorghum in all the land that has beans before the beans germinate. Later, the rest of the land is planted with only corn and sorghum.

This system allows the farmers to accomplish their planting, but it also creates a risk for them. Beans planted in dry soil before adequate moisture is available may receive moisture adequate to initiate germination but inadequate to sustain growth. This could result in a complete loss for the farmer, and is a situation which happens not infrequently.

Several experimental multiple cropping systems planted in May, 1975, are designed to cope with the conditions which the farmers face in this area, yet to increase production and income. They utilize the advantages of the double corn row developed in El Salvador, and are designed to reduce risk by waiting to plant beans until adequate soil moisture is available to sustain growth.

In the most promising system, three rows of beans are planted about 30 cm apart. Between these three rows and the adjacent three rows, sufficient space is left for double rows of corn.[7] After the beans have emerged, the

---

[7]To facilitate adoption by the farmer, local measures are used in the system. The distance between centers of the double rows of corn is 2 "varas" or 1.68 m.

corn is planted. If, as happened this year, the rains stop for a period after bean planting, the corn planting can be delayed without fear of dominance by the beans. In fact, the delay improves the bean crop by reducing even further any competition with the corn.

The beans used this year are a short season variety from El Salvador ('Sensuntepeque') and can be harvested in 60 to 65 days. As soon as the beans are harvested a short season sorghum is planted in the space between the corn rows, and will be growing about a month before the corn is doubled. About two weeks before the corn is doubled, cowpeas (*Vigna* sp.) are planted on the outer edges of these twin rows and the leaves of the corn are used as a mulch to conserve stored soil moisture as the rainy season ends.

The results of this system are still unknown but appear promising. Labor requirements fit in well with availability and only hand tools are required. A local 'criollo' corn variety is being used although a hybrid adapted to more favorable conditions in the region is being tested. The system requires short season beans and sorghum; the beans being used come from a nearby region with similar conditions and appear to be well adapted. The sorghums ('Guatecau' from Guatemala and 'CENTA-S-1' from El Salvador) were developed locally, and produce well in good conditions, but their adaptability to the conditions of these small farmers remains to be seen.

With minimum fertilizer and insecticide use, in accordance with the economic possibilities of these farmers, it is hoped that production potential of corn and sorghum per farm can be increased owing to a doubling of the population of each. The production of beans per farm should be maintained even though the yield may decline somewhat per area planted. This will be partially offset by an increased area planted and partially by an increased yield per plant because of less competition with the corn and sorghum. The increased yield per plant (or per kilogram of seed planted) will please the farmers who calculate yield in this manner rather than in yield per area. However, the use of short season varieties may cancel this effect until improved short season yielders are selected. Any production from cowpeas, which have been raised as a substitute for beans in the area but on a small scale, will be a bonus.

Fertilizer Allocation in Multiple Cropping Systems

In order to improve the recommendations to farmers in the pilot promotion program in El Salvador, an experiment was undertaken to determine the appropriate distribution of nitrogen to each of the six crops fertilized in the system. The crops were: radishes (no fertilizer), beans, corn, cucumbers, cabbage, a second crop of bush beans and onions (*Allium cepa* L.). The system, designed for an onion producing area, was a modification of the basic system.

Without going into detail on the experimental design, the treatments were zero, 130, 260, 390, and 520 kg/ha of elemental nitrogen per year, distributed in fixed proportions between crops. That is, each crop in the 520 kg/ha treatment received twice the N received by the same crop in the 260 kg/ha, or central treatment. Quantities for the central treatment and the proportion for each crop were based on prior information obtained from monoculture trials plus what little information was available from previous work in systems, and were the following in terms of kilograms of N per hectare: corn and cucumbers, 82 kg in two applications; beans, 7 kg in one application; and cabbage and onions, 41 kg in two applications. The soil was high in potassium and previous trials had produced no response to phosphorus, so to keep the experiment simple, only nitrogen was varied. The source of nitrogen was ammonium sulfate. The data on onions were not available at the time this was written; the first crop of beans was lost and the response derived from the second crop; and the analysis of the other data should be considered preliminary, but will serve as an excellent example.

Analysis of each crop individually is by quadratic regression based on the response of each within the system. Each regression equation relating production to nitrogen can be considered as the response of a separate product and the appropriate economic allocation of fertilizer can be made on the basis of the product-product relationships presented earlier. In the case of five crops, the analysis is comprised of a set of either 5 or 6 equations depending on the economic conditions of the farmers for whom the system is designed.

For each crop, and derived from the production function, there is a marginal value product function equating this to a constant value:

$$P_{y_i} (dy_i/dN) = K.$$

The minimum value which K can assume is the price of the input, nitrogen. For a wealthy farmer, these five equations complete the system and K is the price of nitrogen. The solution of the system, distributing the nitrogen between crops, is the one which maximizes profit for the farmer who does not have a limit on the amount of fertilizer he can purchase. If the amount of fertilizer is limited by the farmer in accordance with his economic situation, a sixth equation expressing this limit is required: $\Sigma N_{y_i} = F$. In this equation N_{y_i} is the amount of N to be allocated to the ith crop and F is the total amount of fertilizer the farmer can obtain.

The following biologic production functions were derived from the fertilizer trial. For each function N is 100 pounds (45.4 kg) of N and product is also measured in 100 pound (45.4 kg) units, or *quintals*.

First beans: $F = 7.59 + 41.32\,N_f - 173.26\,N_f^2$
Corn: $M = 33.78 + 28.28\,N_m - 6.98\,N_m^2$
Cucumber: $P = 74.12 + 416.87\,N_p - 97.63\,N_p^2$
Second beans: $B = 13.67 + 74.38\,N_b - 311.87\,N_b^2$
Cabbage: $R = 54.66 + 104.34\,N_r - 16.75\,N_r^2$

Using the following as prices of the products: beans, $20.00/cwt ($0.44/kg); corn, $6.00/cwt ($0.13/kg); cucumbers, $2.50/cwt ($0.06/kg);

and cabbage, \$5.00/cwt (\$0.11/kg); the MVP of nitrogen for each crop or $Py_i(dy_i/dN)$ is shown below and equated to the constant, K:

$$\text{for F}: \quad 826.40 - 6,930.40\,N_f = K \qquad [1]$$
$$\text{for M}: \quad 169.68 - 83.76\,N_m = K \qquad [2]$$
$$\text{for P}: \quad 1,042.18 - 488.16\,N_p = K \qquad [3]$$
$$\text{for B}: \quad 1,487.60 - 12,474.80\,N_b = K \qquad [4]$$
$$\text{for R}: \quad 521.70 - 167.50\,N_r = K \qquad [5]$$

Adding the restriction for the amount of fertilizer the farmer can obtain or is willing to purchase, gives the sixth equation:

$$N_f + N_m + N_p + N_b + N_r = F \qquad [6]$$

Equations [1] to [6] contain seven unknowns, but because either K or F will be given, the system is complete. In the case of a wealthy farmer with no restrictions on purchase of fertilizer, K can be the price of N. When a poorer farmer determines F, then K is the unknown value of the MVP for N in each crop.

If the farmer has no restrictions on fertilizer then $K = 44$, the price of 100 pounds (45 kg) of N (\$0.97/kg), and the solution defines the maximum rational limit on fertilizer use. If a farmer (or his credit source) limits the amount of fertilizer he will purchase to, say 20 hundred pound bags of ammonium sulfate per manzana per year then $F = 4.2$ or 21% of 2,000 pounds, expressed in cwt (equivalent to 191 kg). In this case, the solution from Eqs. [1] to [6] results in $K = 165.7$. The distribution of nitrogen between crops for a wealthy and a poorer farmer and that of the experimental design is compared in Table 1.

These two solutions illustrate the interrelationship between the crop and the effect on optimum allocation as fertilizer quantity is changed. In the experimental design, based on information primarily from monoculture, the three grain crops were alloted 43.7% of the fertilizer. In the system and for the poorer farmer the grains receive only 5.9% and this increases only to 26.1% in the high profit solution of the wealthy farmer. The vegetables yield a greater return on the investment in fertilizer and should be allocated more when considered with the grains than was done in the experimental design. In practice the poor farmer should probably not use any fertilizer on his beans but instead allocate that fertilizer to the corn. Small amounts are difficult or impossible to apply and the additional amount on the corn serves the double purpose of strengthening the stalks which will be used for staking cucumbers.

A MODEL FOR DEVELOPMENT OF MULTIPLE CROPPING SYSTEMS

In my work over the last 2 years, a model for conducting coordinated research on multiple cropping systems has evolved. The model reflects the

Table 1. Nitrogen distribution between crops in a multiple cropping system

Crop	Experimental design	Wealthy farmer		Poor farmer	
	%	kg N/ha	%	kg N/ha	%
First beans	3.1	7.3	1.7	6.2	2.3
Corn	37.5	97.4	22.7	3.1	1.1
Cucumbers	37.5	132.5	30.8	116.6	43.1
Second beans	3.1	7.5	1.7	6.9	2.5
Cabbage	18.8	185.1	43.1	138.0	51.0
Total	100.0	429.8	100.0	270.8	100.0

need for rapid results from research important in most developing countries, but particularly important in El Salvador where traditional procedures of spending several years on vaguely oriented research before recommendations are made is a luxury which can no longer be afforded.

Two completely different situations for which multiple cropping systems are being developed were presented earlier. In each case, the system was being developed for precisely specified agronomic and economic conditions. The basic cropping system designed in El Salvador satisifed the necessities of the farmers as well as the country sufficiently well that it is now being utilized by many farmers (some for as long as 18 months) and is the focus of a national promotion program.

The system was developed without the benefits of a team of agronomists and many more agronomic questions were raised than were answered, yet the farmers for whom it was designed are eager to utilize it. I am convinced the reason for this ready acceptance of a new technology is because it was designed specifically for them. It satisfies their needs because its development was based on a study to determine what these needs were and identify the restrictions relevant to them. The system meets conditions important to this group of farmers and makes it possible for them to use given their economic, social, and agronomic situation.

In the development of the system which finally emerged we had to, and were able to, cast off many traditional concepts which are second nature to a modern agricultural scientist. One of the most interesting is related to our extremely high use of manual labor. Most nonfarmers who visited our experimental plots suggested that we should be able to make the system more "efficient" by the use of small, walking tractors and specialized equipment. This idea never occured to the farmers for whom the system was designed because (i) a tractor, of whatever size, is completely out of the range of possibilities for them for a myriad of reasons, and (ii) they saw the system as a means of providing them gainful employment and increasing their incomes in conditions in which they could work.

An augmented team of foreign and national scientists began a concentrated effort this year to refine the system and to answer many of the agronomic and economic questions which were raised. There is no doubt that

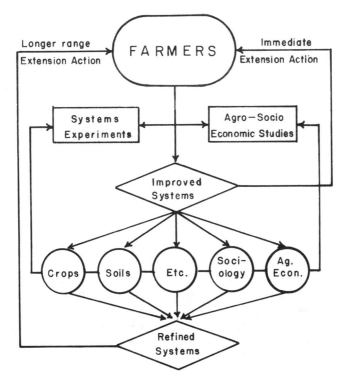

Figure 11. Model for development of multiple cropping systems.

the basic system will be modified to adapt it to differing conditions and each modification can be improved time and time again. But even while this is going on, the basic system is being used and the farmers are benefiting from it.

For multiple cropping systems development in countries which cannot afford to wait for results from traditional research methods, I recommend a procedure structured after the process which evolved in El Salvador and which is being utilized in Guatemala. The model, shown in Figure 11, has three characteristics which are valuable in developing countries. It maximizes the probability of rapidly generating a technology immediately available and highly appropriate to the target group; it provides orientation for more detailed research to follow; and it creates a multidisciplinary environment so vital to successful research in multiple cropping systems.

The focus of the model is on farmers—on a target group whose socio-economic conditions and agricultural situation are sufficiently homogeneous that their needs and capabilities can be readily specified. These farmers are the subjects of a three-pronged attack. The first is an agro-socio-economic survey to determine: (i) What they are doing, (ii) How they are doing it, and (iii) Why they are doing it the way they are. In order to determine the latter it is necessary to understand economic and cultural as well as agronomic restrictions which condition their cropping patterns and practices.

The second prong of the attack is to initiate experiments on improved systems designed specifically for these farmers. For the results to be immediately transferable the experiments must be conducted under the same conditions as those of the farmers. The same person or persons responsible for the agro-socio-economic study should share responsibilities for design of the experimental systems with one or more agronomists. Ideally, the agronomist should also have responsibility in the agro-socio-economic study of the farmers.

I would suggest that the team responsible for the experimental systems be small, just two people may be optimum, and the project should be kept highly flexible to take advantage of all new information as soon as it is available. In Guateamala our current systems experiment is being modified continually. At times, such flexibility can disturb the statistical accuracy of the trial, but the goal of the project is information and not a publication. For this first stage of research, treatments need not be defined so narrowly that only one factor varies between them. The object is to design a *system* that works so treatment differences can be complete changes of systems. Refinements to determine the cause of a particular effect can wait on the second, or refinement stage of the research effort, which is the third prong of the attack. The refinement of the basic system involves more traditional research procedures by more narrowly oriented scientists. Fertilizer use, varietal improvement, disease control, product quality, and timing of production are examples of refinement needs.

The advantage which this model offers is that the effects being made by the specialists are coordinated and oriented toward known conditions. These conditions are those of the farmers as they have been defined in the study of the farmers themselves, from the results of the systems experiment conducted under farm conditions, and later from the results obtained by farmers who have used the "improved" system derived in the first stage of the process.

SUMMARY

Economics and agronomy are inseparable in multiple cropping systems. Unlike monoculture crops, which can have rather wide adaptation, multiple cropping systems must be designed for specific agronomic, economic, and cultural conditions. A farmer's economic situation, which dictates how many and what kind of resources he has to work with, is as important in determining a feasible cropping system as are his soils and climate. Because it is the farmer who makes the decision whether or not to utilize any particular cropping system he needs a unit of comparison between systems which is meaningful to him and which he can interpret in his decision making framework. The only practical unit for measuring production which meets this and four other necessary criteria is market value of the products. Hence, both in use of inputs and in selecting products, the union of agronomy and economics is essential in multiple cropping systems.

Multiple cropping systems, as a field for research endeavor, provide an excellent framework within which to undertake multidisciplinary research and development, but require that many traditional research procedures be reconsidered. Because multiple cropping systems are specific to regions and types of farms, initial experimental research should be undertaken after determining the agro-socio-economic conditions of the farmers for whom the improved system is to be designed. Later, the improved system or systems can be refined with the help of more traditional research procedures, but these efforts will be more productive because they will be oriented toward specific farm situations. The multidisciplinary demands made on us by implicitly considering the needs and conditions of the farmers for whom we are working reflects both the challenge and the promise of multiple cropping systems.

LITERATURE CITED

Andrew, C. O. 1969. Improving performance of the production distribution system for potatoes in Colombia. Instituto Colombiano Agropecuario, Departamento de Economía Agrícola, Boletín No. 4, Tibaitatá, and Ph.D. thesis, Dep. of Agricultural Economics, Michigan State Univ., East Lansing. 70–14981.

Bradford, L. A., and G. L. Johnson. 1953. Farm management analysis. Wiley and Sons, Inc., New York. Chaps. 8–11.

Chacón, Adrián E., and Mario A. Barahona. 1975. Granos básicos en multicultivos. p. 63–76. In XXI Reunión Anual, Programa Cooperativo Centroamericano para el Mejoramiento de Cultivos Alimenticios (PCCMCA). San Salvador, El Salvador, C. A., Vol. I.

Heady, E. O., and J. L. Dillon. 1961. Agricultural production functions. Iowa State University Press.

Hildebrand, P. E., and E. C. French. 1974. Un sistema Salvadoreño de multicultivos. Departamento de Economía Agrícola, Centro Nacional de Tecnología Agropecuaria (CENTA), Ministerio de Agricultura y Ganaderia. San Salvador, El Salvador, C. A.

Hildebrand, P. E., E. C. French, M. A. Barahona, A. E. Chacón, and John Bieber. 1975. Manual para multicultivos. Departamento de Economía Agrícola, Centro Nacional de Tecnología Agropecuaria (CENTA), Ministerio de Agricultura y Ganadería. San Salvador, El Salvador, C. A.

Hildebrand, P. E., and E. G. Luna T. 1974. Unforeseen consequences of introducing new technologies in traditional agriculture. p. 508–509. In "Session No. 5 Public investment in research, education and technology". The future of agriculture: Technology, policies and adjustment. Papers and Reports, International Conference of Agricultural Economists, Fifteenth Conference. Oxford Agricultural Economics Institute, Oxford.

International Rice Research Institute. 1974. Annual Report for 1973. Multiple Cropping. IRRI, Los Banõs, Philippines.

Reiche, C. E., P. E. Hildebrand, S. Ruano, and J. T. Wyld. 1976. El pequeño agricultor y sus sistemas de cultivos en ladera: Jutiapa, Guatemala. Instituto de Ciencia y Technología Agrícolas. Guatemala, Guatemala. In press.

West Pakistan Water and Power Development Authority, and Tipton and Kalmbach Inc., Engineers. 1976. Regional Plan-Northern Indus Plains. Vol. II, Economics, Appendix B. Value of water in the northern Indus Plains. Lahore, Pakistan and Denver, Colorado.

Multiple Cropping: An Appraisal of Present Knowledge and Future Needs

P. A. Sanchez[1]

The purpose of the symposium was to bring together the available knowledge on multiple cropping systems, both ancient and new. Specialists from various parts of the world compiled the available information about what farmers and researchers are doing in different geographical regions, the fundamental concepts of multiple cropping, and specific agronomic practices. This paper reviews the information presented and the discussions which ensued in an attempt to summarize what is known about multiple cropping and what needs to be known if such practices are to bring about significant increases in world food production.

WHAT IS KNOWN

The traditional objective of agricultural research has been to enhance crop production in two dimensions: increasing the cultivated area and increasing yields per unit area per crop. The first section of the symposium documented the widespread use of multiple cropping throughout the world and the various ways in which crop production can be intensified in two additional dimensions: time and space. The development of mutually exclusive definitions for the various forms of multiple cropping in the Andrews and Kassam paper provides a uniform terminology which permits focusing more sharply on the similarities and the differences between them.

The various forms of multiple cropping do not occur haphazardly, but rather follow geographical and energy gradients. The most complex and in-

---

[1] Associate professor of Soil Science, North Carolina State University, Raleigh, North Carolina.

tense forms of intercropping occur in areas where temperature and moisture do not limit growth during most of the year. The papers by Harwood and Price; Pinchinat, Soria, and Bazan; and Okigbo and Greenland provide an extremely comprehensive description of these systems. As temperature and moisture become more limiting with increasing latitude and/or decreasing rainfall, multiple cropping patterns shift to sequential cropping. Multiple cropping is also more intense where power sources are largely human or animal, such as the small farms in the tropics. It is less prevalent in capital- and energy-intensive systems typical of the U. S. agriculture. The most complex and sophisticated forms of intercropping are practiced on farms ranging from 5 ha of arable land to less than 7 ha.

The symposium also emphasized the importance and efficiency of these small farming systems which have been generally considered primitive or marginal and, until recently, virtually ignored by researchers and policy makers. The bulk of food consumed in tropical Asia, Latin America, and Africa is produced on these small farms. This realization has fundamental implications to research and development policies. The papers by Harwood and Price, and Hildebrand clearly demonstrate that many of these systems are efficient in terms of labor utilization, which is the abundant source of energy. Sophistication in terms of agronomic management and decision-making by these "small farmers" is just as complex as linear programming methods used by scientists.

Most authors agree that improving the productivity of the more complex intercropping systems, rather than attempting to replace them with capital- and energy-intensive technology is the appropriate research strategy. Inspired by the pioneering research of Richard Bradfield in the Philippines, there are a number of active and excellent research programs ongoing in several tropical areas.

The potential for intensifying the production via multiple cropping is not limited to tropical areas. Various intercropping combinations have been practiced on small farms in the U. S., but many of them have been essentially eliminated or discouraged by improvements in mechanization and increases in farm size. The dramatic yield increases in American farms during the last few decades are a result of the efficiency of large-scale farming in single crop stands. The rate of yield increases, however, slowed down to the point where agronomists were concerned with "moving off the yield plateau", a subject of an American Society of Agronomy symposium in 1967. With the renewed interest in "all-out food production", sequential double cropping systems based on no-tillage techniques have been developed and have been rapidly adopted by large-scale farmers throughout the U. S. Many farms in the southern, midwestern, and western U. S. which previously produced one crop per year per field now produce two and in some cases, three. The papers by Lewis and Phillips; Gomm, Sneva and Lorenz; Radke and Hagstrom; Unger and Stewart; and Siddoway and Barnett document these trends. For example, in the dryland wheat areas of the upper midwest, previously only one crop could be produced every 2 years because of chronic moisture deficit. Development of strip intercropping techniques to hold snow, increase subsoil moisture, and prevent wind erosion makes it possible to grow a crop every year or three crops in 2 years.

The challenge to intensify food production by multiple cropping has been accepted by farmers and researchers. Much can be gained by studying the techniques developed in the tropics, improving them at their place of origin, and adapting them to the different physical, social, and economic environments of the temperate region.

Intercropping systems practiced by farmers generally produce more total yields of the mixed crops per hectare than when the individual crops are grown in single stands. The various papers indicate that from 20 to 50% more yield per hectare is commonly obtained by intercropping annual crops. The yield advantages are even larger when annual crops are mixed with perennials. This evidence raises two questions. Why is there a yield advantage? Would this advantage disappear with more capital-intensive inputs?

As Trenbath's paper points out, for intercropping to be advantageous, competition between species for available light, water, and nutrients must be lower than competition between plants of the same species in single stands. Farmers have selected those combinations of crops and planting schedules which minimize interspecific competition. That a better utilization of solar radiation is obtained by keeping a vegetative cover on the soil most of the time was documented in the review by Allen, Sinclair, and Lemon. When two crops with differing canopy configurations are mixed, light interception is greater and better distributed, especially if one is a tall-statured crop with relatively erect leaves and the companion crop is short-statured with more horizontal leaf angles. Relay intercropping permits fuller use of solar radiation and available water by planting a second crop before the first one is harvested. The nature of competition below ground for water and nutrients, however, remains largely unknown. There is some evidence that certain intercropped systems accumulate more nutrients from the soil than separate single stands and, in some cases, utilize fertilizer applications more efficiently; but the existing information is too fragmental for asserting that these phenomena occur in most intercropped combinations.

The review by Litsinger and Moody provided extensive evidence that most traditional intercropping patterns are pest-suppressant. The most obvious effect is the reduction of weed infestations as a result of constant crop cover and increased light interception by the crops. By minimizing the amount of time that land lies idle, there are fewer opportunities for weed growth. Certain crop mixtures also reduce insect, pathogen and nematode attacks by various means. Some species produce root exudates which eliminate nematodes that attack a companion crop. Corn-peanut intercropping decreases the incidence of corn borer attack. Other mechanisms involved include the propagation of beneficial insect species, a more even insect population, the decrease of host plants which habor larvae and spores, and in certain cases, the greater physical distance between plants of the same species. Litsinger and Moody conclude that crop diversity in close proximity is crop protection. The pest management advantages in intercropped systems appear to be well established.

All forms of multiple cropping save time, but time is most crucial in the double cropping systems recently developed in the temperate region where two crops have to be squeezed in a limited frost-free growing season. The keys to success lie in early planting, careful management, short season cultivars, modified row arrangements, and most importantly the development of mechanized no-till planting for one or both crops. The papers by Lewis and Phillips, and Unger and Stewart provide ample justification for no-tillage or minimum tillage techniques with weeds controlled by contact herbicides. In areas of limited rainfall, no-till planting is essential for saving soil moisture for growing a second crop. The moisture that is lost with regular tillage commonly prevents successful establishment of the second annual crop. Farm machinery has been redesigned for harvesting the first crop quickly and planting the following one on untilled soil covered with the preceding crop's residues, conditions previously considered unsuitable for planting. The development of these soil management techniques has also provided a built-in mechanism for controlling water and wind erosion, utilizing soil moisture more efficiently, and allowing some degree of nutrient recycling by leaving crop residues on the soil.

The economics of multiple cropping require a change in traditional thinking. Economists can no longer consider input-output relationships for a single crop. The value of the system has to be considered as a whole and as Hildebrand emphasizes, the only way to realistically compare systems is by the value of the total product, in spite of the variable nature of crop prices. It is not possible to make comparisons of corn yields with potato yields on a physical basis. It is seldom that individual species yield as much per hectare in multiple cropping systems as when grown in single stands. However, the profitability of the entire system per hectare is the final arbiter.

This symposium has also shown that certain multiple cropping systems are inferior to growing crops separately in single stands. In some intercropping systems, interspecific competition exceeds intraspecific competition. In a similar manner, the overall profitability of some sequential double cropping systems is less than growing only one crop a year. Certain pest problems are enhanced by growing two crops at the same time or in sequence. Practices profitable for labor-intensive technologies may be unprofitable for capital-intensive technologies. Crop intensification also has its limits. Certain systems involving five or more harvests a year require so much labor that their profitability per unit of labor diminishes even in the smallest farms.

WHAT NEEDS TO BE KNOWN

The symposium papers either directly or by omission have identified serious gaps which require additional research. Some are geographical, like the almost total absence of up-to-date information from some countries of the Middle East as shown by Nasr. Similar gaps occur at the country or sub-country levels throughout the world. In general, however, it appears that researchers are following the farmer's innovations more than supplying new information. The following issues appear to be the most critical problems agronomists must come to grips with in order to increase the productivity of multiple cropping systems. These gaps exist because of the commodity or discipline orientation of most agricultural scientists and their solution requires an interdisciplinary effort among soil scientists, plant breeders, plant pathologists as well as among crop scientists.

Plant breeders have traditionally focused their efforts towards improving yields of single-crop stands. The papers by Francis, Flor, and Temple; and Drolsom and Smith emphasize the need for a completely different breeding strategy for intercropped systems. The breeding objectives must focus on maximizing the profitability of intercropping rather than the individual crop's yields. Trenbath's paper points out that the architecture of some crops need to be modified in order to reduce intercrop competition. For sequential cropping systems, new cultivars need to be developed and adapted to different temperature and photoperiod conditions so that crops can be planted later or earlier than the usual time for growing them in single stands. Although there are a number of research operations following the approach, more such efforts are needed on a worldwide scale to develop the most productive cultivars for specific multiple cropping combinations.

Plant physiologists need to look at these systems as a whole and determine the most efficient patterns for maximizing the utilization of solar radiation, water, and nutrients. Much needs to be learned about planting dates, row spacing, and population density for the various crop combinations as well as developing new combinations not presently used by farmers.

The largest knowledge gap, by far, is what happens below the ground. Basic studies are needed on crop root competition, and how two or more different root systems can better utilize limited supplies of water and nutrients. The paper by Oelsligle, McCollum and Kang showed the lack of information on management of fertilizers in intercropped systems. The increasing awareness of important varietal and species differences in tolerating adverse soil conditions such as subsoil acidity or drought opens significant possibilities for manipulating multiple cropping systems in ways that interspecific competition is minimized and soil and fertilizer nutrients are more efficiently utilized. Intercropping cereals with legumes which fix nitrogen appears to be a promising means for providing nitrogen to a subsequent cereal crop without investing time in growing a green manure crop. Studies on placement, timing, sources and rates of fertilizer applications are extremely limited. This limitation is not only in intercropped systems but in sequential cropping. Although sequential crops are grown in single stands, there is a carryover nutritional effect from one crop to another which needs study and quantification. These effects may be different from what is known about traditional crop rotations because of the shorter time span involved.

Although more information is available on pest management and no-till soil management practices than about plant breeding, mineral nutrition and soil fertility, it is obvious that advances in one discipline are likely to affect practices related to other disciplines. Research on specific multiple cropping systems must be equally as interdisciplinary as the farmers who practice them.

Finally, as pointed out by Erbach and Lovely, mechanization may limit the adoption of the more complex intercropped systems by large-scale farm operations. Advances in mechanization for sequential cropping systems have been impressive. It seems clear that a better use of available human and animal labor in labor-intensive and capital-short farming situations may be most advantageous; however, the possibility of fully mechanizing intercropped systems suitable for labor-short, capital-intensive farming have not been fully explored. Much remains to be done in developing machinery for planting and harvesting row-intercropped combinations.